THE CULTIVATION OF
PARASITES *IN VITRO*

THE CULTIVATION OF PARASITES *IN VITRO*

ANGELA E.R. TAYLOR

B.Sc. Ph.D.

Lister Institute of Preventive Medicine,
Chelsea Bridge Road, London SW1

AND

J.R. BAKER

B.Sc. Ph.D. M.I.Biol.

London School of Hygiene and Tropical Medicine,
Keppel Street, London WC1

BLACKWELL SCIENTIFIC PUBLICATIONS

OXFORD AND EDINBURGH

59/.55
T238

Printed in Great Britain by
ADLARD & SON LTD, DORKING
and bound by
THE KEMP HALL BINDERY, OXFORD

'Whenever I hear the word culture
I reach for my revolver.'

HANNS JOHST

CONTENTS

vii

PREFACE

The primary aim of this book is to provide a laboratory handbook giving full practical details of the more successful methods of growing animal parasites *in vitro*. We have restricted ourselves to methods of cultivation of parasites of animals and not of plants, although reference has been made to a few good papers on the latter subject in the appendix (p. 337) and brief details of the cultivation of plant tissues are given on p. 358. We have disregarded completely methods for growing and maintaining parasites in living animals but have included certain methods of growing parasites in tissue culture, since this technique has been successful with some organisms.

The book is divided into three parts, the first two of these dealing with the Protozoa and Helminths respectively. Each chapter consists of a review of the literature followed by practical details of the more successful techniques; wherever possible these have been grouped under genera but sometimes larger groups have been used where one culture technique can be applied to a variety of genera and species, as is the case with many of the Protozoa. To facilitate reference to the relevant literature, tables are included in each section or chapter; in part I the tables include references to most of the culture media used for each group of parasites whereas in part II the tables list the majority of papers published on all aspects of the cultivation of Helminths. The third part of the book consists of an Appendix giving details of general techniques of *in vitro* culture and of the preparation of media.

Several difficulties arise in the study of parasites; the very nature of a parasite (by definition) makes it impossible to study it in its natural environment because it is so closely associated with its host. This is especially true where behavioural, physiological or biochemical studies are concerned and where the screening of parasitic drugs or the immunogenic properties of the metabolic products of parasites are being investigated. Many of these phenomena can only be investigated *in vitro* and thus advances in these aspects of parasitism have run closely parallel with the development of suitable culture methods. Considerable progress has been made in this field over the past ten years but there still remains much to be done before the majority of parasitic species can be grown throughout their life-cycle *in vitro*.

xi

ACKNOWLEDGEMENTS

We are most grateful to Dr. B. Weitz and Dr. C. A. Hopkins who have read and commented critically on various sections of the text, and to Mr. L. G. Ellis for assistance with the bibliography. We would also like to thank our secretaries Mrs. K. M. Jakeman and Mrs. R. E. Eversden for their skill and patience in preparing the manuscript.

We are indebted to the publishers and editors of the following journals for permission to use material: Annals of the New York Academy of Sciences, Annals of Tropical Medicine and Parasitology, Experimental Parasitology, Journal of Experimental Medicine, Journal of Parasitology, Nature (London), Transactions of the American Microscopical Society, and the following publishers: Baillière, Tindall and Cassell Ltd., E. & S. Livingstone Ltd. and Oliver and Boyd Ltd.

ANGELA E. R. TAYLOR

J. R. BAKER

PART ONE

CULTIVATION OF PROTOZOA

CHAPTER 1

TRYPANOSOMATIDAE

Certain organisms belonging to this family were among the first parasitic Protozoa to be cultivated *in vitro*, certainly the first to be grown axenically (MacNeal & Novy, 1903). Axenic culture is essential as none of these organisms will grow successfully *in vitro* in the presence of bacterial or fungal contaminants. In order to discourage growth of bacteria, antibiotics are frequently added to media: neither penicillin nor streptomycin appears to have significantly harmful effect on most flagellates. However, Krassner (1965) has shown that streptomycin has some inhibitory effect on *Leishmania tarentolae in vitro* even in concentrations as low as 33–133 μg/ml, in the absence of blood in the medium. For the purification of contaminated cultures, Seneca *et al.* (1949) suggested 1,000 units of penicillin and 1,000 units (= 1 mg) of streptomycin per ml; such quantities were shown to be harmless to the flagellates, but for routine cultures (i.e. prevention rather than removal of contamination), many workers use lower concentrations. Weinman (1960a) considered that dihydrostreptomycin was less toxic to trypanosomes than streptomycin, and should therefore be used instead of the latter.

The earlier work on cultivation of this group was directed mainly at *Trypanosoma* spp., and is summarized in the *Bulletin of the Sleeping Sickness Bureau* (1909). More recent reviews include those of Lwoff (1940, 1951), Guttman & Wallace (1964), which deals mainly with the development of defined media, and Tobie (1964), who considers only the trypanosomes of mammals.

Almost always, the digenetic trypanosomatids (those with both vertebrate and invertebrate hosts) *Leishmania* and *Trypanosoma* are cultivated *in vitro* at temperatures within the range of 20–28°c. Prates (1928), von Razgha (1929) and Reichenow (1939), amongst others, pointed out that at these temperatures, trypanosomes grow in the form normally assumed in the invertebrate vector. Little work has been done on the cultivation of the forms normally developing in the vertebrate (see pp. 35–40).

Reichenow (1940) showed that individuals of a readily cultivated strain

2

of *T.gambiense* which had been made akinetoplastic by treatment with acriflavin were unable to develop *in vitro*. Recently it has become possible to understand this in terms of the organisms' ability or inability to perform mitochondrial respiration (see Vickerman, 1965).

Organisms which are infective to the vertebrate host develop in cultures of most species of *Leishmania* and *Trypanosoma*, excepting those species of *Trypanosoma* which are grouped by Hoare (1966) in the section Salivaria (see pp. 31–32).

Speaking generally, the cultural requirements of different members of the family Trypanosomatidae become increasingly stringent as the presumed evolutionary sequence within the family is followed. Thus, the monogenetic trypanosomatids (with only a single invertebrate host) can be cultivated in relatively simple media, and it has proved possible to devise several defined media for members of this group. The requirements of members of the genera *Leishmania* and *Trypanosoma* are more sophisticated and only recently has growth of one more primitive species of both of these genera been achieved in defined media (pp. 23–28). Finally the Salivarian species of *Trypanosoma*, probably the most recently evolved group in the family (Baker, 1963), are the most difficult to cultivate *in vitro*. Most of the 'lower' members of the family can be grown in media designed for the 'higher' groups, but not *vice versa*.

Trypanosomatids grown *in vitro* may be preserved by freezing at either $-70°c$ in solid carbon dioxide (see Baker, 1966) or at $-190°c$ in liquid nitrogen (Resseler *et al.*, 1965).

I. MONOGENETIC TRYPANOSOMATIDAE

The nutritional requirements of this group of organisms have been intensively studied by Lwoff (1940, 1951) and Guttman (1963). Most species (like the digenetic members of the family) need to be supplied with haematin: one apparent exception to this rule is *Crithidia oncopelti* (= *Strigomonas oncopelti*), which can be grown in media devoid of haematin such as those described by Newton (1956) and Horne & Newton (1958) (pp. 7–8). It has been suggested that *C.oncopelti* obtains its haematin from a bacterial endosymbiont capable of synthesizing this compound (Guttman & Eisenman, 1965), but doubt has recently been thrown on this by the work of Newton & Gutteridge (1967).

Guttman (1963) reported a defined medium for several other species of *Crithidia* and for *Blastocrithidia culicis*, which require haematin (p. 6). With the addition of 0·01% glycine, this medium becomes suitable for *Lepto-monas* spp. (Guttman, 1966a): for these species, glutamic acid (essential for *Crithidia* and *Blastocrithidia*) may be omitted. A semi-defined medium for *C.fasciculata*, which also needs haematin, has been reported by Nathan & Cowperthwaite (1955).

TABLE 1.1. Some media which have been used for the cultivation of monogenetic Trypanosomatidae*

Author(s)	Date	Species	Detailed description (if any)
Guttman†	1963, 1966a	*Crithidia* spp. and *Blastocrithidia culicis*	p. 6
Horne & Newton	1958	*C.oncopelti*	p. 7
Nathan & Cowperthwaite	1955	*C.fasciculata*	—
Newton†	1956	*C.oncopelti*	p. 7

* Many or all of these species will also grow in the media listed in Tables 1.2–1.4
† Defined medium.

The work of Guttman and her associates (see Guttman, 1963) resulted in the discovery that certain unconjugated pteridines ('crithidia factor') were essential growth substances for species of *Crithidia*: these could be replaced by unusually large quantities of folic acid (1 μg/ml). A method of assaying crithidia factor by the growth of *Crithidia* spp. in a partially-defined medium lacking any 'indigenous' factor, was described a year later (Guttman, 1964).

Halevy & Sarel (1965) found that growth of *L.culicidarum* was increased about three-fold if the cultures were shaken throughout incubation at a frequency of about 250 per minute. Wallace & Clark (1959) cultivated *Herpetomonas muscarum* and *C.luciliae* in Diamond & Herman's (1954) SNB-9 medium (p. 13), using a slightly lower concentration of sodium chloride (0·55% instead of 0·6%): the insects were dissected with sterile instruments after being immersed for 5 minutes in benzalkonium chloride (Zephiran chloride, Winthrop) solution (1:1,000). There is little doubt that most or all of the monogenetic trypanosomatids would grow in the various diphasic blood-agar media described in the next section of this chapter.

Defined medium for monogenetic trypanosomatids
(Guttman, 1963 and 1966a)

MEDIUM

1 Composition
(final concentrations in mg per 100 ml)

L-Arginine HCl.................50	Iron (as $Fe(NH_4)_2(SO_4)_2.6H_2O$).....0·1	
L-Glutamic acid*.................100	Manganese (as $MnSO_4.H_2O$).......14	
L-Histidine HCl 30	Magnesium sulphate $7H_2O$ 65	
DL-Isoleucine 10	Potassium phosphate (K_3PO_4).......15	
DL-Leucine 10	Zinc (as $ZnSO_4.7H_2O$) 5	
L-Lysine HCl....................40	Adenine* 1	
DL-Methionine..................10	Sucrose* 1,500	
DL-Phenylalanine 6	Biotin ....0·001	
DL-Tryptophan 8	Calcium pantothenate.............0·3	
L-Tyrosine......................6	Folic acid ....0·1	
DL-Valine 5	Nicotinic acid...................0·3	
EDTA..........................60	Pyridoxamine 2HCl ....0·1	
Boron (as H_3BO_3) ....0·05	Riboflavin....................0·06	
Calcium (as $CaCl_2$)* ....0·5	Thiamine HCl ....0·6	
Cobalt (as $CoSO_4.7H_2O$).........0·25	Haemin* ....2·5	
Copper (as $CuSO_4.5H_2O$)........0·25	Triethanolamine* 500	

* See notes on preparation below.

2 Preparation

(a) Final pH should be adjusted to 7·8–8·0 with sulphuric acid or potassium hydroxide (if necessary).

(b) All ingredients *except the vitamins* may be prepared and stored at fourfold concentration.

(c) Glutamic acid should be free of methionine: Grade 'A' of the California Biochemical Corporation is satisfactory.

(d) Calcium chloride is prepared by acidifying calcium carbonate with hydrochloric acid.

(e) Adenine may be replaced by any purine base or riboside.

(f) Sucrose may be replaced by glucose (and certain other sugars: see original paper).

(g) Haemin and triethanolamine (T.E.A.) are prepared as follows. Make a stock solution of haemin (5 mg/ml) in 50% w/v T.E.A. When making the medium, first add half the required quantity of T.E.A. (250 mg/100 ml), which brings the pH to 7: then add the haemin solution (0·5 ml/100 ml) which automatically adds the remainder of the T.E.A.

(h) Although not stated, sterilization of this medium is presumably effected by filtration.

TECHNIQUE

This medium supports *Crithidia, Blastocrithidia* and *Trypanosoma ranarum*. For growth of *Leptomonas* spp., glycine (10 mg/100 ml) must be added and the glutamic acid may be omitted (see Guttman, 1966a). With further defined supplements of (as yet unspecified) amino-acids and lipids, Guttman (1966b) has been able to cultivate *T.mega* in this medium.

Undefined medium for *Crithidia oncopelti* (= *Strigomonas oncopelti*)
(Horne & Newton, 1958)

MEDIUM

Peptone (Bacteriological, Evans
    Medical Supplies)...............3 g
Glucose ....0·5 g
Sodium chloride................0·5 g
Water to.....................100 ml

Initial pH 7·4. Sterilize by autoclaving at 15 lb for 20 min.

TECHNIQUE

The medium is used in 5 ml, 50 ml or 500 ml volumes as required (presumably in tubes or flasks respectively), incubated at 25°C. Transfers to fresh medium should be made every 2 days.

Defined medium for *Crithidia oncopelti* (= *Strigomonas oncopelti*)
(Newton, 1956)

MEDIUM

Composition

Methionine ....200 mg
Adenine......................10 mg
Thiamine.....................1 mg
Nicotinamide ....1 mg
Calcium pantothenate ....1 mg
Pyridoxine hydrochloride........1 mg
p-Aminobenzoic acid ....1 mg
Biotin ....0·01 mg
Trace metals solution (see below)..10 ml

Glucose ....5 g
Ammonium chloride ....5 g
Disodium hydrogen phosphate
  $2H_2O$ ....0·25 g
Potassium dihydrogen phosphate.0·08 g
Sodium chloride................9·0 g
Potassium chloride.............0·42 g
Water to.........................1 l.

Initial pH 7·2. Sterilize by autoclaving at 10 lb for 10 min.
   Trace metals solution:

> Magnesium sulphate 7H$_2$O ......20 g
> Ferrous sulphate ....0·5 g
> Zinc sulphate 7H$_2$O.............0·5 g
> Manganese sulphate 3H$_2$O ......0·5 g
> Copper sulphate 5H$_2$O ....0·5 g
> 0·1 N sulphuric acid to ....1 l.

TECHNIQUE

Cultures are incubated at 25°c, and transfers to fresh medium are made
every 3–4 days. Further details are not given.

NOTES: (1) A solid version of the medium can be prepared by adding
0·7% w/v agar to the above. *C.oncopelti* grows on this in discrete colonies:
such cultures survive for 3–4 weeks.

   (2) Nathan (1958) supplemented this liquid medium with L-glutamic
acid (0·1%), L-histidine (0·02%) and L-arginine (0·03%).

II. *LEISHMANIA* AND *TRYPANOSOMA*
(EXCEPT SALIVARIA)

1. DIPHASIC (UNDEFINED) MEDIA

The first successful cultivation of any trypanosomatid—indeed probably
the first successful growth *in vitro* of any parasitic protozoon—was achieved
in 1903 by Novy & MacNeal, who grew *Trypanosoma lewisi* in the
'condensation water' which collected at the base of a mixture of nutrient
agar and blood which had been allowed to solidify in test-tubes. The
following year MacNeal (1904) reported that a medium of this type was
also suitable for the growth of *T.brucei*, though a higher proportion of
blood was necessary (1 part of agar to 2 parts of blood, in place of the 3:1
or 1:1 ratios which were satisfactory for *T.lewisi*) and it grew much less
readily than *T.lewisi*. Novy & MacNeal used only rabbit blood but
Mathis (1906) modified their technique by heating the medium to not
more than 100°c, and found that other bloods (goose, goat, dog) were
equally satisfactory for non-pathogenic trypanosomes like *T.lewisi*. He
also added a few drops of saline if insufficient condensation water appeared
at the base of the tube, the completed tubes being allowed to stand for 2
or more days before use for dissolution of the nutrients in the solid slant.

Nicolle (1908a, b) simplified Novy & MacNeal's medium by omitting the nutrients (extract of beef, and peptone): he found that *Leishmania tropica* grew at least as well in the condensation water developed from a mixture of plain agar, marine salt and rabbit's blood. Nicolle's modified medium subsequently became known as NNN medium from the initial letters of the names Novy, MacNeal (ignoring the prefix in the interests of euphony!) and Nicolle. All the diphasic media which have been described and used since this time for the growth of Trypanosomatidae have been based on one or other of the original recipes of Novy & MacNeal or of Nicolle. The latter is frequently used unaltered, save for the substitution of pure sodium chloride for marine salt (p. 14). Following the suggestion of Mathis (1906), many workers have added about 1 ml of a suitable physiological solution (e.g. 0·9% sodium chloride or Ringer's, Locke's or Hanks's salines) to the tubes as an overlay to increase the available fluid in which the organisms grow: if this is done it is best to allow the concentrations of nutrients in the slope to equilibriate with those in the overlay for a day or two before use. The addition of such an overlay usually prolongs the life of the culture (Nattan-Larrier & Grimard-Richard, 1934) and also results in the production of larger total numbers of flagellates (not necessarily in higher concentrations per unit volume). However, if the cultures are being used solely for diagnosis, it may be preferable not to add any fluid to the condensation water, as growth will be detectable sooner in the smaller volume of rich liquid: Dr R. Lainson (personal communication) has shown that promastigote (i.e. leptomonad—see Hoare & Wallace, 1966) forms of *Leishmania mexicana* could be detected in tubes without added liquid in less than one week after inoculation with material from a human lesion, whereas in tubes to which 0·5 ml of Locke's solution had been added, 3–4 weeks elapsed before the flagellates were detected.

Innumerable varieties of these blood-agar media have been developed. Some of these are listed in Table 1.2. The use of a nutrient agar base usually results in more luxuriant growth, and may be an advantage if large numbers of organisms are required or if attempts are being made to grow a more fastidious organism. The preparation of two of the modern versions of Novy & MacNeal's medium is detailed below (pp. 13 & 14). Nöller (1917) introduced the use of such media in Petri dishes, a method which enables beautiful preparations to be obtained by touching a cover-slip on to the agar surface on which the colonies of flagellates are growing, removing it, fixing in osmium tetroxide vapour (before allowing the organisms to dry) and subsequently staining with Giemsa's stain (see Minchin, 1909, for details of the technique of fixation and staining). Either

TABLE 1.2. Some diphasic media which have been used for the cultivation of *Trypanosoma* (except Salivaria) and *Leishmania* at temperatures below 37°C.

Author(s)	Date	Name	Species*	Detailed description (if any)
Baker	1966	4N	Trypanosomes of birds	p. 13
Bonacci	1934	—	*T.cruzi*	—
von Brand *et al.*	1946	—	*T.cruzi*	—
Chang	1947 ⎫			
Chang & Negherbon	1947 ⎬ —		*Leishmania, T.cruzi*	—
Deane & Deane	1961	—	*T.conorrhini*	—
Diamond & Herman	1954	SNB-9	Several	p. 13
Herbert	1961 ⎫			
Herbert	1965 ⎬ —		*T.theileri*	—
Herrer *et al.*	1966	—	Several	—
Jackson	⎧ 1962	—	*L.enriettii*	—
	⎩ 1693	—	*T.lewisi*	—
Johnson	1947	—	*T.conorrhini*	—
Lehmann	1959	—	Trypanosomes of amphibia	—
Lehmann	1966	NNL, SNBL	Ditto and *T.cruzi*	—
M(a)cNeal & Novy	1903	NN	*T.lewisi*	—
Mathis	1906	—	Several	—
McConnell	1963	—	*Leishmania*	—
Neal & Miles	1963	—	*Leishmania, T.cruzi*	p. 14
Neva *et al.*	1961	—	*T.cruzi*	—
Nicolle	1908b	NNN	*L.tropica*	p. 14
Nöller	1917	—	Many	—
Pessat	1961	—	*T.cruzi*	—
Salle & Schmidt	1928	—	*L. tropica*	—
Seneca & Henderson	1951 ⎫			
Seneca & Wolf	1955 ⎬ —		*L.donovani, T.cruzi*	—
Senekji(e)	1939	—	*L.tropica*	—
Senekjie	1943	—	*T.cruzi*	—
Senekjie & Lewis	1945	—	*Leishmania*	—
Tom	1943	—	*T.cruzi*	—
Young & van Sant	1923	—	*L.donovani*	—

* Species for which medium was originally used: others may grow equally well.

plain or nutrient agar media may be used in this way: the plates are incubated upside down, dehydration and contamination being avoided by maintaining a layer, 1–2 mm deep, of 2–3% aqueous mercuric chloride solution in the lid of the Petri dish (which here serves as the base of the inverted plate). The plates are inoculated by 'streaking' or placing a drop of liquid containing flagellates from an ordinary tube culture, on to the surface of the agar (with aseptic precautions).

The use of diphasic media which have been autoclaved after the addition of blood to the base (instead of before as in the classical NNN method) has been investigated by a few authors. The advantages of this procedure are (i) easy attainment of sterility, even under conditions where the aseptic collection and addition of blood may be difficult, and (ii) the production of a firmer base from which erythrocytes will not be liberated into the fluid part of the medium: this is an advantage for certain biochemical and immunological procedures, when pure suspensions of flagellates are required. The main disadvantage of autoclaved media is that they are usually less adequate for supporting growth: however, autoclaved diphasic media have been reported adequate for *T.cruzi* (Tom, 1943) and for *T.cruzi* and several species of *Leishmania* (Neal & Miles, 1963; p. 14). Lehmann (1960, 1964) had some success in the growth of salivarian trypanosomes in autoclaved media, and it is likely that other species of *Trypanosoma* and *Leishmania* would grow at least equally well in his media, which are discussed below (p. 31).

A few investigations have been made into the effect of using different types of blood. For example, Ray (1932) tested various bloods in a nutrient agar-blood medium, without added overlay, for the growth of *Leishmania* spp., and found that they could be arranged as follows in descending order of suitability: human, rabbit, guinea-pig, horse, sheep. Satisfactory growth was, however, obtained with all these bloods. MacNeal & Novy (1903) found rat blood equally satisfactory for the growth of *T.lewisi*, and rhesus monkey's blood is satisfactory for at least certain species of *Leishmania* (Lainson, personal communication). Bray & Munford (1967) have shown that, for certain strains of *L.braziliensis*, rat blood is better than that of the rabbit. By far the most commonly used blood, however, is that of the rabbit. Defibrination of the blood appears to have no effect on its suitability as a substrate (it may sometimes be a convenience in handling the blood): neither does inactivation by heating to 56°c for half an hour (this may not be true, however, of blood used in media for the salivarian trypanosomes: see below). It is important that the blood which is used should be fresh (preferably stored for not longer than 1 week at 4°c): commercially prepared bloods are generally less satisfactory than those collected just before use.

Much research has been aimed at identifying substances required by the haemoflagellates *in vitro*, and has been summarized by Lwoff (1951) and Guttman & Wallace (1964). It was at one time thought that some of these organisms (*Leishmania* spp. and *T.cruzi*) could develop in media devoid of erythrocyte constituents (Adler, 1934; Senekjie, 1943; Senekjie & Lewis, 1945): but Lwoff (1951) showed that haemin at least was required, and suggested that sufficient haemin may have been present in the serum used by the earlier workers to support growth of the parasites. Chang (1947) used a medium in which serum and 'haemoglobin solution' (presumably an erythrocyte extract) were added separately, for the growth of *Leishmania* spp. and *T.cruzi*, thus avoiding the contamination of the suspension of flagellates by cellular elements from the blood. Tobie & Rees (1948) have serially cultivated *T.cruzi* inside dialysis sacs suspended in the overlay of a diphasic nutrient agar-blood medium, overlaid with Locke's solution, thus demonstrating that at least this species requires only dialyzable substances for its growth *in vitro* and does not need pre-formed proteins.

Packchanian (1934, 1943) and Packchanian & Sweets (1947) investigated the longevity of individual cultures, and the duration of retention of infectivity to the vertebrate hosts, using a variety of species maintained in nutrient agar-blood cultures: *T.lewisi* retained its infectivity for not more than 1 year, while *T.cruzi* remained infective for at least 13 years (involving 81 serial passages). They recorded also that motile *T.cruzi* were seen in individual culture tubes which had been kept at room temperature for about 6 years; the majority of the species with which they worked, however, survived in individual cultures for only 1–4 months.

Most species of *Leishmania* and *Trypanosoma* (except the Salivaria) will grow in any of the diphasic media mentioned above. Packchanian (1943) records successful growth of *T.rotatorium*, *T.avium*, *T.theileri* (= *T.'americanum'*), *T.melophagium*, *T.lewisi*, *T.duttoni*, *T.cruzi*, *Leishmania tropica* and *L.donovani* in nutrient agar-blood medium at room temperature; Preston (1966) has used similar media at about 20°C for *T.rajae*. Wallace (1956) and Lehmann (1962b) have grown *T.ranarum* in Diamond & Herman's (1954) SNB-9 (p. 13) at 20–25°C; and Lehmann (1966) has obtained even better growth of this species in SNB-9 prepared with lysed instead of whole blood; Rioux *et al.* (1966) have grown *T.pestanai* of the badger in NNN medium at 25°C. Desowitz (1963) grew *T.conorrhini* in a similar medium at 25–27°C: at 37°C he found that haematozoic (blood-stream) forms developed (this subject will be discussed in more detail in the next section). Shaw (1964) used NNN and other diphasic media, as well as several monophasic media, for *Endotrypanum schaudinni*. In contrast, Grewal (1957) failed to obtain development of *T.nabiasi* (from rabbits) in NNN and other media (including Noguchi-Wenyon, see p. 22 below), and Dr T.D. Cotton (personal communication) has evidence that there is at least one species of trypanosome of birds which will not develop in various blood-agar media.

4N nutrient agar–blood medium
(Baker, 1966)

MEDIUM

1 *Preparation of base*

Add 40 g Oxoid blood agar base no. 2 (Oxo Ltd) to 1 l. of distilled water, mix and dissolve by steaming or autoclaving. Dispense while molten in 5 ml aliquots into screw-capped glass bottles (30 ml capacity) and autoclave again if necessary. When cooled to about 45°c, add aseptically to each bottle 20 drops (about 1 ml) of fresh rabbit blood and allow base to set in a slant at the base of the bottle. The composition of the base (before addition of the blood) is stated by the manufacturers to be:

> Proteose peptone ....15 g/l.
> Liver digest ....2·5 g/l.
> Yeast extract.................5 g/l.
> Sodium chloride...............5 g/l.
> Agar........................12 g/l.

pH approximately 7·4.

2 *Overlay*

Modified Locke's solution as used by Tobie *et al.* (1950: see p. 32), containing 200 units benzylpenicillin B.P. and streptomycin sulphate B.P. equivalent to 2 mg of base, is added, 1 ml to each bottle containing 5 ml of agar.

3 After addition of the overlay, the bottles are incubated at 37°c for 12–24 hr to check sterility and then stored at about 4°c, for 24 hr or more before use (to allow for equilibriation between base and overlay).

TECHNIQUE

Cultures on this medium may be incubated at 28°c, or at room temperature. Transfers, using a bacteriological wire loop, to fresh medium will usually need to be made once or twice a week.

SNB-9 medium
(Diamond & Herman, 1954)

MEDIUM

1 *Preparation of base*

Dissolve 0·6 g sodium chloride, 2 g neopeptone (Difco) and 2 g agar in 100 ml water by autoclaving (16 lb, 20 min). Cool to 50°c, and add

25 ml sterile defibrinated rabbit blood. Dispense in 2 ml aliquots to suitable test-tubes and allow to set in a slant.

2 *Overlay*

Add to each tube (after solidification) 0·5 ml sterile broth (prepared as for the base but with agar omitted).

TECHNIQUE

After incubating at 37°c to check sterility in the usual way, cultures are inoculated and incubated at room temperature (or at 28°c, if required).

Heated blood-agar medium
(Neal & Miles, 1963)

MEDIUM

1 *Preparation of base*

A conventional nutrient agar (see the two media described immediately above) plus 10% defibrinated rabbit blood is steamed at atmospheric pressure for 10–15 min, and allowed to solidify in a slant in suitable vessels.

2 *Overlay*

To each vessel containing base, is added (in proportions not specified) a solution of sodium chloride (0·85%) and glucose (1%) in distilled water.

TECHNIQUE

No details are given: the medium is presumably used similarly to those described immediately above.

NOTE: This medium is suitable for *L.donovani*, *L.tropica*, *L.enriettii*, *L.braziliensis*, *L.adleri* and *T.cruzi*: growth up to 40,000 to 100,000 flagellates per mm^3 is achieved after 3–5 days.

NNN medium
(Wenyon, 1926, slightly modified)

MEDIUM

Dissolve (by heat) 14 g agar and 6 g sodium chloride in 900 ml distilled water. Autoclave, dispense into tubes (about 5 ml each): autoclave again if necessary, cool to 50°c and add aseptically to each tube 20 drops (about 1 ml) fresh rabbit blood. Allow to set in a slant and then incubate at 37°c for 1 or more days to check sterility. Refrigerate before use. If screw-capped tubes are not used, cotton plugs and rubber caps must be employed to prevent contamination and dessication.

TECHNIQUE

This medium may be incubated (after inoculation) at room temperature or 28°c. Transfers to fresh medium are usually necessary every 1 or 2 weeks.

NOTE: The original recipes did not include the addition of any overlay: sufficient liquid is expelled from the base during the initial incubation and refrigeration. However, for ease of handling and the production of larger numbers of flagellates, many workers now add 1–2 ml of a suitable overlay (saline, glucose-saline, Locke's fluid, etc.) to each tube: cf. Nattan-Larrier & Grimard-Richard (1934) and the 4N and heated blood-agar media described above.

2. MONOPHASIC (UNDEFINED) MEDIA

It is convenient to consider separately those monophasic media designed especially for *T.cruzi*, and those used mainly for other species of *Trypanosoma* and for *Leishmania*. Some media are known to be suitable for organisms of both groups, and this is likely to be true of many of the others also.

(i) *Trypanosoma cruzi*
The Noguchi-Wenyon medium, originally designed for *Leishmania* and certain non-pathogenic trypanosomes but subsequently found to be suitable for the long-term maintenance of *T.cruzi* also, is described on pp. 22–23. Other variants of this medium have been used exclusively for *T.cruzi* by Kelser (1936) and Silva (1954). Using a similar medium, Lwoff (1938) showed that for growing *T.cruzi*, whole blood could be replaced by serum, haemin and *l*-ascorbic acid, all three being essential. Boné & Parent (1963) identified the essential constituent of serum as stearic acid, but this was questioned by Lambrecht (1966). Various other monophasic media have been devised for *T.cruzi*: some are listed in Table 1.3. The medium described by Little and his co-workers (Little & Subbarow, 1945;

TABLE 1.3. Some monophasic media which have been used for the cultivation of *Trypanosoma* (except Salivaria) and *Leishmania* at temperatures below 37°c.

Author(s)	Date	Name	Species*	Detailed description (if any)
Adler	1934	—	Many	—
Adler & Ashbel	1934	—	*Leishmania*	—
Archetti	1938	—	*Leishmania*	—
Baracchini	1965	—	*T.cruzi*	—
Boné & Parent†	1963	T2	*T.cruzi*	p. 24
Boné & Steinert	1956	—	*T.cruzi, T.mega*	p. 19
Camargo	1964	—	*T.cruzi*	—
Chang	1947	—	*Leishmania, T.cruzi*	—
Citri & Grossowicz	1954	—	*T.cruzi*	—
Deane & Deane	1961	HLS	*T.conorrhini*	—
Deane & Kirchner	1963	No. IV	*T.conorrhini*	—
de Freitas & Hausmann	1954	DP-40	*T.cruzi*	—
Fromentin	1964	—	*T.therezieni*	—
Fulton & Joyner	1949	—	*Leishmania*	p. 20
Halevy & Gisry	1964	—	*T.ranarum*	—
Hoare	1923	—	*T.melophagium*	—
Jadin (see Wéry & de Groodt-Lasseel	1966)	—	Many	p. 20
Kelser	1936	—	*T.cruzi*	—
Kligler	1924	—	*L.tropica*	—
Kligler	1926	—	*L.tropica*	—
Little (see Sampath & Little	1949)	—	*T.cruzi*	p. 21
Little & Oleson†	1951	—	*T.cruzi*	p. 25
Lwoff (see Jadin & Pierreux	1960)	—	*T.cruzi*	—
Noguchi & Lindenberg	1925	—	*L.tropica*	—
Ponselle	1923	—	*T.inopinatum*	—
Salle & Schmidt	1928	—	*L.tropica*	—
Seneca & Henderson	1951	—	*T.cruzi, L.donovani*	—
Silva	1954	—	*T.cruzi*	—
Simpson & Green	1959	—	*T.theileri*	—
Trager†	1957	C	*L.tarentolae*	p. 26
Wallace	1956	—	*T.ranarum*	—
Warren	1960	—	*T.cruzi*	—
Wenyon	1921	Noguchi-Wenyon	Many	p. 22
Zeledon	1959	—	*T.cruzi*	p. 23

* Species for which medium was originally used: others may grow equally well.
† Defined or nearly-defined media.

Sampath & Little, 1949) can be sterilized by autoclaving and is suitable for use in large volumes (up to 5 l.) (p. 21). Zeledon (1959) used a medium in which *T.cruzi* developed, but *T.rangeli* did not grow unless fresh rabbit's blood dialysate were added (p. 23): this medium could be of practical use as a supplement to the morphological differential diagnosis of these two organisms. Boné & Steinert (1956) described a medium for *T.cruzi* (p. 19) which was subsequently developed into a nearly defined medium for the same species (see p. 24). Jadin and his colleagues (Jadin & Pierreux, 1960; Jadin & Wéry, 1963; Wéry & de Groodt-Lasseel, 1966) have described a medium (p. 20) in which *T.cruzi* has been maintained for 600 passages without losing its infectivity to mice, rats and rabbits (Jadin, Wéry, LeRay & Gatti, 1966); several other species of *Trypanosoma* (including Salivaria) and of *Leishmania*, as well as *Strigomonas oncopelti*, grow in this medium with greater or lesser success. Wéry & de Groodt-Lasseel (1966) divided growth in this medium into three phases: logarithmic multiplication (days 2–5), stationary phase (days 5–16), and phase of gradual death and lysis (days 15–180). The maximum number of flagellates developing in the medium was 1,160,000 per mm^3.

Seneca & Henderson (1951) and Fife & Kent (1960) grew *T.cruzi* inside sacs of dialysis tubing; the former used the medium described by Senekjie (1943), while the latter authors used Little & Subbarow's (1945) recipe (later modified by Sampath & Little, 1949).

(ii)   Leishmania *and other species of* Trypanosoma

Wenyon (1921) added whole blood instead of serum to a semi-solid medium used by Noguchi for cultivating spirochaetes, and found it suitable for the growth of *L.donovani*, *L.tropica*, *T.lewisi*, *T.melophagium* and *Leptomonas* sp. This medium (p. 22), known as 'Wenyon-Noguchi' or, more correctly, 'Noguchi-Wenyon' medium, is suitable for all species of *Leishmania* and many of *Trypanosoma* (though not the Salivaria). Its main advantage is that cultures in it grow slowly and hence survive for several weeks or months (at room temperature) without the need for transfer (if dessication is prevented). From such cultures, luxuriant growth in more nutritious diphasic blood-agar media (e.g. NNN or 4N, pp. 13, 14) can be readily obtained when required.

Kligler (1924) similarly modified Noguchi's medium for use with *L.tropica*, and Noguchi & Lindenberg (1925) reported growth of this species in Noguchi's medium enriched with erythrocyte extract. Subsequently, Kligler (1926) reported growth of *L.tropica* in this medium with added glucose, and serum instead of blood. Other authors have obtained growth of this and other trypanosomatids in monophasic media containing serum instead of blood (Adler, 1934; Adler & Ashbel, 1934; Marinkelle, 1965), presumably due to the presence of sufficient haematin in the serum (Lwoff, 1951: see p. 12 above). Adler & Theodor (1926) noticed that, when homologous antiserum was used in preparing Kligler's medium, the parasites developed as agglutinated masses of amastigote ('L.D.') forms; an observation subsequently developed as a serological method of identification of species of *Leishmania* (Adler *et al.*, 1966).

Among the simpler monophasic media are the mixture of equal parts of rabbit's blood and water in which Ponselle (1923) obtained growth of *T.inopinatum* of the frog (but not, apparently, of *T.rotatorium* from the same host), and Archetti's (1938) mixture of equal volumes of citrated blood and Ringer's solution for *L.donovani*. Diamond & Herman (1954) tried to obtain growth of avian trypanosomes in Ponselle's medium, with little success.

More sophisticated types of monophasic media include that of Jadin and his colleagues (p. 20), in which *L.tropica*, *L.donovani*, *L.enriettii*, *T.lewisi*, *T.rangeli*, *T.theileri* (after patient adaptation), as well as *T.cruzi* and salivarian trypanosomes, have been grown (Jadin & Wéry, 1963). A similar medium has been used by Halevy & Gisry (1964) for *Trypanosoma ranarum* of the frog; these authors added, instead of whole blood, haemin (1 mg%) and rabbit serum (5%) to the basal medium (Hanks's BSS with added nutrients). Multiplication of the parasite also occurred for at least one or two consecutive sub-cultures in their medium without serum. Wallace (1956) grew the same species (*T.ranarum*) in a modification of Diamond & Herman's (1954) SNB-9 medium (see p. 13) without agar and containing only 5% (v/v) of defibrinated rabbit blood. He found, however that growth was less good than in the conventional diphasic SNB-9 medium, a fact which he ascribed to the action of the solid part of the medium as a 'reserve of nutrients which diffuse into the small amount of liquid'.

Simpson & Green (1959) cultivated *T.theileri* in a commercially-available nutrient broth (trypticase soy broth, Baltimore Biological Laboratory) plus 2% of a solution prepared by lysing whole bovine blood with ten times its volume of water and removing the debris by centrifugation. They added 12·5 ml blood from the ox being investigated to 50 ml of this medium, and the cultures were incubated (surprisingly) at 37°c. It is a pity that the authors were not explicit about the morphology of the flagellates developing in this medium: Ristic & Trager (1958) found that haematozoic forms of *T.theileri* developed in a very similar medium at 37°c (see p. 38). Herbert (1965), however, was unable to obtain growth of *T.theileri* in Ristic & Trager's medium (*loc. cit.*) at 37°c, although growth was satisfactory at 28°c. Simpson & Green's method is closely similar to the technique used by Hoare (1923) to diagnose infections of *T.melophagium* in sheep: Hoare merely added defibrinated blood from the sheep being examined to bacteriological nutrient broth (in proportions of 1:1 or 1:2), incubated the cultures at 30°c, and examined them after about 1 week.

Fromentin (1964) cultivated *T.therezieni* of the badger in a monophasic medium consisting of tissue culture medium 199 (see p. 355) enriched either with 5% of the liquid phase of Tobie's medium (p. 32), prepared with human blood, or by incubation at 37°c for 24 hr with rat erythrocytes, which were subsequently removed by centrifugation. The organism also grew in Tobie's diphasic medium.

A monophasic medium has been developed especially for *Leishmania donovani* by Fulton & Joyner (1949) (p. 20). The medium of Boné & Steinert (1956), referred to above in connection with *T.cruzi*, is suitable for the growth of *T.mega* (of frogs) and possibly other species also. For growth of *T.mega*, the medium can be used without added serum.

T. mega and *T. cruzi*
(Boné & Steinert, 1956)

MEDIUM

1   *Composition*

Sodium chloride ....4 g
Sodium phosphate ($Na_3PO_4.12H_2O$) 5 g
Potassium chloride ....0·4 g
Glucose ....2 g
Bacto-tryptose (Difco) ....15 g
Oxoid liver infusion (Oxo) ....1 g
Haemin (see below) ....20 mg
Water ....1 l.

pH 7·8.

2   *Preparation*

(a)   Haemin is added as a solution prepared by grinding 20 mg of haemin in 10 ml of ethanol and 10 ml of 0·025 molar sodium hydroxide (Steinert, 1958b).

(b)   Sterilize the complete medium by autoclaving (10 lb, 10 min), during which the ethanol evaporates.

TECHNIQUE

After inoculation, incubate at 24°–26°c.

NOTE: As constituted above, the medium is suitable for *T.mega*. With

3

the addition of 2% v/v fresh calf serum, it is also suitable for *T.cruzi* (Boné & Parent, 1963). Some workers find 20% serum better.

Leishmania spp.
(Fulton & Joyner, 1949)

MEDIUM

1   Mix 1 l. of 0·9% aqueous sodium chloride with 20 ml of 1·15% aqueous potassium chloride, add 2 g of glucose and autoclave.

2   Prepare a nutrient solution as follows:

(a)   Steam 1 lb (0·45 kg) minced ox liver in 1 l. slightly acid tap water for 2 hr and filter.

(b)   Lyse 1 volume of defibrinated rabbit blood in 2 volumes of distilled water, centrifuge to remove deposit.

(c)   Mix the following:

> Liver extract (a above) ....50 ml
> Erythrocyte extract (b above) ....40 ml
> Rabbit serum.................100 ml
> 20% w/v aq. Bacto-peptone
> (Difco).....................10 ml

3   Mix 30 ml saline (1 above) with 6 ml nutrient solution (2c above), adjust pH to 8·0–8·2 and sterilize by filtration.

TECHNIQUE

Dispense the medium aseptically either in 3–4 ml aliquots in test-tubes or 36 ml aliquots in 100 ml conical flasks. After inoculation, incubate at 25°c. Maximum numbers occur after 10–12 days, but serial transfers to fresh medium are usually made weekly.

T.cruzi and other trypanosomatids
(Jadin & Wéry, 1963; Wéry & de Groodt-Lasseel, 1966)

MEDIUM

> Hanks's BSS (see p. 350) ....850 ml
> Lactalbumin hydrolysate (Difco) ....5 g
> Glucose ....1 g
> Beef blood (Difco)* ....150 ml
> Calf serum ....200 ml
> Penicillin................200 units/ml
> Streptomycin..............200 µg/ml

* An aqueous solution of ox haemoglobin.

TECHNIQUE

The above medium (presumably sterilized by filtration) is used in 300 ml aliquots in flasks. Cultures are incubated at 28°C after inoculation; transfers to fresh medium are made twice weekly.

T.cruzi
(Sampath & Little, 1949)

MEDIUM

1   *Basal medium*
(per 100 ml)

Bacto-peptone (Difco)	1 g
Casamino acids (Difco)	1 g
Sodium chloride	0·5 g
Glucose	0·2 g
β-Alanine	10 mg
Glycine	10 mg
Folic acid	2 mg
Nicotinamide	2 mg
Thiamine	2 mg
Choline	2 mg

Adjust pH to 7·5.

The life of cultures is prolonged if 1% 'corn steep liquor' (made alkaline, filtered and neutralized before use) is added to the medium, but this is not essential.

2   *Red cell coagulum*
(Little & Subbarow, 1945)
One hundred millilitres of fresh rabbit erythrocytes are poured into 1 l. of rapidly boiling distilled water, mixed thoroughly and boiled for 10 min. The resulting wet coagulum is collected while hot by filtration through cheesecloth. When partially dry, it can either be used as described under 3(a) below or transferred to trays lined with absorbent paper and completely dried at 37°C for 48 hr with regular stirring to aid granule formation. The dry granules (ground to powder if required) can be stored indefinitely in a dry place: they contain about 90·5% protein and 7·8% haematin.

3   *Preparation*
(a)   The basal medium (1 above) may be mixed with the fresh, semi-dry coagulum (10 g/100 ml) in a mechanical homogenizer (Waring blender),

and filtered. This 'activated filtrate' forms the complete medium, which can be autoclaved and stored for several months in a refrigerator.

(b)   Alternatively, aliquots of basal medium (5 ml) and dried granules of coagulum (100 mg) may be mixed in test-tubes and autoclaved (15 lb for 20 min). Larger volumes of medium, up to 5 l., may be used (in flasks), the basal medium and coagulum being mixed in the proportions of 1 l. to 10 g.

TECHNIQUE

After inoculation, the medium is incubated at 28°c. Maximum numbers occur after 5–8 days; cultures may be subinoculated (0·2–0·5 ml amounts) after 1 or 2 weeks.

Noguchi-Wenyon medium for many species of trypanosomatids
(Wenyon, 1921)

MEDIUM

1   Mix the following (easier if warmed):

> 0·85% sodium chloride solution
>   (pH 7·6) ....270 ml
> 2% nutrient agar* ....30 ml

* Any commercial nutrient agar is suitable: e.g. 'Oxoid' (Oxo Ltd).

2   Dispense 10 ml aliquots into narrow test-tubes ($8 \times \frac{1}{2}$ in, $20 \times 1\cdot25$ cm, are suitable), with cotton plugs: autoclave.

3   Cool to 50°c and add to each tube 20 drops (c. 1 ml) or less of fresh rabbit blood. Do not mix, but allow to cool in a vertical position.

4   Incubate for about 24 hr at 37°c to check sterility.

TECHNIQUE

The medium is inoculated with a sterile Pasteur pipette just (about 0·5 cm) below the surface, and incubated at room temperature. Depending on the strain of organisms, cultures will remain viable for weeks or months. The flagellates form a whitish zone in the semi-solid agar, which gradually moves down the tube: transfers to fresh medium (or to other media such as NNN) are made by removing a small amount of material from this zone with a sterile Pasteur pipette and inoculating it to the new medium.

Because the tubes are narrow, dessication is seldom a problem: however, they may be capped if desired.

NOTE: This medium is usually used for long-term maintenance; if the organisms are multiplying too fast (so that frequent subinoculation becomes necessary), growth may be slowed by reducing the amount of blood added but some blood is essential.

Medium for distinguishing
T.cruzi from *T.rangeli*
(Zeledon, 1959)

MEDIUM

Add 10% sheep blood which has been frozen and thawed (or 10% horse serum and 3 mg/100 ml haematin) to Difco brain–heart infusion and heat to boiling. Filter (through ordinary filter paper) and autoclave.

TECHNIQUE

Technical details are not given: presumably the medium is used in test-tubes at about 24–28°c. *T.cruzi* grows in this medium, whereas *T.rangeli* does not: however, *T.rangeli* can grow if fresh rabbit blood contained in a sac of dialysis membrane is placed in the medium.

3. DEFINED AND ALMOST DEFINED MEDIA

Citri & Grossowicz (1955) and Boné & Parent (1963) have each devised media for growing *T.cruzi* with only one constituent which is undefined, casein hydrolyzate and Bacto-tryptose (Difco) respectively. Little & Oleson (1951) used a defined medium plus an erythrocyte supplement in the form of a 50% saline suspension of washed chick erythrocytes absorbed on to filter paper and autoclaved (see p. 26). During the development of this medium, they found that Bacto-tryptose (Difco), 15 mg/ml, could be replaced by a mixture of adenylic, orotic and cytidylic acids and glutamine (20 µg/ml each) and sodium acetate (5 µg/ml). Whether this mixture could successfully replace the Bacto-tryptose in Boné & Parent's (1963) recipe (p. 24), so producing a completely defined medium for *T.cruzi* is, apparently, unknown.

The only report to date of growth of a species of *Trypanosoma* in a completely defined medium is that of Guttman (1966b). She has grown

T.ranarum in her defined medium for monogenetic trypanosomatids (p. 6), and *T.mega* in the same medium 'supplemented with energy-yielding amino acids and lipids'. In these media, both species become transformed to the trypomastigote (i.e. trypanosome) form upon addition of blood to the culture, an interesting observation which should assist experimental study of this morphogenetic process (see below, pp. 35–36).

Trager (1957) has grown *Leishmania tarentolae* (a parasite of lizards) in both partially and wholly defined media. The defined medium (p. 26) was developed from the undefined by replacing the supplemented casein hydrolysate ('Parenamine', Winthrop-Stearns) by a known amino acid mixture, omitting bovine plasma fraction V, adding certain metals and doubling the concentration of folic acid. Trager (*loc. cit.*) was unable to cultivate *L.donovani* in this medium, and Jackson (1963) obtained only limited success in modifying it to support *L.enriettii*.

Krassner (1965) found that the growth of *L.tarentolae* in Trager's defined medium at 28°C was enhanced by the addition of human erythrocyte extract; clearly the defined medium does not completely supply the parasite's nutritional requirements. Growth at 33°C was impossible without the erythrocyte extract.

Medium T2 for *T.cruzi*
(Boné & Parent, 1963)

MEDIUM

1 *Composition*

Bacto-tryptose (Difco)	15 g
Glucose	2 g
Thiamine	1 mg
Folic acid	3 mg
Haemin (see note 1)	20 mg
Sodium stearate (see note 2)	25 mg
Sodium chloride	4 g
Sodium phosphate ($Na_3PO_4.12H_2O$)	5 g
Potassium chloride	0·4 g
Water	1 l.

2 *Preparation*

(a) See p. 19 for details of addition of haemin.

(b) Sodium stearate is added as a freshly prepared colloidal solution of 20 mg stearic acid in 1·7 ml 0·1 N sodium hydroxide and 98·3 ml distilled water; the mixture is heated at 70°C for 30 min with constant stirring.

(c) Adjust pH to 7·6 and autoclave at 115°c for 10 min.

TECHNIQUE

Details are not given: the medium is presumably used in test-tubes at about 24–28°c.

NOTE: Lambrecht (1966) questioned the need for stearate: he found much better growth in this medium when supplemented with the overlay from Johnson's (1947) medium which had been in contact with the base for 48 hr.

Nearly defined medium for *T.cruzi*
(Little & Oleson, 1951)

MEDIUM

1 *Liquid phase*

(a) Prepare five stock solutions (i)–(v) at 10 times the final concentration shown: these stock solutions may be stored in a refrigerator.

(i) Amino acids	mg/l.
DL-Aspartic acid	200
L-Glutamic acid	180
L-Arginine	50
L-Histidine	50
L-Lysine	50
L-Cystine	60
L-Cysteine	50
DL-Methionine	100
DL-Phenylalanine	100
L-Tyrosine	30
DL-Tryptophan	220
L-Proline	110
Hydroxy-L-proline	75
Glycine	100
DL-α-Alanine	100
DL-Serine	100
DL-Threonine	50
DL-Valine	100
L-Leucine	50
DL-Isoleucine	100
DL-Norleucine	100

(ii) Buffer	g/l.
Sodium phosphate (Na_3PO_4)	5
Sodium chloride	4
Potassium chloride	0·4

(iii) Vitamins	mg/l.
Thiamine	0·40
Riboflavin	0·80
Ca-pantothenate	0·80
Pyridoxine	1·60
p-Aminobenzoic acid	0·80
Meso-inositol	0·80
Choline chloride	1·60
Pteroylglutamic acid	1·00
Biotin	0·40
Nicotinamide	0·80

(iv) Carbohydrate	
Glucose	2,500

(v) Miscellaneous	
Guanosine	30
Adenine sulphate	20
Uracil	50
Uric acid	15
Urea	140
Creatine	20
Creatinine	30
Nucleic acid (yeast)	100

(b)   Mix equal volumes of the stock solutions, dilute tenfold with distilled water and add the following:

Adenylic acid	20 μg/ml
Glutamine	20 μg/ml
Orotic acid	20 μg/ml
Cytidylic acid	20 μg/ml
Sodium acetate	5 μg/ml

(If near-definity is not required, these ingredients can all be replaced by Bacto-tryptose (Difco) at 15 mg/ml.)

(c)   Adjust pH to 7·2 with normal hydrochloric acid (about 38 ml/l.).

(d)   If a semi-solid medium is required, add agar (Difco), 0·2% (*T.cruzi* will grow in either the liquid or semi-solid version).

2   'RBC strips'

Sheets of Whatman No. 2 filter paper are dipped into a 50% suspension of washed erythrocytes (chick or rabbit) in saline, immediately drained and hung up to dry. When dry, the sheets are cut into strips measuring $1 \times \frac{3}{8}$ in (2·5 × 1 cm) and placed in Petri dishes for autoclaving and storage.

3   *Final preparation*

(1)   Dispense in 5 ml aliquots in test-tubes ($6 \times \frac{5}{8}$ in, 15 × 1·5 cm) containing one previously autoclaved 'RBC strip' per tube.

(2)   Autoclave completed tubes at 120°c for 20 min.

TECHNIQUE

Further details are not given: incubation is presumably at 24–28°c.

Defined medium C for *Leishmania tarentolae*
(Trager, 1957)

MEDIUM

1   *Composition of stock solutions*

Final
concentration
in mg/100 ml

(a)

NaCl	200
Na_2HPO_4	125
KH_2PO_4	50

Final
concentration
in mg/100 ml

Haemin ....2·5
L–Arginine HCl..................30
L–Histidine 15
L–Isoleucine 60
L–Leucine 150
L–Lysine HCl....................125
DL–Methionine 30
DL–Phenylalanine 40
DL–Threonine 50
DL–Tryptophan 20
DL–Valine 50
DL–Alanine 70
DL–Aspartic acid 120
Glycine 10
L–Glutamic acid.................190
L–Proline 50
DL–Serine.......................40
L–Tyrosine 40
Total amino acids . . 1090

(b)

Riboflavin, thiamine, pyridoxine,
   pyridoxal pyridoxamine . . . each 0·2
Calcium pantothenate ....0·8
p-Aminobenzoic acid..............0·3
Nicotinamide ....0·5
Biotin...........................0·02
Inositol, choline chloride . . . . each 0·3
Adenine, guanine, xanthine,
   uracil .... each 0·17
Cytidylic acid ....0·05
Glucose 500

(c)

Folic acid.......................0·16

(d)

$CaCl_2$...........................2·6

(e)

$MgSO_4.7H_2O$...................100

(f)

	Metal	Salt
$ZnSO_4.7H_2O$............	0·50	2·2
$FeSO_4.7H_2O$	0·20	1·0
$MnSO_4.4H_2O$	0·10	0·4
$CuSO_4$....................	0·02	0·05
$CoSO_4.7H_2O$	0·01	0·044
H_3BO_3..................	0·002	0·011

2 *Preparation of stock solutions*

(a) Solution (a) is prepared at twice the final concentration by first dissolving the amino acids in about three-fifths the final volume of boiling water. The salts are then added, followed by the haemin which has been previously dissolved by grinding with a little 0·05 N sodium hydroxide. The pH is adjusted to 7·8–8·0, the solution diluted to the required volume and autoclaved (15 lb for 15 min).

(b) Solution (b) contains its ingredients at 10 times their final concentration. The purines and pyrimidines are dissolved separately in 2 ml of 6 N HCl and the resulting solution diluted and brought to pH 6·7–6·8 before being added to a solution of the vitamins. The mixture is diluted to the required volume, the glucose added and the whole sterilized by filtration.

(c) Solution (c) contains 5 mg of folic acid dissolved, with the aid of 3 drops of 0·01 N NaOH and gentle heating, in 100 ml of water: it is sterilized by autoclaving. The final pH is 6·7–6·8.

(d) Solutions (d), (e) and (f) contain the salts at 100 times their final concentration and are sterilized by autoclaving: in solution (f) a fine red precipitate forms which is stirred into even suspension before removing a measured volume.

3 *Final preparation*

Mix the stock solutions aseptically in the following proportions in sterile 25 ml conical (Erlenmeyer) flasks plugged with cotton: the total volume in each flask is brought to 3 ml with sterile distilled water.

Stock solution	Ml per total volume (3 ml)
(a)	1·5
(b)	0·3
(c)	0·1
(d), (e), (f) each	0·03
	1·99

TECHNIQUE

Inoculate each flask with 3 drops of suspension from a previous 7 days old culture (or with washed leptomonads from such a culture) and incubate at 26–27°C. Transfer to fresh medium weekly, when the population should be about 20–50 million parasites per ml.

III. SALIVARIAN TRYPANOSOMES

(i)   *Methods of cultivation*
This group is dealt with separately as it has proved the most refractory to cultivation of all members of the family: neither growth in defined media, nor development of the haematozoic forms, has yet been achieved. Some of the media which have been used are listed in Table 1.4.

TABLE 1.4. Some media which have been used for the cultivation of salivarian trypanosomes at temperatures below 37°C.

Author(s)	Date	Name	Species	Detailed description (if any)
Brutsaert & Henrard	1938	—	*T.b. gambiense*	—
Dodin & Fromentin	1962	—	*T.b. gambiense*	—
Lehmann	1960	MM-7	*T.brucei* sspp.	—
		NN-auto	*T.brucei* sspp.	—
Lehmann	1961b	T-H	*T.brucei* sspp.,	—
		NAB	*T.congolense*	
Lehmann	1964	NAB-AS	*T.brucei* sspp.	—
Nicoli	1961	—	*T.b. gambiense*	—
Novy & M(a)cNeal	1903, 1904	NN	*T.b. brucei*	—
Ponselle	1924	—	*T.brucei* sspp. *T.dimorphon*	—
von Razgha	1929	—	*T.brucei* sspp.	—
Reichenow	1934	—	*T.gambiense, T.cruzi T.congolense*	—
Thomson & Sinton	1912	—	*T.brucei* sspp.	—
Tobie *et al.*	1950	—	*T.brucei* sspp., *T.congolense*	p. 32
Weinman	1944	—	*T.b. gambiense*	—
Weinman	1960a	—	*T.brucei* sspp.	p. 33

Amongst the earlier workers, Novy & MacNeal (1903, 1904) and Thomson & Sinton (1912) obtained some success in growing *T.brucei** in diphasic blood-agar medium, but agreed that this species was very difficult to grow, and success was erratic.

Ponselle (1924) used a monophasic medium consisting of an alkaline

---

* *T.rhodesiense* and *T.gambiense* are here treated as subspecies of *T.brucei*: see Hoare (1966).

saline solution of peptone and gelatine containing whole blood (rabbit): he considered that the concentration of sodium chloride should be varied for different species from 0·3% (*T.brucei brucei*) to 0·8% (*T.b.rhodesiense* and *T.dimorphon*). Prates (1928) found that Ponselle's method was unreliable, and that the saline concentration was of no importance (within the range used by Ponselle).

Von Razgha (1929) and Reichenow (1934) reported some success in growing *T.b. gambiense* and *T.b. rhodesiense* (and, in the latter paper, *T.congolense* and *T.cruzi*) in a simple suspension of citrated human blood in Ringer's solution (with 0·6% NaCl): the proportions of blood, citrate and Ringer's solution were 3:1:4 (von Razgha) and 2:2:4 (Reichenow). Brutsaert & Henrard (1938) used an almost identical medium for the cultivation of *T.b. gambiense*, but obtained far more reliable results than the previous workers by using Liquoid (Roche) as anticoagulant when collecting blood samples from patients for diagnosis of sleeping sickness. They obtained positive cultures from human blood in which microscopical demonstration of parasites had failed. In their medium (as in von Razgha's) the erythrocytes settled at the bottom of the tube and growth of trypanosomes occurred mainly at the surface of this layer. According to the Merck Index (Stecher, 1960), Liquoid is sodium polyanetholesulfonate, a substance which inhibits coagulation and is also anti-complementary. It was doubtless the anti-complementary property of this substance which accounted for Brutsaert and Henrard's success in isolating *T.b. gambiense* from human blood.

Weinman (1944, 1946) evolved a diphasic medium which supported subcultures of *T.b. gambiense* apparently indefinitely: when he too used an anti-complementary substance (polyvinyl sulphuric acid or PVSA) as anti-coagulant when collecting blood samples, Weinman (1960a) obtained reproducible success in the use of his medium (p. 33) for diagnosis and isolation from both blood and cerebrospinal fluid, as well as for routine maintenance, of *T.brucei* sspp. It seems likely that Liquoid could be used instead of PVSA in Weinman's medium, which might simplify its production.

Tobie *et al.* (1950) described a diphasic nutrient blood–agar medium for the routine maintenance of *T.brucei* sspp. which closely resembles Weinman's medium, but rabbit blood was used instead of human, and the erythrocytes were not separated before inactivation of the plasma. It is possible that this medium (p. 32) would serve equally well for diagnosis by isolation of trypanosomes if either PVSA or Liquoid were used when collecting the blood inoculum. Subsequently, Tobie (1958) showed that *T.congolense* could be isolated and maintained in this medium, though not without some difficulty: isolation was achieved only when human (rather than rabbit) blood was used in the base.

Lehmann (1960, 1961b, 1962a, 1964) has studied the cultivation of *T.b. brucei* and *T.b. rhodesiense* in a variety of diphasic blood-agar media, including autoclaved media (Lehmann, 1960 and 1964); he has obtained some indications of differential nutritional requirements and growth patterns of different strains, and thinks these may possibly represent sub-specific differences.

A few authors have tried to obtain growth of salivarian trypanosomes in media of a type which might ultimately lead to the development of a defined medium. Nicoli (1961) has grown a strain of *T.b. gambiense* in a balanced saline (Earle's or Ringer's) solution of lactalbumin hydrolysate (Difco), calf serum, extract of human erythrocytes (lysed) and glucose: the lactalbumin hydrolysate could be replaced by thirteen (unspecified) amino acids. An inoculum of about 100 trypanosomes per mm^3 increased to about 32,000 per mm^3 after 96–120 hr at 26°c. Dodin & Fromentin (1962) reported rather similar results, using an unpublished modification of tissue culture medium 199 and various blood fractions. The medium used by Jadin and his colleagues for several other trypanosomatids (see p. 20) is also suitable for *T.vivax* and the three subspecies of *T.brucei* (Jadin & Wéry, 1963).

(ii) *Infectivity of cultures of the Salivaria*

Gordon & Miller (1961) demonstrated that a culture of *T.b. rhodesiense* (in Weinman's medium) was infective to *Glossina morsitans*: of a few tsetse flies which fed on the culture through a membrane of guinea-pig skin, one developed metacyclic trypanosomes in its salivary glands 27 days later. Reichenow (1939) had earlier conducted a similar experiment using *T.b. gambiense* and *T.congolense*, but had obtained rather equivocal results as none of his flies produced metacyclic trypanosomes.

There have been several reports of sporadic infectivity of cultures of *T.brucei* sspp. to laboratory rodents. At one time this was thought to be due to the addition of trehalose or other sugars to the medium (Weinman, 1960b; Geigy & Kaufmann, 1964) and, since these substances were also present in tsetse fly tissues, speculation arose that they might be responsible for the reacquisition of infectivity by the flagellates at the end of their developmental cycle in the fly. However, Lehmann (1961a) was not able to reproduce this effect, and Bowman et al. (1960) showed that trehalose is rapidly hydrolyzed to glucose by a specific enzyme (trehalase) present in the blood of many vertebrates: hence in culture media containing blood, trehalose itself would be unlikely to remain unchanged long enough to exert any effect on the trypanosomes. When the trehalase was inactivated by autoclaving, Bowman et al. (loc. cit.) obtained no evidence that trehalose was utilized by trypanosomes. Finally, the matter was cleared up by Amrein et al. (1965), who showed that trehalose was not involved in the phenomenon of sporadic acquisition of infectivity by cultures: factors which did, however, play a part were (a) the age of the culture, (b) the (human) donor of the blood used in preparing the medium (Weinman's), and (c) the length of time for which the medium was stored before use.

Maintenance of *T.brucei* sspp. and
T. congolense
(Tobie, von Brand & Mehlman, 1950)

MEDIUM

1 *Solid phase*
(a)   Dissolve 1·5 g Bacto-beef (Difco); 2·5 g Bacto-peptone (Difco); 4·0 g sodium chloride and 7·5 g Bacto-agar (Difco) in 500 ml distilled water (see Note 4). Adjust the pH to 7·2–7·4 with sodium hydroxide and autoclave (15 lb for 20 min).
(b)   Cool this mixture until it can be comfortably held in the hand (about 45°c) then add whole rabbit blood, which has been inactivated at 56°c for 30 min, in the proportion of 25 ml of blood to 75 ml of base. (Coagulation of the whole blood is prevented by using 0·5% sterile sodium citrate.)
(c)   Dispense in amounts of 5 ml or 25 ml into test-tubes or flasks, respectively. The test-tubes are kept in a slanted position and the flasks upright until the base has solidified.

2 *Liquid phase*
Sterile, modified Locke's solution of the following composition: NaCl, 8 g; KCl, 0·2 g; $CaCl_2$, 0·2 g; KH_2PO_4, 0·3 g; glucose, 2·5 g; and distilled water, 1 l. Add this to the solidified base in amounts of 2 ml and 10–15 ml respectively. The tubes and flasks are closed with cotton plugs which need not be capped since subcultures must be made before evaporation becomes serious.

TECHNIQUE

After inoculation, cultures are incubated at 24–25°c. Maximum population (about 21,000/mm^3) is reached between 10 and 14 days after inoculation. Transfers to fresh medium are made every 1–2 weeks.

NOTES: (1) Human blood can be used instead of rabbit blood, but is no better.

(2) If used for isolation from an infected laboratory rodent, the first culture should be allowed to grow for 3 weeks before subinoculation.

(3) A monophasic medium can be prepared by allowing the overlay of the diphasic medium to remain in contact with the base for 6 days and then removing it and using it as the culture medium. In this liquid, maximum growth is less (about 9,000/mm^3 after 8–12 days).

(4) The solid components of the base (excluding the blood elements) are contained in Difco 'Nutrient Agar 1·5%' (Weinman, 1946): hence this product, 15·5 g/500 ml water, can be substituted for the ingredients listed in paragraph 1(a) above.

Diagnosis of *T.brucei* sspp.
(Weinman, 1960a)

MEDIUM

Preparation of base

(a) Dissolve 31 g of Difco 'Nutrient Agar 1·5%' (for composition see the medium described immediately above) and 5 g of plain agar in 1 l. of distilled water: dispense 5 ml aliquots into screw-capped test-tubes and autoclave.

(b) Collect 400–500 ml human blood (using 75 ml of 2·5% sodium citrate as anticoagulant) and separate the erythrocytes from the plasma by centrifugation: inactivate the plasma at 56°C for 30 min, wash the erythrocytes (by centrifuging) 3 times with at least 3 times their volume of isotonic saline, and then recombine the cells and plasma in equal parts by volume.

(c) When the autoclaved agar, (a) above, has cooled to 45°C, add the reconstituted blood (warmed to 45°C) in the proportion of 1 volume to 3 volumes of agar. Mix gently and allow to set in a sloping position.

(d) Incubate the tubes at 37°C for 24 hr and then store in a refrigerator for up to 6 months.

NOTE: No overlay is added to this medium.

Preparation of polyvinyl sulphuric acid (PVSA) (Chargaff *et al.*, 1936)

Suspend 1·04 g dry polyvinyl alcohol in 24 g dry pyridine and slowly add 6 g chlorosulphonic acid to the *chilled* mixture. When the reaction abates, incubate the mixture at 70°c for 1½ hr. Decant the supernatant liquid, and dissolve the rubbery reaction product in 20 ml water (made alkaline with 2 N potassium hydroxide). Add 80 ml ethanol to the solution, cool and collect the precipitate by centrifugation. Re-dissolve the precipitate in 75 ml warm water, filter through cotton wool, and reprecipitate it by the addition of 150 ml alcohol. Repeat the precipitation process twice. Yield: 1·85 g of the potassium salt of PVSA as a white, water-soluble powder. For use, dissolve 0·5 g in 100 ml physiological saline, adjust pH to 7·5 if necessary, and sterilize by filtration.

TECHNIQUE

(a)   For diagnosis, blood is collected from the patient using polyvinyl sulphuric acid (see above for preparation) as anti-coagulant, 0·1 ml of a 0·5% w/v solution in saline for every 1 ml of blood. It is recommended to inoculate 2 ml of blood and anti-coagulant to each of 2 tubes of medium: this must be done promptly since coagulation is inhibited for only about 15 min.

(b)   Antibiotic (usually 0·5 mg of dihydrostreptomycin sulphate or 2,000 units of penicillin, in 0·1 ml of saline) is added to each ml of the inoculated blood.

(c)   The blood is spread over the surface of the agar by tilting the tube a few times, and the latter is then incubated at 25°c in the dark. Cultures should be first examined 5 days after inoculation: if not positive by 30 days they may be discarded. Examination should be made by washing the agar slope with liquid from the bottom of the tube, using a Pasteur pipette, and finally withdrawing a drop of the fluid for microscopic examination: it is recommended that the agar should be gently rubbed with the tip of the pipette during the washing, since trypanosomes often grow as colonies on its surface.

NOTES: (1) This medium is suitable for routine maintenance as well as for isolation of *T.brucei* sspp.

(2) It is possible that Liquoid (Roche Products) would be equally suitable as an anticomplementary anticoagulant: if so, the technique would be simplified since the preparation of PVSA could be omitted.

IV. STAGES OF *LEISHMANIA* AND *TRYPANOSOMA* NORMALLY FOUND IN THEIR VERTEBRATE HOSTS

1. METHODS OTHER THAN TISSUE CULTURE AND THE USE OF CHICK EMBRYOS

As stated earlier, almost all work on the cultivation of *Trypanosoma* and *Leishmania* has involved the growth of the forms normally seen in the invertebrate vector: in their vertebrate hosts, species of *Trypanosoma* are always represented by trypomastigote forms (except, in some species, when dividing), and *Leishmania* always by amastigote forms.

Among the salivarian trypanosomes, true cultivation of the forms found in the vertebrate (the haematozoic forms) has never been achieved. At best, maintenance of the organisms for about 24–48 hr (without increase in numbers) has been obtained. This was first done by Yorke *et al.* (1929), who found that *T.b. rhodesiense*, *T.b. gambiense* and *T.equiperdum* survived for up to 48 hr at 37°C in parasitized blood mixed with serum (or serum diluted with up to twice its volume of Ringer's saline containing 0·1–0·5% glucose) to give a suspension of not more than 1,000 trypanosomes per mm³. Their method has been recently re-investigated by Williamson & Rollo (1952), who recorded survival in undiminished numbers of *T.b. rhodesiense* at 37°C for about 4 hr in a balanced buffered saline solution containing 0·2% glucose and 0·1% serum. They then found that equally good if not better survival could be obtained by replacing the serum with a mixture of amino-acids and metals: survival in this synthetic medium (p. 39) was, on average, 4·5 hr (maximum 7 hr) at 37°C.

A similar medium was used by D'Alesandro (1962) to maintain haematozoic forms of *T.lewisi* (a stercorarian species) for about 24 hr at 37°C (p. 37). D'Alesandro obtained more consistent results if rat serum and an extract of lysed rat erythrocytes were added to the medium. The trypanosomes commenced multiplication in this supplemented medium, provided that the serum had been obtained from non-immune rats. Ristic & Trager (1958) cultivated *T.theileri* at 37°C in a medium consisting of whole blood, serum plus erythrocyte lysate and glucose (p. 38). Various forms developed, including numerous trypanosomes, and the fifth subculture (after a total of 24 days *in vitro*) was infective to a calf. However, Herbert (1965) was unable to obtain growth of another strain of *T.theileri* at 37°C in this medium.

The factors inducing transformation from 'insect' forms (pro- and

4

epimastigote) to haematozoic trypanosomes *in vitro* have received a little study. Deane & Deane (1961) and Deane & Kirchner (1963) obtained transformation of some individuals of *T.conorrhini in vitro* in certain media at 37°c. Desowitz (1963) also obtained transformation to haematozoic forms of some individuals of the same species in diphasic (NNN) medium, by raising the temperature to 37°c: he thought that this transformation was 'induced solely by temperature'. Baker (1966), however, who observed a similar phenomenon in cultures of *T.avium* growing in another diphasic medium (4N, see p. 13) when kept at 40°c, thought that factors other than the temperature must also be involved.

The subject has been studied in much more detail by Steinert and his co-workers, using *T.mega*, a parasite of poikilothermic hosts (amphibia): temperature is unlikely to play any part in morphogenetic transformation of this species. Steinert & Boné (1956) first showed that addition of serum to the medium (Boné & Parent, 1963: see p. 19) induced transformation, and Steinert (1958b) found that this would occur only if the cultures were 'competent', (i.e. about 6 days old or more). The functional constituent of the serum was shown by Steinert (1958a) to be urea: the highest average transformation rate (about 10%) was induced by the addition of commercial urea to the medium at 0·4 mg/ml. Subsequently, Steinert & Steinert (1960) found that organisms which had undergone this transformation in the presence of urea no longer incorporated tritiated thymidine into their nuclei (i.e., their synthesis of nuclear deoxyribonucleic acid was 'blocked'); whether this was a cause or effect of the morphogenetic transformation was not determined. As mentioned earlier, Guttman (1966b) induced transformation of this species and of *T.ranarum* growing in a defined medium (p. 6), by the addition of blood.

TABLE 1.5. Some media used for attempted cultivation of certain digenetic Trypanosomatidae at 37°c.

Author(s)	Date	Species	Detailed description (if any)
D'Alesandro	1962	*T.lewisi*	p. 37
Lemma & Schiller	1964	*Leishmania* spp.*	—
Ristic & Trager	1958	*T.theileri*	p. 38
Trager	1953	*L.donovani**	—
Williamson & Rollo	1952	*T.b. rhodesiense*	p. 39
Yorke *et al.*	1929	*T.bruceis* spp., *T.equiperdum*	—

* Only physiologically abnormal forms survived.

Muniz & de Freitas (1945, 1946) studied transformation *in vitro* of *T.cruzi* from haematozoic trypanosomes to epimastigote forms, as it occurs at the beginning of the cycle in the invertebrate host. They concluded that this 'reversion' occurs independently of temperature, but depends on the presence of 2 factors—haemoglobin and an unidentified 'metamorphosis-producing' factor which is present in erythrocytes, nutrient broth, meat infusion, peptone and blood extracts. Deane & Kirchner (1963) observed that reversion in *T.conorrhini* was temperature dependent, since it occurred *in vitro* at 25–28°c but not at 37°c: it also required the presence of intact erythrocytes.

Growth of species of *Leishmania in vitro* at 37°c occurs readily in tissue culture (see next section), but much less readily extracellularly. Trager (1953) obtained limited success in growing *L.donovani* at 37°c in a cell-free medium composed of human erythrocyte extract and human or hamster serum, inoculated with a suspension of parasites prepared from infected hamsters' spleens: sub-cultures were made into this medium enriched with nutrient broth. The forms which grew were regarded as being morphologically and physiologically intermediate between the true amastigote leishmania and promastigote leptomonads, though they were aflagellate.

More recently, Lemma & Schiller (1964) have repeated these experiments: by gradually acclimatizing *L.donovani*, *L.tropica* and *L.brasiliensis* in blood-agar cultures, to successively higher temperatures, extracellular growth of amastigote forms was obtained at 34°c in a diphasic nutrient agar-blood medium overlaid with Hanks's balanced salt solution containing antibiotics: subcultures were successful. However, these leishmania were clearly not physiologically normal since, when injected into hamsters' spleens they did not produce permanent infection (they could not be recovered more than 3 days after inoculation). Since neither Trager nor Lemma & Schiller have succeeded in cultivating physiologically normal leishmanias, their methods will not be cited in detail.

T.lewisi (haematozoic forms)
(D'Alesandro, 1962)

MEDIUM

1 *Composition*

  (a) Hanks's balanced salt solution
        (p. 350) 40%
        Rat serum.....................40%
        Nutrient solution...............20%
        (Lactalbumin hydrolysate, Difco 5·0 g

Yeast extract . . . . .1·0 g
Sodium bicarbonate . . . . .1·1 g
Glucose .4·5 g
Phenol red, 1% . . . . 1·6 ml
Hanks's balanced salt solution . . . .1 l.)

(b) To the above are added:
Penicillin . . . . .100 units/ml
Streptomycin . . . . .100 μg/ml
Glucose . . . . .2·5 mg/ml
Lysed rat blood . 1 drop (c.0·05 ml)/1·5 ml

pH 7·4–7·7.

2 Preparation of lysed rat blood

Defibrinated rat blood is centrifuged cold at 950 g for 30 min and the serum stored in a refrigerator while the packed cells are lysed by freezing in a solid carbon dioxide-ethanol bath and thawing in an ice-water bath; the lysate is then mixed with all the homologous serum and centrifuged cold at 1350 g for 1 hr. The supernatant liquid is either used immediately or stored in deep-freeze.

TECHNIQUE

The medium is used in 1·5 ml aliquots in Porter flasks (3·5 cm diameter). Each flask is inoculated with a mixture of 4–5 million trypanosomes and rat erythrocytes in saline (prepared by centrifuging infected rat blood and resuspending the deposit in saline). Cultures are incubated at 37°C. Trypanosomes survive for 24 hr and some multiplication occurs.

T.theileri (haematozoic forms)
(Ristic & Trager, 1958)

MEDIUM

1 Composition

Into each 50 ml conical (Erlenmeyer) flask place the following:

Whole, uninfected ox blood
(see Note 1) . . . . .1·0 ml
Glucose, 5% w/v solution . . . . . .0·2 ml
Lysed, uninfected ox blood . . . . .1·8 ml

2 Preparation of lysed blood

Centrifuge 20 ml ox blood (defibrinated) in the cold at 2,500 rev/min for 30 min; the serum is stored in the refrigerator while the packed cells are lysed by freezing in a solid carbon dioxide-ethanol bath and thawing at 0°c. The lysate is then mixed with 5 ml of homologous serum and centrifuged cold at 4,500 rev/min for 1 hr. The supernatant is either used immediately or stored at −10°c.

TECHNIQUE

(a)   For isolation, 1 ml whole blood (see Note 1) from the animal under investigation is added to each flask containing 3 ml of the above medium. The flasks (plugged with cotton wool and capped with aluminium foil) are incubated at 36–37·5°c.

(b)   For maintenance, transfers to fresh medium at 36–37·5°c are made with inocula of 1 ml of fluid from a positive culture, every 4 days.

NOTES: (1)   The blood samples are collected into one-tenth of their volume of a saline solution of heparin containing 30 mg/100 ml.

(2)   Six transfers were made successfully; the numbers of flagellates rose from about 1,000/ml in the first culture to about 500,000/ml in the second and subsequent ones. The organisms present were mainly epimastigote (crithidia), a few promastigote (leptomonads) and 'numerous' trypomastigote (blood forms). Material from the fifth sub-culture was infective to a calf.

(3)   Herbert (1965) failed to obtain growth at 37°c in this medium, using a strain of *T.theileri* isolated in Eire, although growth was satisfactory at 28°c (presumably without the production of blood forms): strain differences may be involved here, as that used by Ristic & Trager was isolated in the U.S.A.

T.b.rhodesiense (haematozoic forms)
(Williamson & Rollo, 1952)

MEDIUM

The ingredients are prepared as four stock solutions (a)–(d) (final concentrations in $\mu g/ml$). Solution (d) can be replaced by vitamin-free casein hydrolysate (Ashe) at 500 $\mu g/ml$.

(a)

Sodium chloride..............4,000	Sodium bicarbonate............1,000
Potassium chloride 100	Potassium dihydrogen phosphate..1,800
Calcium chloride (anhyd.).........100	Disodium hydrogen phosphate
Magnesium chloride $6H_2O$.........25	(anhyd.) 7,570

(b)

Glucose 2,000

(c)

Ferric chloride $6H_2O$ . . . . 0·15	Nickel sulphate . . . . 0·013
Copper sulphate $5H_2O$ . . . . 0·12	Cobalt sulphate $7H_2O$ . . . . 0·024
Manganese sulphate $4H_2O$ . . . . 0·012	Zinc sulphate $7H_2O$ . . . . 22·0

(d)

DL-Threonine 126	DL-Methionine 126
L-Valine 63	L-Phenylalanine 26
L-Leucine 158	L-Histidine 26
L-Isoleucine 53	L-Tryptophan 21
L-Lysine HCl 79	
L-Arginine HCl 79	(Total amino acids . . . . 757)

TECHNIQUE

Cultures are maintained at 37°c and the organisms remain motile and in undiminished numbers for an average of $4\frac{1}{2}$ hr (up to 7 hr in 1 culture). Survival is about the same in the salts and glucose solution (a+b) plus 0·1% v/v serum.

Air is adequate as a gas phase: carbon dioxide-free air is, however, toxic and better results are obtained with 5% carbon dioxide in air: best of all is a mixture of 5·6% carbon dioxide, 7·8% oxygen and 86·6% nitrogen The original paper should be consulted for details of certain substances which prolonged survival by 1–2 hr: these included adenine, adenosine, nucleic acids, etc. (concentrations unspecified).

2. TISSUE CULTURE AND CHICK EMBRYOS

Only a brief summary of these methods is given, with the exception of Trager's (1959) technique. Good reviews have been published by Pipkin (1960) and Zuckerman (1966).

Trypanosoma cruzi and *Leishmania* spp., in the form normally occurring in the vertebrate host, grow readily in tissue cultures of a variety of cell types and in chick embryos. Several species of *Trypanosoma* belonging to the subgenus *Trypanozoon* have also been grown in chick embryos: there seems to have been little success in cultivating *T.congolense* in this way. Very little work has been done on the growth of any trypanosome except *T.cruzi* in tissue cultures, presumably because most of these species, as far as is known, lack an intracellular stage. References to all this work are given in the two reviews cited above. In addition, Muniz & de Freitas (1946) obtained the development at 37°c of *T.cruzi* through the entire cycle which it normally follows in the vertebrate host. They used ascitic fluid collected from the peritoneal cavity of guinea-pigs which had previously been inoculated intraperitoneally with sterile glucose nutrient broth, to induce secretion of a larger volume of the fluid. Fluid from other cultures, containing metacyclic trypanosomes, was added to this ascitic fluid and the complete developmental cycle occurred if the leucocytes, normally present in the fluid, were allowed to remain in the culture: if the leucocytes were removed by centrifugation, transformation from amastigote leishmanias into haematozoic trypanosomes did not occur. When transformation occurred in cultures containing leucocytes, it did not necessarily do so intracellularly.

Lundholm *et al.* (1959) discovered trypanosomes (probably *T.theileri*) contaminating their monolayer cultures of foetal bovine kidney cells in Roux flasks (Madin *et al.*, 1957). The trypanosomes, presumably derived from the ox foetus, multiplied in the tissue culture fluid (modified Hanks's balanced salt solution plus 0·5% lactalbumin hydrolysate or culture medium 199, both with 10% lamb serum) with or without foetal kidney cells; multiplication appeared to be more rapid in the presence of the cells.

The growth of trypanosomes in cultures of tsetse-fly tissues is a recent development of considerable interest. This work was commenced by Trager (1959) who not only grew explants of tsetse-fly tissue *in vitro* (the first time this had been achieved for a dipteran insect), but also cultivated *T.vivax*, *T.congolense* and *T.b. brucei* in the fluid phase of such tissue cultures (p. 42), the first time that *T.vivax* had been grown *in vitro* in any type of medium. Trager (*loc. cit.*) was able to infect sheep with his cultures, but only when the latter had been incubated at 38°c for 19 hr before inoculation. He concluded that factors other than the raised temperature were involved in the development of infective forms since his results were variable and not all cultures survived exposure to 38°c for 19 hr. *T.b. brucei* and *T.congolense*, although growing readily in the cultures, did not produce infective forms; whereas *T.vivax* grew only at 30–32°c, the former species could be cultivated at a lower temperature (28°c). Serial subcultures of all three species were readily obtained, and it proved possible to transfer the *T.vivax* strain to NNN medium on which it was also maintained (though growth was much lighter than in the tissue cultures).

Nicoli & Vattier (1964) repeated Trager's work using *T.b. rhodesiense* and omitting the trehalose and organic acids from the medium. The trypanosomes grew for 6–10 days, and were not infective to rats. They were considered to represent the type normally developing in the mid-gut of *Glossina*, but in the published drawings they appeared to be more like the stumpy blood forms. Amrein *et al.* (1965) maintained *T.brucei* sspp., which had been cultivated previously in Weinman's medium, in tissue culture medium 199 containing isolated pieces of tissue from *Glossina* spp. for periods up to 6–7 days. The flagellates showed a marked attraction towards pieces of mid-gut, salivary gland and muscle, but not towards malpighian tubes, gonads or fat tissue. Such cultures were not infective to mice.

Tsetse–fly tissue culture technique for *T.vivax*, *T.b.brucei* and *T.congolense*
(Trager, 1959)

I. TISSUE–CULTURES

1 *Composition and preparation of stock solutions*

(a)	mg/100 ml
Sodium chloride	90
Potassium chloride	300
Sodium dihydrogen phosphate H_2O	110
Magnesium sulphate $7H_2O$	370
Calcium chloride (anhyd.)	80
Glucose	150
Lactalbumin hydrolysate	1,000
Yeast extract (Difco)	200
Trehalose	50
L–Malic acid	50
α–Ketoglutaric acid	25
Succinic acid	5

All ingredients are dissolved in re-distilled water, pH adjusted to 6·8–6·9 with N sodium hydroxide and sterilized by filtration.

(b)	mg/10 ml
Reduced glutathione	200
Ascorbic acid	2

Sterilize by filtration.

2 *Preparation of medium*

Various media were used, based on the above solutions: the most complete, and one of the most successful versions (D4) was composed of

Solution (a)	8 ml
Solution (b)	0·5 ml
Sheep serum	2 ml

In 1 ml of this mixture, two sterilized (see below) pupae of *Glossina palpalis* were gently crushed with a pipette (harsh crushing releases tyrosinase and spoils the medium): after centrifuging at 2,000 rev/min for 15 min, the supernatant fluid (plus the resuspended fatty layer) constitutes the tissue-culture medium (pH 6·7–6·9).

3   *Culture technique*

Various tissues were dissected aseptically from sterilized pupae (see below), or from adults emerging from sterilized pupae kept on sterile sand in sterile glass vials plugged with cotton: after emergence, such adults were kept in sterile glass tubes, of which one end was plugged with cotton wool and the other closed with gauze, and allowed to feed daily on an area on the back of a rat which had been shaved and disinfected with alcohol. Between feeds, the gauze-covered end of the tube was covered with a closely fitting sterile glass vial.

Successful outgrowth was obtained from a variety of tissues; the original paper should be consulted for details of these. Cultures were set up either as hanging-drop preparations on coverslips or in small Carrel flasks, with 0·3 ml of medium forming a thin layer over the bottom of the flask, which was closed with a silicone-rubber bung. All tissue-cultures (without trypanosomes) were kept at 28°c and the medium was changed when necessary (usually at intervals of 1–2 weeks).

2. TRYPANOSOME CULTURES

Cultures of proboscis, alimentary tract and salivary gland from very late pupae or newly-emerged adults were used, as described above.

Trypanosomes were introduced into these cultures as minute droplets of either whole infected blood (with heparin) or a centrifuged concentrate of organisms from such blood (centrifuged at 800 rev/min for 10 min; supernatant centrifuged again at 2,500 rev/min for 10 min; sediment resuspended in 0·4 ml culture medium for inoculation). Serial transfers were made weekly (usually) with small drops of positive culture fluid.

Successful growth of *T.vivax* was achieved only when the inoculum was obtained from a sheep with an infection of long duration, and when the cultures were incubated at 30°c (once the strain was established, it also grew at 28°c). Heavy cultures were obtained, and the strain was maintained *in vitro* for 3 months. When such cultures were exposed to a temperature of 38°c for 19 hr, they occasionally became infective to sheep.

T.brucei and *T.congolense* grew readily in the tissue-cultures. *T.brucei* did not, however, become infective, even after exposure of cultures to 38°C: *T.congolense* was not tested in this way.

3. STERILIZATION OF TSETSE PUPAE

Batches of not more than ten puparia were immersed for 15 min in White's solution (mercuric chloride 0·25 g, sodium chloride 6·5 g, hydrochloric acid 1·25 ml, ethanol 250 ml, distilled water 750 ml): Nicoli & Vattier (1964) used 0·1% aqueous sodium merthiolate solution for this purpose. The puparia floated in the solution, but were submerged by sterile forceps three times during their immersion, washed in sterile distilled water and dried on sterile filter paper. These procedures were carried out in sterile Petri dishes.

V. CHOICE OF A SUITABLE MEDIUM, WITH NOTES ON OBTAINING DIAGNOSTIC MATERIAL

Clearly this will depend on one's particular requirements. For diagnosis or routine maintenance of many of the monogenetic trypanosomatids as well as species of *Leishmania* and many species of *Trypanosoma*, including those of poikilothermic vertebrates, birds and mammals (including *T.cruzi* but excluding the salivarian trypanosomes), one of the simple blood-agar media (e.g. NNN, SNB-9, etc.) would probably be the medium of choice (pp. 13–15). When using cultivation for diagnosis, great care must be taken to ensure that the material inoculated into the medium is bacteriologically sterile. Blood from small vertebrates can be obtained aseptically from the heart if the animal is alive: if however it is dead, contamination of the blood may have occurred. Blood obtained by clipping the tail-tip, or a digit, is more likely to become contaminated, unless great care is taken to sterilize the skin (with alcohol, which must be allowed to evaporate before the blood is withdrawn). Blood of larger vertebrates, including man, is most readily collected aseptically from a vein. *Leishmania* may be obtained by aseptic biopsy or puncture of an infected organ. If the organ of choice is the skin, this must be sterilized with great care: Herrer *et al.* (1966) recommend the use of iodine, followed by ether (before the iodine is dry): the segment of skin should then be chopped up finely in a saline solution containing 500 units of penicillin and 1 mg of streptomycin per ml, and left for 24–72 hr at 4–6°C before being inoculated into the medium.

For diagnosis of *T.brucei* sspp. or *T.congolense*, Weinman's (1960a) medium is recommended (p. 33). For the maintenance of these species, this medium or that of Tobie *et al.* (1950) would be suitable (p. 32).

As an aid in distinguishing between *T.cruzi* and *T.rangeli*, Zeledon's (1959) medium (p. 23) could be useful.

REFERENCES

ADLER S.(1934). Culture of leishmanias and other Trypanosomidae in haemoglobin-free media. *Trans. R. Soc. trop. Med. Hyg.* **28:** 201–204.

ADLER S. & ASHBEL R. (1934). Il metabolismo della *Leishmania*. *Archiv. zool. ital.* **20:** 521–527.

ADLER S., FONER, ANNIE & MONTIGLIO B. (1966). The relationship between human and animal strains of *Leishmania* from the Sudan. *Trans. R. Soc. trop. Med. Hyg.* **60:** 380–386.

ADLER S. & THEODOR O. (1926). The identity of *Leishmania tropica* Wright, 1903, and *Herpetomonas papatasii* Adler, 1925. *Ann. trop. Med. Parasit.* **20:** 355–364.

AMREIN Y.U., GEIGY R. & KAUFFMAN, MARIANNE (1965). On the reacquisition of virulence in trypanosomes of the *brucei*-group. *Acta trop.* **22:** 193–203.

ARCHETTI I. (1938). Ein einfacher Nährboden für Leishmanien. *Arch. Schiffs-u. TropenHyg.* **42:** 547–549.

BAKER J.R. (1963). Speculations on the evolution of the family Trypanosomatidae Doflein, 1901. *Expl Parasit.* **13:** 219–233.

BAKER J.R. (1966). Studies on *Trypanosoma avium*. IV. The development of infective metacyclic trypanosomes in cultures grown *in vitro*. *Parasitology* **56:** 15–19.

BARACCHINI O. (1965). Meio de cultura líquido esterilizável pelo calor para *Trypanosoma cruzi*. *Revta Inst. Adolfo Lutz* **22/23:** 91–92. [Vol. dated 1962–63.]

BONACCI H. (1934). Nuevo medio de cultivo para el *Trypanosoma cruzi* Chagas, 1909. *Revta Inst. bact., B. Aires* **6:** 242–247.

BONÉ G.J. & PARENT G. (1963). Stearic acid, an essential growth factor for *Trypanosoma cruzi*. *J. gen. Microbiol.* **31:** 261–266.

BONÉ G.J. & STEINERT M. (1956). Isotopes incorporated in the nucleic acids of *Trypanosoma mega*. *Nature, Lond.* **178:** 308–309.

BOWMAN I.B.R., BRAND T. VON & TOBIE, ELEANOR J. (1960). The cultivation and metabolism of trypanosomes in the presence of trehalose with observations on trehalase in blood serum. *Expl Parasit.* **10:** 274–283.

BRAND T. VON, JOHNSON, ELEANOR M. & REES C.W. (1946). Observations on the respiration of *Trypanosoma cruzi* in culture. *J. gen. Physiol.* **30:** 163–175.

BRAY R.S. & MUNFORD, FRANCES (1967). On the maintenance of strains of *Leishmania* from the Guianas. *J. trop. Med. Hyg.* **70:** 23–24.

BRUTSAERT P. & HENRARD C. (1938). L'hémoculture comme moyen auxiliaire de diagnostic de la maladie du sommeil. *C. r. Séanc. Soc. Biol.* **127:** 1469–1472.

CAMARGO E.P. (1964). Growth and differentiation in *Trypanosoma cruzi*. I. Origin of metacyclic trypanosomes in liquid media. *Revta Inst. Med. trop. S Paulo* **6:** 93–100.

CHANG S.L. (1947). Studies on haemoflagellates. I. A semi-solid medium and a fluid medium with a solid base for growing various species of *Leishmania* and *Trypanosoma cruzi*. *J. infect. Dis.* **80:** 164–171.

CHANG S.L. & NEGHERBON W.O. (1947) Studies on haemoflagellates. II. A study of the growth rates of *Leishmania donovani*, *L.brasiliensis*, *L.tropica* and *Trypanosoma cruzi* in culture. *J. infect. Dis.* **80:** 172–184.

CHARGAFF E., BANCROFT F.W. & STANLEY-BROWN, MARGARET (1936). Studies on the chemistry of blood coagulation. II. On the inhibition of blood clotting by substances of high molecular weight. *J. biol. Chem.* **115:** 155–161.

CITRI N. & GROSSOWICZ N. (1954). A liquid medium for the cultivation of *Trypanosoma cruzi*. *Nature, Lond.* **173:** 1100–1101.

CITRI N. & GROSSOWICZ N. (1955). A partially defined culture medium for *Trypanosoma cruzi* and some other haemoflagellates. *J. gen. Microbiol.* **13:** 273–278.

D'ALESANDRO P.A. (1962). *In vitro* studies of ablastin, the reproduction-inhibiting antibody to *Trypanosoma lewisi*. *J. Protozool.* **9:** 351–358.

DEANE, MARIA P. & DEANE L.M. (1961). Studies on the life-cycle of *Trypanosoma conorhini*. *In vitro* development and multiplication of the bloodstream trypanosomes. *Revta Inst. Med. trop. S Paulo* **3:** 149–160.

DEANE, MARIA P. & KIRCHNER, ELFRIEDE (1963). Life-cycle of *Trypanosoma conorhini*. Influence of temperature and other factors on growth and morphogenesis. *J. Protozool.* **10:** 391–400.

DESOWITZ R.S. (1963). The development and survival of the blood-stream forms of *Trypanosoma conorhini* in culture. *J. Protozool.* **10:** 390–391.

DIAMOND L.S. & HERMAN C.M. (1954). Incidence of trypanosomes in the Canada goose as revealed by bone marrow culture. *J. Parasit.* **40:** 195–202.

DODIN A. & FROMENTIN H. (1962). Premier essai de culture de trypanosomes en milieu synthétique. *Bull. Soc. Path. exot.* **55:** 797–804.

FIFE E.H. JR. & KENT J.F. (1960). Protein and carbohydrate complement fixing antigens of *Trypanosoma cruzi*. *Am. J. trop. Med. Hyg.* **9:** 512–517.

FREITAS G. DE & HAUSMANN R.L. (1954). Sôbre o crescimento de *Schizotrypanum cruzi* em meios livres de proteinas nativas. *Anais Acad. bras. Cienc.* **26:** 531–535. [Seen only in *Trop. Dis. Bull.* (1955) **52:** 1175–1176.]

FROMENTIN H. (1964). Mise en culture de *Trypanosoma therezieni* Brygoo 1963. *Bull. Soc. Path. exot.* **57:** 219–224.

FULTON J.D. & JOYNER L.P. (1949). Studies on Protozoa. Part I. The metabolism of Leishman-Donovan bodies and flagellates of *Leishmania donovani*. *Trans. R. Soc. trop. Med. Hyg.* **43:** 273–286.

GEIGY R. & KAUFFMANN M. (1964). On the effect of substances found in *Glossina* tissues on culture trypanosomes of the *brucei*-subgroup. *Acta Trop.* **21:** 169–173.

GORDON R.M. & MILLER J.K. (1961). Cyclical infection of *Glossina morsitans* with culture forms of *Trypanosoma rhodesiense*. *Nature, Lond.* **191:** 1317.

GREWAL M.S. (1957). The life cycle of the British rabbit trypanosome, *Trypanosoma nabiasi* Railliet, 1895. *Parasitology* **47:** 100–118.

GUTTMAN, HELENE N. (1963). Experimental glimpses at the lower Trypanosomatidae. *Expl Parasit.* **13:** 129–142.

GUTTMAN, HELENE N. (1964). Crithidia assays for unconjugated pteridines. In *Pteridine chemistry*: 255–266. Pfleiderer W. & Taylor E.C. (eds). New York: Pergamon Press.

GUTTMAN, HELENE N. (1966a). First defined media for *Leptomonas* spp. from insects. *J. Protozool.* **13:** 390–392.

GUTTMAN, HELENE N. (1966b). The first defined medium for *Trypanosoma* spp. *J. Protozool.* **13** Suppl.: 18. [Abstract only.]

GUTTMAN, HELENE N. & EISENMAN R.N. (1965). 'Cure' of *Crithidia* (*Strigomonas*) *oncopelti* of its bacterial endosymbiote. *Nature, Lond.* **206**: 113–114.

GUTTMAN, HELENE N. & WALLACE F.G. (1964). Nutrition and physiology of the Trypanosomatidae. In *Biochemistry and physiology of Protozoa*, **3**: 459–494. Hutner S.H. (ed). New York & London: Academic Press.

HALEVY S. & GISRY O. (1964). Lipid composition of *Trypanosoma ranarum*. *Proc. Soc. exp. Biol. Med.* **117**: 552–555.

HALEVY S. & SAREL S. (1965). Isolation of ergosterol from the trypanosomatid *Leptomonas culicidarum*. *J. Protozool.* **12**: 293–296.

HERBERT I.V. (1961). Bovine trypanosomiasis due to *Trypanosoma theileri* Laveran, 1902 and its occurrence in Eire. *Ir. Vet. J.* **15**: 230–236.

HERBERT I.V. (1965). Some observations on the isolation and *in vitro* culture of two mammalian trypanosomes, *Trypanosoma theileri* Laveran, 1902, and *T.melophagium* Flu, 1908, with special reference to *T.theileri*. *Ann. trop. Med. Parasit.* **59**: 277–293.

HERRER A., THATCHER V.E. & JOHNSON C.M. (1966). Natural infections of *Leishmania* and trypanosomes demonstrated by skin culture. *J. Parasit.* **52**: 954–957.

HOARE C.A. (1923). An experimental study of the sheep-trypanosome (*T.melophagium* Flu, 1908), and its transmission by the sheep-ked (*Melophagus ovinus* L.). *Parasitology* **15**: 365–424.

HOARE C.A. (1966). The classification of mammalian trypanosomes. *Ergebn. Mikrobiol. ImmunForsch. exp. Ther.* **39**: 43–57.

HOARE C.A. & WALLACE F.G. (1966). Developmental stages of trypanosomatid flagellates: a new terminology. *Nature, Lond.* **212**: 1385–1386.

HORNE R.W. & NEWTON B.A. (1958) Intracellular structures in *Strigomonas oncopelti*. *Expl Cell Res.* **15**: 103–111.

JACKSON G.J. (1962). On axenic cultures of certain protozoan and worm parasites of insects. *Trans. N.Y. Acad. Sci.*, Ser. II, **24**: 954–965.

JACKSON G.J. (1963). *Leishmania enriettii* leptomonads in various culture media, including defined and antibody containing ones. *Progress in Protozoology*: 549. Ludvík J., Lom J. & Vavrá J. (eds). Proceedings of the first international congress on Protozoology, Prague, 1961. Prague: Czechoslovak Academy of Science.

JADIN J. & PIERREUX G. (1960). Un milieu de culture pour trypanosomides. *Annls Soc. belge Méd. trop.* **40**: 903–906.

JADIN J. & WÉRY M. (1963). La culture des Trypanosomidae. *Annls Soc. belge Méd. trop.* **43**: 831–842.

JADIN J., WÉRY M., LE RAY D. & GATTI F. (1966). Au sujet de la transmission de certains caractères biologiques chez les Trypanosomidae. *Bull. Séanc. Acad. r. Sci. (colon.) outre Mer* **3**: 453–465.

JOHNSON, ELEANOR M. (1947). The cultivation of *Trypanosoma conorhini*. *J. Parasit.* **33**: 85.

KELSER R.A. (1936). A complement-fixation test for Chagas' disease employing an artificial culture antigen. *Am. J. trop. Med.* **16**: 405–415.

KLIGLER I.J. (1924). On the cultivation and biological characters of *Leishmania tropica*. *Am. J. trop. Med.* **4**: 69–76.

KLIGLER I.J. (1926). The cultural and serological relationship of *Leishmania*. *Trans. R. Soc. trop. Med. Hyg.* **19**: 330–335.

KRASSNER S.M. (1965). Effect of temperature on growth and nutritional requirements of *Leishmania tarentolae* in a defined medium. *J. Protozool.* **12**: 73–78.

LAMBRECHT F.L. (1966). Notes on the growth curve of *Trypanosoma cruzi* Chagas 1909 as determined by optical density. *Revta Inst. Med. trop. S Paulo* **8**: 249–254.

LEHMANN D.L. (1959). The cultivation of some trypanosomes from urodeles. *J. Protozool.* **6**: 340–343.

LEHMANN D.L. (1960). Some culture differences between *Trypanosoma rhodesiense* and *T.brucei* in autoclaved diphasic media. *Ann. trop. Med. Parasit.* **54**: 419–427.

LEHMANN D.L. (1961a). Investigations on the infectivity of early cultural forms of rhodesian trypanosomiasis. *Ann. trop. Med. Parasit.* **55**: 151–153.

LEHMANN D.L. (1961b). Attempts at the selective cultivation of *Trypanosoma rhodesiense*, *T.brucei* and *T.congolense*. *Ann. trop. Med. Parasit.* **55**: 440–446.

LEHMANN D.L. (1962a). Differential effects of osmotic pressure and of suramin upon cultures of *T.congolense* and *T.rhodesiense*. *Ann. trop. Med. Parasit.* **56**: 1–3.

LEHMANN D.L. (1962b). Culture forms of *Trypanosoma ranarum* (Lankester, 1871). II. Effect of temperature upon reproduction and cyclic development. *J. Protozool.* **9**: 325–326.

LEHMANN D.L. (1964). An autoclaved medium for the growth and possible differentiation of African trypanosomes. *Ann. trop. Med. Parasit.* **58**: 6–8.

LEHMANN D.L. (1966). Culture media for *Trypanosoma ranarum* and *Trypanosoma cruzi*. *Ann. trop. Med. Parasit.* **60**: 452–454.

LEMMA A. & SCHILLER E.L. (1964). Extracellular cultivation of the leishmanial bodies of species belonging to the protozoan genus *Leishmania*. *Expl Parasit.* **15**: 503–513.

LITTLE P.A. & OLESON J.J. (1951). The cultivation of *Trypanosoma cruzi*. *J. Bact.* **61**: 709–714.

LITTLE P.A. & SUBBAROW Y. (1945). A practical liquid medium for cultivation of *Trypanosoma cruzi* in large volumes. *J. Bact.* **50**: 57–60.

LUNDHOLM B.D., STORZ J. & McKERCHER D.G. (1959). *Trypanosoma theileri* as a contaminant of tissue origin in cultures of fetal bovine kidney cells *in vitro*. *Virology* **8**: 394–396.

LWOFF, MARGUERITE (1938). L'hématine et l'acide ascorbique, facteurs de croissance pour le flagellé *Schizotrypanum cruzi*. *C.r. hebd. Séanc. Acad. Sci., Paris* **206**: 540–542.

LWOFF, MARGUERITE (1940). *Recherches sur le pouvoir de synthèse des flagellés trypanosomides*. Paris: Masson et Cie.

LWOFF, MARGUERITE (1951). The nutrition of parasitic flagellates (Trypanosomidae, Trichomonadinae). In *Biochemistry and physiology of Protozoa* **1**: 129–176. Lwoff A. (ed). New York: Academic Press Inc.

MacNEAL W.J. (1904). The life-history of *Trypanosoma lewisi* and *Trypanosoma brucei*. *J. infect. Dis.* **1**: 517–543.

M[A]CNEAL W.J. & NOVY F.G. (1903). On the cultivation of *Trypanosoma lewisi*. In *Contributions to medical research dedicated to Victor Clarence Vaughan . . . :* 549–577. Ann Arbor, Michigan: G. Wahr.

MADIN S.H., ANDRIESE P.C. & DARBY N.B. (1957). The *in vitro* cultivation of tissues of domestic and laboratory animals. *Am. J. vet. Res.* **18**: 932–941.

MARINKELLE C.J. (1965). Influence of temperature on the morphology of *Trypanosoma conorrhini*. In *Progress in Protozoology*: 75. Proceedings of the 2nd international Congress on Protozoology, London, 1965. Amsterdam etc.: Excerpta Medica Foundation (International Congress Series No. 91).

MATHIS C. (1906). Sur un modification au milieu de Novy-MacNeal pour la culture des trypanosomes. *C.r. Séanc. Soc. Biol.* **61**: 550–552.

McCONNELL E. (1963) Leptomonads of wild-caught Panamanian *Phlebotomus*: culture and animal inoculation. *Expl Parasit.* **14**: 123–128.

MINCHIN E.A. (1909). The structure of *Trypanosoma lewisi* in relation to microscopical technique. *Q. Jl microsc. Sci.* **53**: 755–808.

MUNIZ J. & DE FREITAS G. (1945) Estudo sôbre o determinismo da transformação das formas sanguìcolas do *Schizotrypanum cruzi* em critídias. *Revta bras. Med.* **2**: 995–999.

MUNIZ J. & DE FREITAS G. (1946). Realização *in vitro* do ciclo do *S. cruzi* no vertebrado, em meios de caldolìquido peritoneal. *Revta bras. Biol.* **6**: 467–484.

NATHAN, HELENE A. (1958). Purine biosynthesis by the trypanosomid flagellate, *Strigomonas oncopelti*. *J. Protozool.* **5**: 194–195.

NATHAN, HELENE A. & COWPERTHWAITE, JEAN (1955). 'Crithidia factor'—a new member of the folic acid group of vitamins. *J. Protozool.* **2**: 37–42.

NATTAN-LARRIER L. & GRIMARD-RICHARD L. (1934). Culture des *Leishmania* sur le milieu N.N.N. 'mouillé'. *Bull. Soc. Path. exot.* **27**: 656–658.

NEAL R.A. & MILES R.A. (1963). Heated blood agar medium for the growth of *Trypanosoma cruzi* and some species of *Leishmania*. *Nature, Lond.* **198**: 210–211.

NEVA F.A., MALONE, MARY F. & MYERS, BARBARA R. (1961). Factors influencing the intracellular growth of *Trypanosoma cruzi in vitro*. *Am. J. trop. Med. Hyg.* **10**: 140–154.

NEWTON B.A. (1956). A synthetic growth medium for the trypanosomid flagellate, *Strigomonas (Herpetomonas) oncopelti*. *Nature, Lond.* **177**: 279–280.

NEWTON B.A. & GUTTERIDGE W.E. (1967). The putative 'bacterial endosymbiont' of *Crithidia oncopelti*: a reappraisal. *J. Protozool.* **14** Suppl.: 41. [Abstract only.]

NICOLI J. (1961). Étude préliminaire sur les conditions de culture de *Trypanosoma gambiense*. *Bull. Soc. Path. exot.* **54**: 77–83.

NICOLI J. & VATTIER G. (1964). Culture de *Trypanosoma rhodesiense* sur tissues de pupes de glossines. *Bull. Soc. Path. exot.* **57**: 213–219.

NICOLLE C. (1908a). Nouvelles acquisitions sur le kala-azar: cultures; inoculations au chien; étiologie. *C.r. hebd. Séanc. Acad. Sci., Paris* **146**: 498–499.

NICOLLE C. (1908b). Culture du parasite du bouton d'Orient. *C.r. hebd. Séanc. Acad. Sci., Paris* **146**: 842–843.

NOGUCHI H. & LINDENBERG A. (1925). The isolation and maintenance of *Leishmania* on the medium employed for the cultivation of organisms of the leptospira group of spirochetes. *Am. J. trop. Med.* **5**: 63–68.

NÖLLER W. (1917). Blut- und Insektenflagellatenzüchtung auf Platten. *Arch. Schiffs-u. TropenHyg.* **21**: 53–94.

NOVY F.G. & MACNEAL W.J. (1903). The cultivation of *Trypanosoma brucei*. A preliminary note. *J. Am. med. Ass.* **41**: 1266–1268.

NOVY F.G. & M[A]cNEAL W.J. (1904). On the cultivation of *Trypanosoma brucei*. *J. infect. Dis.* **1**: 1.

PACKCHANIAN A. (1934). On the cultivation of seven species of trypanosomes *in vitro*. *Science, N.Y.* **80**: 407–408.

PACKCHANIAN A. (1943). On the viability of various species of *Trypanosoma* and *Leishmania* cultures. *J. Parasit.* **29**: 275–277.

PACKCHANIAN A. & SWEETS H.H. JR. (1947). Infectivity of *Trypanosoma cruzi* after cultivation for thirteen years *in vitro* without animal passage. *Proc. Soc. exp. Biol. Med.* **64**: 169.

PESSAT O.A.N. (1961). Milieu diphasique pour la culture de *Trypanosoma cruzi*. *Bull. Soc. Path. exot.* **54**: 16–19.

PIPKIN A.C. (1960). Avian embryos and tissue culture in the study of parasitic Protozoa. II. Protozoa other than *Plasmodium*. *Expl Parasit.* **9**: 167–203.

PONSELLE A. (1923). La culture de *Trypanosoma inopinatum*, trypanosome pathogène de la grenouille. *Annls Parasit. hum. comp.* **1**: 155–158.

PONSELLE A. (1924). Culture des trypanosomes pathogènes. *C.r. hebd. Séanc. Acad. Sci.*, *Paris* **178**: 1219–1221.

PRATES M.M. (1928). Cultures of polymorphic trypanosomes (*brucei, gambiense* and *rhodesiense*). *Final Report of League of Nations international Commission on human Trypanosomiasis*: 169–178. Geneva: League of Nations (C.H. 629).

PRESTON T.M. (1966). *In vitro* cultivation of *Trypanosoma rajae*. *Trans. R. Soc. trop. Med. Hyg.* **60**: 10.

RAY J.C. (1932). Cultivation of various leishmania parasites on solid medium. *Indian J. med. Res.* **20**: 355–367.

RAZGHA A. VON (1929). Über die Züchtung der menschenpathogenen Trypanosomen. *Z. Parasitkde* **2**: 55–56.

REICHENOW E. (1934). Die Züchtung der pathogenen Trypanosomen. *Arch. Schiffs-u. TropenHyg.* **38**: 292–302.

REICHENOW E. (1939). Über die Entwicklungsfähigkeit der Kulturformen von *Trypanosoma gambiense* und *T.congolense* in *Glossina*. *Arch. Schiffs-u. TropenHyg.* **43**: 197–202.

REICHENOW E. (1940). Zur Frage der Bedeutung des Blepharoplasts der Trypanosomen. *Archos Inst. Biol., S Paulo* **11**: 433–436.

RESSELER R., LE RAY D. & GOEDVRIEND J. (1965). Conservation de protozoaires, particulièrement en culture, à la température de l'azote liquide. *Annls Soc. belge Méd. trop.* **45**: 665–678.

RIOUX J.-A., ALBARET J.-L., BRES A. & DUMAS A. (1966). Présence de *Trypanosoma pestanai*, Bettencourt et França, 1905 chez les blaireaux du sud de la France. *Annls Parasit. hum. comp.* **41**: 281–288.

RISTIC M. & TRAGER W. (1958). Cultivation at 37°c of a trypanosome (*Trypanosoma theileri*) from cows with depressed milk production. *J. Protozool.* **5**: 146–148.

SALLE A.J. & SCHMIDT C.L.A. (1928). The metabolism of *Leishmania tropica*. *J. infect. Dis.* **43**: 378–384.

SAMPATH A. & LITTLE P. (1949). Cultivation of *Trypanosoma cruzi* in liquid media. *J. Bact.* **57**: 265.

SENECA H. & HENDERSON E. (1951). Growth of hemoflagellates in dialyzing sacs and the production of growth inhibitory factor. *Am. J. Hyg.* **53**: 17–21.

SENECA H., HENDERSON E. & HARVEY, MARTHA (1949). Purification of hemoflagellate cultures with antibiotics. *Am. J. trop. Med.* **29**: 41.

SENECA H. & WOLF A. (1955). *Trypanosoma cruzi* infection in the Indian monkey. *Am. J. trop. Med. Hyg.* **4**: 1009–1014.

SENEKJI[E] H.A. (1939). Studies on the culture of *Leishmania tropica*. *Trans. R. Soc. trop. Med. Hyg.* **33**: 267–269.

SENEKJIE H.A. (1943). Biochemical reactions, cultural characteristics and growth requirements of *Trypanosoma cruzi*. *Am. J. trop. Med.* **23**: 523–531.

SENEKJIE H.A. & LEWIS, RUTH A. (1945). An inquiry into the growth factor or factors of certain blood and tissue flagellates. *Am. J. trop. Med.* **25**: 345–348.

SHAW J.J. (1964). *Studies on members of the Trypanosomatidae in sloths, with special reference to* **Endotrypanum schaudinni**. Thesis for Ph.D. degree, Faculty of Science, University of London. [To be published as a memoir of the London School of Hygiene and Tropical Medicine.]

SILVA I.I. (1954). Metodo de cultivo del *Trypanosoma (Schizotrypanum) cruzi* para la preparacion de antigenos. *An. Inst. Med. reg., Tucum'n* **4:** 71–75.

SIMPSON C.F. & GREEN J.H. (1959). Cultivation of *Trypanosoma theileri* in liquid medium. *Cornell Vet.* **49:** 192–193.

Sleeping Sickness Bureau (1909). The cultivation of trypanosomes on artificial media. *Bull. Sleep. Sickn. Bur.* **1:** 287–294 and 325–326.

STECHER P.G., ed. (1960). *The Merck index of chemicals and drugs*: 611. Ed. 7. Rahway, N.J., U.S.A.: Merck & Co. Inc.

STEINERT M. (1958a). Action morphogénétique de l'urée sur le trypanosome. *Expl Cell Res.* **15:** 431–433.

STEINERT M. (1958b). Études sur la determinisme de la morphogénèse d'un trypanosome. *Expl Cell Res.* **15:** 560–569.

STEINERT M. & BONÉ G.J. (1956). Induced change from culture form to blood-stream form in *Trypanosoma mega*. *Nature, Lond.* **178:** 362.

STEINERT M. & STEINERT G. (1960). Inhibition de la synthèse de l'acide désoxyribonucléique de *Trypanosoma mega* par l'urée à faible concentration. *Expl Cell Res.* **19:** 421–424.

THOMSON J.G. & SINTON J.A. (1912). The morphology of *Trypanosoma gambiense* and *Trypanosoma rhodesiense* in cultures: and a comparison with the developmental forms described in *Glossina palpalis*. *Ann. trop. Med. Parasit.* **6:** 331–356.

TOBIE, ELEANOR J. (1958). The cultivation of *Trypanosoma congolense in vitro*. *J. Parasit.* **44:** 241–242.

TOBIE, ELEANOR J. (1964). Cultivation of mammalian trypanosomes. *J. Protozool.* **11:** 418–423.

TOBIE, ELEANOR J., BRAND T. VON & MEHLMAN B. (1950). Cultural and physiological observations on *Trypanosoma rhodesiense* and *Trypanosoma gambiense*. *J. Parasit.* **36:** 48–54.

TOBIE, ELEANOR J. & REES C.W. (1948). The cultivation of *Trypanosoma cruzi* in dialysate medium. *J. Parasit.* **34:** 162–163.

TOM N. (1943). A modification of the N.N. medium for cultivating *Trypanosoma cruzi*. *Am. J. trop. Med.* **23:** 615–616.

TRAGER W. (1953). The development of *Leishmania donovani in vitro* at 37°C. Effects of the kind of serum. *J. exp. Med.* **97:** 177–188.

TRAGER W. (1957). Nutrition of a hemoflagellate (*Leishmania tarentolae*) having an interchangeable requirement for choline or pyridoxal. *J. Protozool.* **4:** 269–276.

TRAGER W. (1959). Tsetse-fly tissue culture and the development of trypanosomes to the infective stage. *Ann. trop. Med. Parasit.* **53:** 473–491.

VICKERMAN K. (1965). Polymorphism and mitochondrial activity in sleeping sickness trypanosomes. *Nature, Lond.* **208:** 762–766.

WALLACE F.G. (1956). Cultivation of *Trypanosoma ranarum* on a liquid medium. *J. Protozool.* **3:** 47–49.

WALLACE F.G. & CLARK T.B. (1959). Flagellate parasites of the fly, *Phaenicia sericata* (Meigen). *J. Protozool.* **6:** 58–61.

WARREN L.G. (1960). Metabolism of *Schizotrypanum cruzi* Chagas. I. Effect of culture age and substrate concentration on respiratory rate. *J. Parasit.* **46:** 529–539.

WEINMAN D. (1944). Cultivation of *Trypanosoma gambiense in vitro* in cell-free medium. *Proc. Soc. exp. Biol. Med.* **55**: 82–83.

WEINMAN D. (1946). Cultivation of African sleeping sickness trypanosomes on improved, simple, cell-free medium. *Proc. Soc. exp. Biol. Med.* **63**: 456–458.

WEINMAN D. (1960a). Cultivation of the African sleeping sickness trypanosomes from the blood and cerebrospinal fluid of patients and suspects. *Trans. R. Soc. trop. Med. Hyg.* **54**: 180–190.

WEINMAN D. (1960b). Trehalose metabolism of trypanosomes. *Nature, Lond.* **186**: 166.

WENYON C.M. (1921). [Untitled demonstration.] *Trans. R. Soc. trop. Med. Hyg.* **15**: 153–155.

WENYON C.M. (1926). *Protozoology* **2**: 1300–1304. London: Baillière, Tindall & Cox. [Reprinted 1966 by Baillière, Tindall and Cassell.]

WÉRY M. & DE GROODT-LASSEEL M. (1966). Ultrastructure de *Trypanosoma cruzi* en culture sur milieu semi-synthétique. *Annls Soc. belge Méd. trop.* **46**: 337–348.

WILLIAMSON J. & ROLLO I.M. (1952). Stimulating effect of amino-acids on the survival at 37°C of *Trypanosoma rhodesiense* in a serum-free synthetic medium. *Nature, Lond.* **170**: 376–377.

YORKE W., ADAMS A.R.D. & MURGATROYD F. (1929). Studies on chemotherapy. I. A method for maintaining pathogenic trypanosomes alive *in vitro* at 37°C for 24 hours. *Ann. trop. Med. Parasit.* **23**: 501–518.

YOUNG C.W. & VAN SANT, HELEN M. (1923). *Leishmania donovani* in the peripheral blood. *J. exp. Med.* **38**: 233–256.

ZELEDON R. (1959). Differentiation of *Trypanosoma rangeli* and *Schizotrypanum cruzi* in a liquid medium, with notes on the nutrition of hemoflagellates. *J. Parasit.* **45**: 652.

ZUCKERMAN, AVIVAH (1966). Propagation of parasitic Protozoa in tissue culture and avian embryos. *Ann. N.Y. Acad. Sci.* **139**: 24–38.

CHAPTER 2

SPOROZOA

Almost all the work on the cultivation *in vitro* of this group has concerned the malaria parasites (*Plasmodium* spp.), and has tended to follow four well-defined lines: cultivation of (i) the erythrocytic stages intracellularly, (ii) the same stages extracellularly, (iii) the sporogonic stages which normally develop in mosquitoes, and (iv) the exoerythrocytic schizonts. The methods grouped under sections (i) and (iii) might perhaps be regarded as tissue-culture techniques, in so far as they involve the simultaneous cultivation of erythrocytes and mosquito tissues respectively, together with the parasites; however, it seems more proper to treat them as mono-xenic cultures of the malarial organisms. The methods grouped under the fourth heading are frankly tissue cultures which have been experimentally infected with the parasite and, as such, will not be discussed in any detail in this book. There has been a considerable amount of work done on the growth in avian embryos of those species of *Plasmodium* which infect birds, which also is regarded as being outside the scope of this book: the subject has been ably reviewed by Pipkin & Jensen (1958) and Zuckerman (1966). Long (1966) has reported on the growth of some species of *Eimeria* in avian embryos.

I. *PLASMODIUM*

1. INTRACELLULAR CULTIVATION OF INTRAERYTHROCYTIC STAGES

(i) *Early work*

The earliest successful attempts to cultivate malaria parasites were reported by Bass (1911) and Bass & Johns (1912). Their method (p. 58) allowed the completion of one or two (rarely three) cycles of schizogony of *P.vivax*, *P.falciparum* and *P.malariae*: by making subinoculations at intervals of 48 hr, they succeeded in carrying *P.falciparum* through four successive cycles. A variety of minor modifications of this technique was subsequently developed (see Trager, 1941, for references), including a simplification of it by Row (1928), in which a few drops of infected defibrinated blood were inoculated into a small, flat-bottomed tube containing serum and glucose solution and incubated (in the dark) either at 40°c or at room temperature (in Bombay—about 30–32°c): in these simple cultures, *P.falciparum* and *P.vivax* completed one schizogonic cycle.

Manwell & Hewitt (1937) obtained some development through one, or possibly more, schizogony cycles with heparinated avian blood infected with *P.relictum*, which was merely sealed in capillary tubes and incubated at 25°c. Hewitt (1938) subsequently obtained schizogony of *P.cathemerium* in canary blood which had been introduced to a diphasic medium composed of a slant of coagulated egg overlaid with saline containing glucose (0·5%) and rabbit serum (5%) and incubated at 37°c. However the merozoites produced in such cultures failed to re-invade newly added erythrocytes.

(ii)   *Later developments in the cultivation of mammalian malaria parasites*
Almost all subsequent work on the intraerythrocytic cultivation of these parasites has been done on *P.knowlesi* and reported in a series of papers by E.G. Ball *et al.* (1945), McKee *et al.* (1946), Geiman *et al.* (1946), Anfinsen *et al.* (1946), Geiman (1949, 1951) and Geiman *et al.* (1966b). These authors formulated a culture medium ('Harvard' medium) to simulate as nearly as possible the constitution of monkey plasma, and then designed a culture apparatus which would provide optimum physical conditions, including the rapid dilution or removal of substances such as lactic acid, excreted by the parasites. Subsequently, the medium has been modified, notably by the introduction of glycyl glycine (0·005 M) as a buffer. Using this method (p. 58), growth of the parasites *in vitro* has been maintained for up to 6 successive cycles of schizogony (by making serial transfers every 20–24 hr). *P.knowlesi* multiplied, usually about 4-fold, in the initial cultures and the first 3 or 4 subcultures; rather less multiplication (about 1·8 times) was obtained in the later subcultures. Latterly, *P.coatneyi*, *P.cynomolgi* and *P.falciparum* have multiplied in this medium (Geiman *et al.*, 1966b). Trigg (1967) has also grown *P.falciparum* in a slightly simplified version of it. Geiman *et al.* (1966a) have been able to replace whole plasma in this medium with a commercially available fraction of human plasma, Cohn's fraction IV–4 (Nutritional Biochemicals Corporation).

Trager (1958) also reported some success in growing *P.falciparum* within human erythrocytes, at 37·5–38°c, in a medium developed by McGhee & Trager (1950) for *P.lophurae* (p. 65) and supplemented with folic acid (0·2 ml of a solution containing 0·5 g/l. folic acid added to each culture flask containing 6 ml of medium). Polet (1966) achieved growth but no multiplication of *P.knowlesi* and *P.berghei* in blood diluted with enriched Eagle's medium.

(iii) *Later developments in the cultivation of avian malaria parasites*

Before the introduction of the 'Harvard' medium for *P.knowlesi*, Trager (1941, 1943) had achieved survival of the avian parasite *P.lophurae* in duck erythrocytes for up to 2 weeks *in vitro* at $40·5°c$ (but with virtually no multiplication of the parasite occurring) in a medium consisting of a balanced salt solution (with glucose), extracts of duck erythrocytes and chick embryos, and serum, with added glutathione and calcium panto-thenate. About one half to one third of the total volume of medium was replaced daily (the erythrocytes having been allowed to sediment). Subsequently, Anfinsen *et al.* (1946) reported some success in growing *P.lophurae* in the 'Harvard' medium and Trager (1947), using this medium with pyridoxamine and with the concentrations of purines and pyrimidines increased 8- or 10-fold, obtained some growth and multiplication of *P.lophurae* for up to 48 hr. By subinoculating to fresh medium every 2 days, Trager (*loc. cit.*) maintained the parasites *in vitro* for 8 days, during which period they increased in number 170 times. Subsequently McGhee & Trager (1950) found that adding glutathione (100 mg%) improved the medium. Sherman (1966) continued these investigations on the suitability of modified 'Harvard' medium for the cultivation of *P.lophurae*: he found that, while certain of the constituents used by Trager (1947), including, surprisingly, the glutathione, could be omitted with little or no deleterious effect, the addition of heparin (30 mg%) to the medium was beneficial. After 1950, Trager turned his attention to the possibility of cultivating *P.lophurae* extracellularly (see below), and work on the intracellular growth of avian malaria parasites was continued by Manwell and others (see Manwell & Brody, 1950; Manwell & Glenn, 1953; Glenn & Manwell, 1956; Spandorf & Manwell, 1960; and Nydegger & Manwell, 1962). These writers found that *P.relictum* and *P.hexamerium* grew fairly well in 'Harvard' medium, while *P.cathemerium*, *P.elongatum*, *P.vaughani* and *P.gallinaceum* did little more than survive in it for periods of up to 72 hr. *P.hexamerium*, which was found to grow more readily in 'Harvard' medium than any of the other species investigated by Manwell and his co-workers, developed even better if the medium was enriched with vitamin B_{12}, folic acid and porcine liver coenzyme concentrate (Glenn & Manwell, 1956): *P.circumflexum* also grew quite well in this enriched medium (Spandorf & Manwell, 1960). This work culminated in the development of a complex medium (p. 62) in which *P.hexamerium* could be maintained for 96 hr without changes of medium (though the

numbers of organisms decreased after 48 hr). Subcultures were successfully started (without the addition of extra serum) at 48 and 72 hr, and
in one instance a 'line' was subcultivated twice at 72-hr intervals and so
survived *in vitro* (though in decreasing numbers) for 9 days.

Anderson (1953) obtained very satisfactory growth of *P.gallinaceum* in
chicken erythrocytes suspended in a mixture of serum and erythrocyte

TABLE 2.1. Some media used for the cultivation of malaria parasites.

Author(s)	Date	Species	Detailed description (if any)
Anderson	1953	*P.gallinaceum*	p. 57
Anfinsen *et al.*	1946	*P.knowlesi*	—
Ball	1947, 1948, 1954	*P.relictum**	—
Ball & Chao	1957, 1960, 1961	*P.relictum**	—
Bass & Johns	1912	*P.vivax, P.malariae, P.falciparum*	p. 58
Chao & Ball	1964	*P.relictum**	p. 70
Clarke	1952	*P.gallinaceum*†	—
Geiman	1951	*P.knowlesi, P.vivax, P.cynomolgi*	—
Geiman *et al.*	1966b	*P.knowlesi* and others	p. 58
Glenn & Manwell	1956	*P.hexamerium*	—
Hewitt	1938	*P.cathemerium*	—
Manwell & Brody	1950	*P.hexamerium* and others	—
Manwell & Glenn	1953	*P.hexamerium* and others	—
Manwell & Hewitt	1937	*P.relictum*	—
McGhee & Trager	1950	*P.lophurae*	—
Nydegger & Manwell	1962	*P.hexamerium*	p. 62
Polet	1966	*P.knowlesi, P.berghei*	—
Row	1928	*P.vivax, P.falciparum*	—
Sherman	1966	*P.lophurae*	—
Spandorf & Manwell	1960	*P.hexamerium* and others	—
Trager	1941, 1943, 1947	*P.lophurae*	—
Trager	1958	*P.falciparum*	—
Trager	1950, 1952, 1953, 1958, 1964	*P.lophurae*†	p. 65
Trigg	1967	*P.falciparum*	—

* Sporogonic stages.
† Extracellular growth of erythrocytic stages.

extract, with added glucose (below): the medium was changed daily, and subcultures were inoculated about every 40 hr. In this way, 10 successful transfers were made before the culture was voluntarily discontinued after a total of 427 hr *in vitro*. During this time the increase in parasite numbers had been, in aggregate, nearly 20,000-fold. This seems to be the most successful attempt at cultivation of intraerythrocytic malaria parasites yet achieved.

Cultivation of
Plasmodium gallinaceum
(Anderson, 1953)

MEDIUM

Normal chicken blood is defibrinated by shaking with glass beads, then centrifuged to pack the cells. The serum is removed, heated for 1 hr at 60°c, then cooled and equilibriated with 7% carbon dioxide in air. Meanwhile the packed cells are frozen in dry ice, then slowly thawed at room temperature. The heated serum is mixed with the lysed cells and the mixture then centrifuged for 1 hr in the cold at about 10,000 rev/min. The supernatant fluid is collected and stored at −70°c. Before use it is thawed and again equilibriated with 7% carbon dioxide in air.

TECHNIQUE

Normal chicken erythrocytes (from blood to which has been added 10% v/v of a saline solution of heparin containing 2 mg/ml) are suspended in the above medium to produce a concentration similar to that of whole normal chicken blood. Sufficient erythrocytes from an infected bird are then added to give about 1–2% of parasitized cells. Five to seven millilitres of the cell suspension are placed in wide mouthed culture vessels of about 60 ml capacity; 0·15 ml of 5% glucose solution and 0·1 ml of a solution of penicillin G (potassium salt, 20,000 units/ml of physiological saline) are added.

The vessels are incubated at 40–42°c, rocked 13 times per minute and gassed with 7% carbon dioxide in air. The medium is changed every 24 hr (the erythrocytes being sedimented by centrifugation). Subcultures are prepared after about 40 hr, by inoculating some of the existing culture into 3–5 times its volume of a fresh suspension of uninfected cells in serum-lysate medium.

Short-term cultivation of
malaria parasites
(Bass & Johns, 1912)

MEDIUM AND TECHNIQUE

1   Infected blood is collected aseptically into 1/100th of its volume of 50% glucose solution and defibrinated by gentle stirring: frothing should be avoided.

2   The blood is then centrifuged slowly to sediment the cells. The serum is removed and placed in flat-bottomed culture tubes (12·5 × 1·25 cm) to a depth of about 1 cm.

3   To each tube is added about 0·1–0·2 ml of the deposit of infected red cells from the centrifuged blood (avoiding the upper layer of leucocytes): the cells are allowed to sediment.

4   The tubes are incubated at 40°c. Transfers can be made every 48 hr by removing some cells from an old culture, mixing them with about 5 times their volume of fresh uninfected human erythrocytes, and inoculating the mixture into new tubes prepared as in (2) above.

NOTE: Better results are obtained if the culture tubes are first partially filled with whole blood to a depth of 1–2 cm and centrifuged while coagulation occurs. The defibrinated serum and glucose is then placed on top of the coagulated, layered blood, and the infected cells (0·2–0·4 ml) added as before.

Improved 'Harvard' method for cultivation
of *P. knowlesi* (and other species)
(Geiman *et al.*, 1966b)

MEDIUM

1   *Preparation of stock solutions*

(a)   g/l.
Magnesium chloride 6H$_2$O ......0·406
Calcium chloride (anhydrous) ....0·112
Potassium chloride..............0·820
Sodium chloride...............11·650
Disodium hydrogen phosphate ...0·602
Sodium carbonate ....1·480

Equilibriate the above aqueous solution with carbon dioxide until clear;

autoclave; store overnight at room temperature (20–25°c). Then add the following:

	g/l.
Glucose	6·0
Glycerol	0·5
Sodium acetate 3H$_2$O	0·5

Resterilize by filtration through Millipore filter (Millipore Corporation), grade HA (0·45 μ pores).

(b)
Amino acids ('Parenamine'*	
15% solution)	2·15 ml
Glycine	0·02 g
Histidine	0·02 g
0·85% aqueous sodium chloride	20·75 ml

Sterilize by filtration through fritted glass: store at 4°c.

(c) *Vitamins*
(i) Riboflavin	12·5 mg
1·7% aqueous sodium chloride	
	12·5 ml

Warm in water bath to dissolve.

(ii) Biotin	0·25 mg†
Water (glass distilled)	12·5 ml

(iii) Mix solutions (i) and (ii) and add:

	g/25 ml
Thiamine	0·025
Niacin	0·025
Nicotinamide	0·025
Cocarboxylase	0·010
d-Calcium pantothenate	0·0125
Pyridoxine	0·0125
Ribose	0·0125
Choline	0·0125

After dissolving the above, add:

Potassium dihydrogen phosphate 0·00625

---

* Parenamine (Winthrop Laboratories) was an acid hydrolysate of casein, the detailed composition of which is given by Ball (1954). It is no longer obtainable, but (at least for the growth of *P.lophurae*) the amino acid mixture in which it was included may be replaced by lactalbumin hydrolysate at 0·75% (Trager, 1964) or 0·56% (Sherman, 1966).

† The concentration shown in the original paper is misprinted, and should read 20 μg/ml (Geiman, personal communication).

Sterilize by filtration through fritted glass: store at 4°C in a brown bottle.

(d)
Ascorbic acid ....90 mg
Water (glass distilled) ....10 ml

Prepare freshly for each experiment. Sterilize by filtration through fritted glass and store at 4°C.

(e)
p–Amino benzoic acid ....10 mg
0·85% aqueous sodium chloride..100 ml

Sterilize by filtration through fritted glass and store at 4°C.

(f)   g/50 ml
Xanthine ....0·0125
Guanine......................0·0125
Thymine ....0·00625
Adenine......................0·0125
Uracil........................0·0125
Cytosine ....0·00625

Dissolve the above in 0·85% aqueous sodium chloride by adding a few drops of 10 N sodium hydroxide solution; neutralize with N hydrochloric acid; sterilize by filtration (presumably: not stated by authors) and store at 4°C (a precipitate may form, and should be resuspended before dispensing).

(g)
Glycyl glycine................5·28 g
Water (glass distilled) ....100 ml

Sterilize by filtration (presumably).

2   *Preparation of final medium*
Mix the above stock solutions in the following proportions:

(a).........................48·61 ml
(b)..........................0·5 ml
(c)..........................0·1 ml
(d)..........................0·33 ml
(e)..........................0·1 ml
(f)...........................0·1 ml
(g)..........................1·65 ml
Add glass–distilled water......48·61 ml
                            _____
                            100·00 ml

Equilibriate the final mixture with CO_2 (5 % in air) to give pH $7·45 \pm 0·1$.

TECHNIQUE

Originally 2 main types of apparatus were described (Geiman *et al.*, 1946), in one of which ('rocker-dilution' technique) blood and medium were mixed; in the other ('rocker-perfusion') apparatus, the parasitized blood was separated from the medium by a cellophane dialysis membrane (Fig. 2.2). A later version of the latter (perfusion) apparatus is illustrated by Geiman *et al.* (1966b), but since most recent developments of this method have used the rocker-dilution method, this is described below.

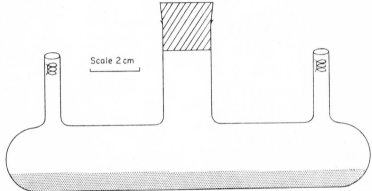

FIGURE 2.1 Diagram of rocker–dilution vessel used in 'Harvard' method of cultivating malaria parasites. The gas phase is passed through 2 cotton-plugged tubes at either end of the cylindrical vessel, and the medium and inoculum are introduced through the larger, central tube, which is closed with a rubber bung. (From Geiman *et al.*, 1946.)

Heparinated blood from heavily-infected monkeys is mixed with normal monkey blood to give a final proportion of about 16 million infected cells per ml (Geiman *et al.*, 1946): this is mixed with the final medium in the proportion of 1 volume of blood to 6 volumes of medium and introduced aseptically into a culture vessel containing either 6–9 ml of medium plus blood (Fig. 2.1) or only 1·5 ml. The vessels are placed in a water-bath at 38–39°c and rocked gently at about 20 cycles/min. A slow stream of 5% carbon dioxide in air (about 1 bubble per sec) is passed through the vessel above (not through) the medium.

Subinoculations are made (if required) every 24 hr, by removing some parasitized blood from the old culture, diluting it with fresh uninfected monkey blood to give an initial parasite count of 1–3%, and transferring it to a fresh apparatus containing new medium. Up to 3 serial sub-inoculations have been achieved with *P.knowlesi* (Ball *et al.*, 1945). In 132 experiments, the average increase achieved in each initial 24 hr period was 4-fold (Geiman *et al.*, 1946): multiplication during subcultures is not quoted. (Using the rocker-perfusion technique, 5 serial subcultures were achieved, although the multiplication rate decreased after the third.)

NOTE: A simplified version of this medium was described by Geiman (1951) in which stock solutions c, e and f were omitted (the use of solution g was not introduced until later), being replaced by liver extract no: 3649-34 (Lederle Laboratories) at 10 ml/l.: this simplification is not now used (Geiman *et al.*, 1966b).

Cultivation of
Plasmodium hexamerium
(Nydegger & Manwell, 1962)

MEDIUM

1   *Composition of stock solutions*

(a)

Magnesium chloride 6H$_2$O . . . . .0·406 g
Potassium chloride . . . . .0·820 g
Calcium chloride (anhydrous) . .0·137 g
Sodium chloride . . . . .11·650 g
Water to make . . . . .1 l.

(b)

Sodium carbonate (anhydrous). .14·80 g
Disodium hydrogen phosphate
    7H$_2$O . . . . .4·57 g
Potassium dihydrogen phosphate .0·57 g
Water . . . . .100 ml

(c)

Water . . . . .50·0 ml
Cocarboxylase . . . . .8·0 mg
Thiamine phosphate hydrochloride
                        20·0 mg
Niacin. . . . . .20·0 mg
Nicotinamide . . . . 20·0 mg
d-Calcium pantothenate . . . . . .10·0 mg
Pyridoxine hydrochloride . . . . .10·0 mg
Riboflavin 5-phosphate (sodium)
                        10·0 mg
Choline chloride . . . . .10·0 mg
Biotin . . . . .8 μg
Potassium dihydrogen phosphate 5·0 mg
1·7% sodium chloride solution. .61·0 ml
Modified Ringer's solution . . . .20·0 ml
Xanthine .5·0 mg

Guanine hydrochloride . . . . .5·0 mg
Thymine .2·5 mg
Adenine sulphate 2H$_2$O . . . . .5·0 mg
Uracil . . . . .5·0 mg
Cytosine . . . . .2·5 mg
p-Aminobenzoic acid . . . . .2·0 mg
L-Histidine monohydrochloride 40·0 mg
Glycine . . . . .40·0 mg
L-Glutamic acid . . . . .20·0 mg
DL-Serine . . . . .10·0 mg
L-Proline . . . . .10·0 mg
DL-Alanine . . . . .10·0 mg
Parenamine† . . . . .4·3 ml
Folic acid . . . . .200 μg
Vitamin B$_{12}$ (0·1%) . . . . .20·0 mg
Thioctic acid . . . . .200 μg
Water to make* . . . . .250·0 ml

(d)

Glucose . . . . .15·0 g
Sodium acetate 3H$_2$O . . . . .1·25 g
Glycerol. . . . . .1·0 ml
Water to make . . . . .100 ml

(e)

Adenosine triphosphate . . . . . . .17·0 mg
Coenzyme A . . . . .17·0 mg
Porcine liver coenzyme concentrate
                        333·0 mg
Ribose . . . . .10·0 mg
Water to make* . . . . .100·0 ml

* It is suggested that sodium malate and sodium pyruvate, prepared by neutralizing malic or pyruvic acid with sodium hydroxide, be added in final concentrations of 0·0002 M to either stock solutions (c) or (e).
† See footnote on p. 59

2 Preparation and storage of stock solutions

Stock solutions (a) and (b) are sterilized by autoclaving, the remainder by filtration. Solutions (c) and (e) should be stored deep-frozen, the others at about 4°c.

3 Preparation of final medium

(a) To prepare 200 ml of medium, mix the stock solutions in the proportions shown below and add penicillin, etc. as indicated:

Stock solution (a)	100·0 ml
Stock solution (b)	2·0 ml
Stock solution (c)	2·5 ml
Stock solution (d)	4·0 ml
Stock solution (e)	1·0 ml
Penicillin	1,000 units
Ascorbic acid	7·2 mg
Phenol red indicator	4 drops
Heparin	400 units
Water to make	200 ml

The penicillin and ascorbic acid are weighed and added immediately before use. The heparin is added from a separate stock solution of suitable concentration.

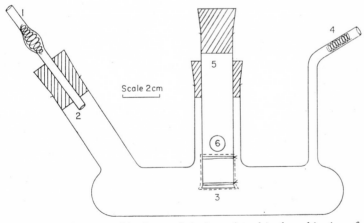

FIGURE 2.2 Diagram of 'rocker-perfusion' vessel used in the cultivation of malaria parasites in small amounts of blood. (1) Gas entry tube; (2) tube for introduction of medium; (3) cellophane membrane tied over base of wide glass tube to form culture chamber; (4) gas exit; (5) culture chamber: the inoculum is introduced through its upper end, normally closed with a rubber bung; (6) hole in wall of culture chamber for gaseous equilibration. (From Geiman et al., 1946.)

(b)   The complete medium is gassed with sterile carbon dioxide until equilibrium is attained (pH = 7·0). If necessary it may be sterilized again by filtration: if this is done, additional gassing with carbon dioxide will probably be necessary afterwards to restore neutrality.

TECHNIQUE

The medium is used in the rocker-perfusion apparatus described by Geiman et al. (1946), illustrated in Fig. 2.2. About 0·5 ml of blood is contained in a glass tube closed at the lower end with cellophane dialysis membrane and just immersed* in about 30 ml of medium. The apparatus is incubated at 38–39°c on a rocking platform (about 20 cycles/min) and a slow (about one bubble per sec) stream of sterile 5% carbon dioxide in air is passed through the flask above (not through) the medium.

2. EXTRACELLULAR CULTIVATION OF INTRAERYTHROCYTIC STAGES

All the work to be discussed in this section has been done by Trager, using *P.lophurae* maintained in ducklings, with the single exception of a paper by Miss Clarke (1952), recording 'some' extracellular growth of *P.gallinaceum* in lysed, infected blood, a method substantially similar to that used by Trager (1950) in his earlier work along these lines. Trager's work has been reported in a series of papers (Trager, 1950, 1952, 1953, 1958, 1964); its culmination was the development of a medium (p. 65) in which growth and schizogony of the intraerythrocytic forms of *P.lophurae* continued, outside the cells, for periods of up to 5 (occasionally 6) days in a single flask (with regular changes of medium). The organisms grow as a 'scum' on a thin layer of fibrin clot which lines the flasks: apart from the organisms themselves the medium is free of intact cells but it does contain duck erythrocyte nuclei. Bowman (1964) has raised the interesting question of whether the presence of these nuclei is essential to the growth of the parasites. This is the nearest approach yet achieved to the axenic cultivation *in vitro* of a species of *Plasmodium*. In connection with this work, a most ingenious apparatus for automatically changing the culture medium has been described by Trager & Jernberg (1961): details should be sought in the original publication. The method depends upon the fact that the parasites grow as a scum on the layer of fibrin

---

* The membrane must be only half submerged in the medium at the point of maximum tilt of the rocking platform, or too much dilution will occur.

and thus are not removed with the old medium: this would prevent the use of Trager's and Jernberg's device with most other types of *in vitro* culture.

Trager's method for extracellular cultivation of *Plasmodium lophurae*
(Trager, 1950, 1952, 1958, 1964)

MEDIUM

A. NUTRIENT SOLUTION

1 *Composition of stock solutions*

No.		Concentration g/l.	Amount of stock solution ml/l.	Concentration mg/l.
1	Sodium chloride	66·0	50	3,300
	Potassium chloride	88·0		4,400
2	Sodium dihydrogen phosphate H_2O	5·5	25	138
	Dipotassium hydrogen phosphate	62·7		1,568
3	Sodium bicarbonate	50·0	18	900
4	Calcium chloride	2·6	15	39
5	Manganese sulphate $4H_2O$	2·2	20	44
6	Sodium acetate $3H_2O$	25·0	10	250
	Glycerol	25·0		250
7	Glucose	50·0	43	2,150
8	Hexose diphosphate (Mg salt)	50·0	14	700
9	Glutathione	20·0	50	1,000
	Ascorbic acid	0·2		10
	Nicotinamide	80·0		4,000
10	Lactalbumin hydrolysate (Nutritional Biochemical Corporation)	375·0	20	7,500
11	Bovine plasma fraction V	20·0	300	6,000
12	Gelatin	180·0	400	72,000
13g	Riboflavin	0·05	10	0·5
	Thiamin HCl	0·05		0·5
	Pyridoxin HCl	0·05		0·5
	Pyridoxamine HCl	0·01		0·1
	Pyridoxal HCl	0·01		0·1
	Inositol	0·10		1·0
	Choline Cl	0·10		1·0

1   *Composition of stock solutions*—contd.

No.		Concentration g/l.	Amount of stock solution ml/l.	Concentration mg/l.
			Final mixture	
13b	Calcium pantothenate	2·0	5	10·0
13d	*p*-Aminobenzoic acid	1·0	1	1·0
14B	Biotin	0·05	0·1	0·005
14F	Folic acid	0·05	0·2	0·01
15	Adenine sulphate	0·05	10	0·5
	Guanine HCl	0·05		0·5
	Xanthine	0·05		0·5
	Uracil	0·05		0·5
	Cytidylic acid	0·02		0·2

2   *Preparation of stock solutions*

(a)   *No. 8:* Some preparations of hexose diphosphate produce a very acid solution: if this occurs it should be adjusted to pH 5·8–6·0 with 0·5 N potassium hydroxide solution.

(b)   *Nos. 14B and F:* 5 mg biotin and folic acid respectively are dissolved in 3 drops of 0·1 N sodium hydroxide solution with gentle warming, and then diluted to 100 ml.

(c)   *No. 15:* 5 mg each of adenine, guanine, xanthine and uracil, and 2 mg of cytidylic acid are dissolved by heating in 2 ml of 6 N hydrochloric acid solution. After dilution with a little water, the pH is adjusted to between 6 and 7 with 2 N sodium hydroxide and the volume is then made up to 100 ml.

3   *Sterilization of stock solutions*

Stock solutions 1–7, 10, 13 b, 13 d, 14 B, 14 F and 15 may be autoclaved; solution 12 is steamed for 20–30 min on each of 3 successive days; the others are filtered.

4   *Storage of stock solutions*

All stock solutions may be stored at about 4°c for up to 3 months *except* Nos. 13 g, b, d (which should be stored deep-frozen) and No. 9 (which should be freshly made or stored frozen for not more than 2 days).

5   *Preparation of final nutrient solution*

The stock solutions are mixed in the proportions shown under (1) above. To each 100 ml of the mixture is added 15 ml of unheated serum from ducks (7–11 weeks old: this is collected during the preparation of the erythrocyte extract—see (B) below).

B. ERYTHROCYTE EXTRACT

Forty-five to fifty millilitres of blood from ducks (7–11 weeks old) are defibrinated by shaking with glass beads for 35 min and centrifuged in the cold for 20 min; the serum is removed and stored in the refrigerator for subsequent use. The packed cells are rapidly frozen in a mixture of solid carbon dioxide and alcohol, stored at $-70°c$ for 1–3 days, thawed by immersion in cold water, re-suspended in $1\frac{1}{3}$ times their volume of nutrient medium (see above) and centrifuged for 1 hr at 2,300 rev/min. The supernatant is collected (and must not be stored, even in a refrigerator, for more than 24 hr). The pH of the final mixture is adjusted, if necessary, to 7·0 with decinormal solutions of either hydrochloric acid or potassium hydroxide.

C. ADDITIONAL INGREDIENTS

1   0·5 g yeast adenylic acid is suspended in 10 ml water and dissolved by the addition of drops of normal sodium hydroxide solution until the pH is 5·8: 0·8 g l-malic acid is then added and the pH is readjusted to 5·8 by adding just over 2 ml of 5 n potassium hydroxide solution. 0·1 g of cozymase (65%) is added, and the solution diluted to 20 ml. It is sterilized by filtration and stored in a deep-freeze.

2   To each 10 ml of the red cell extract medium is added 0·2 ml of the above solution, giving final concentrations (in mm/l.) of adenylic acid, 1·4; l-malic acid, 6·0; and cozymase, 0·15.

TECHNIQUE

1   *Preparation of flasks*

(a)   The flasks used are either 50 ml conical (Erlenmeyer) flasks or special vessels designed for automatic media exchange (Trager & Jernberg, 1961), provided with tubes for inflow and outflow of gas.

(b)   Into each flask is placed 0·25 ml plasma (prepared from blood collected without anticoagulant from the jugular vein of uninfected ducklings, 2–3 weeks old, and centrifuged at 2,000 rev/min) and 0·02 ml of chick embryo extract as a source of thromboplastin. (The chick embryo extract is prepared by grinding one 10-day-old embryo in a glass tissue-grinder with 4 ml isotonic glucose-saline solution, and centrifuging: p. 345.) The flask is then rotated rapidly in a nearly horizontal position while clotting occurs, so that a thin layer of fibrin is formed over the lower part of the wall of the flask.

(c)   To each flask is added the following:

6

(i) 3 ml of nutrient medium (including erythrocyte extract and additional ingredients).

(ii) 0·05 ml of adenosinetriphosphate and pyruvate solution, prepared as follows: 1 g sodium pyruvate (preferably made in the laboratory by neutralizing an alcoholic solution of pyruvic acid with alcoholic sodium hydroxide and re-crystallizing the product once) and 2 g adenosinetriphosphate (potassium salt) are dissolved in 10 ml water, the pH is brought to 5·8 with 0·5 N potassium hydroxide, and the volume made up (with water) to 25ml. The solution is sterilized by filtration and stored at −70°C.

(iii) 0·2 ml coenzyme A solution, consisting of 0·5 g (7,500 Lipmann units) Armour's liver coenzyme concentrate ground in a mortar and dissolved in 14 ml water plus 1·9 ml phosphate buffer (stock solution 2, see above): the pH is brought to 6·5 with 0·5 N potassium hydroxide, the volume is made up to 57 ml, the solution is sterilized by filtration and stored at −70°C.

(iv) 0·04 ml folinic acid solution (1 ampoule of Lederle's leucovorin containing 3 mg calcium salt of formyltetrahydropteroylglutamic acid in 1 ml, added aseptically to 4 ml sterile water and stored in a deep-freeze), giving a final concentration of about 5 μg/ml.

(v) 0·3 ml of inoculum (see 2 below).

(d) Each flask is then placed on a rocking table (16 cycles/min) and incubated at 40–40·5°C. A slow current of 5% carbon dioxide in air is passed through each flask (not more than two flasks being arranged in series).

2 *Preparation of inoculum*

Three millilitres of blood, with about 80–100 parasites per 100 erythrocytes and about 90% uni-nucleate trophozoites, are collected from a 2–3 week-old duckling with a synchronous infection: the blood is withdrawn into 0·3 ml of a solution containing 27 mg of heparin in 100 ml of 0·85% saline. The blood is lightly centrifuged, the plasma is discarded and the erythrocytes are resuspended in 4 times their volume of nutrient medium plus erythrocyte extract (see above). To 2 ml of the suspension (contained in a 50 ml conical flask) are added 1·6 ml of additional erythrocyte extract, 0·07 ml of guinea-pig serum (as a source of complement) and 0·4 ml of anti-duck erythrocyte serum prepared in rabbits. This mixture is incubated on a vibratory shaker for ½ hr at 37°C, and 0·3 ml aliquots are placed in the prepared culture flasks. The mixture contains erythrocyte membranes, some containing parasites, free red cell nuclei and free parasites: after 1 day's incubation the contained parasites become free, but if desired for observations extending over a period of 1 day or less the entrapped parasites may be removed at the start of the experiment by centrifugation for 50 sec to a maximum speed of 500 rev/min, less than $100 \times g$.

3 Subsequent procedures

If the cultures are set up about 4 p.m., by next morning about half the free parasites should have become attached to the fibrin layer as a visible 'scum' near the interface between medium and air. Observations may be made on portions of this scum withdrawn with fine capillary pipettes (sterile). The medium is changed, either by pipette or automatically (Trager & Jernberg, 1961), after the first 18 hr of incubation and subsequently every 12 hr: the adherence of the parasites to the fibrin means that medium exchange can be effected with virtually no loss of parasites. Maximum survival obtained up to 1964 was 5, and occasionally 6, days.

NOTES: (1) Culture flasks should be heat-sterilized so that they are quite dry.

(2) As little delay as possible should ensue between collecting the infected blood and inoculating it into the flasks (usually 1–1·5 hr).

(3) If all procedures are done aseptically, antibiotics should not be needed.

3. CULTIVATION OF SPOROGONIC STAGES

All work on the growth in vitro of the stages in the life-cycle of Plasmodium which normally occur in the mosquito has been done by G.H. Ball and his associates, using P.relictum (maintained in canaries) and Culex tarsalis. From the earliest attempts at maintenance in vitro of oocysts on isolated mosquito midguts (Ball, 1947, 1948), the technique has been progressively improved (Ball, 1954; Ball & Chao, 1957, 1960, 1961) until all the stages from fertilization to the production of viable sporozoites can be produced in vitro, though not in any one culture (Chao & Ball, 1964). Each culture continues to develop for only about 5 days, but by starting each culture with material isolated from mosquitoes at the stage at which the previous culture ended, the entire development has been undergone stepwise in vitro in about 20 days at 27°c (about twice as long as comparable development in vivo at the same temperature). Development occurs at any temperature between 18° and 31°c. Ball & Chao (1957) found that oocysts isolated from the midgut would also undergo some development in vitro, but the method has no advantage over the simpler one of handling the oocysts on the entire midgut. Antibiotics have been found to have an inhibiting effect on both midgut contractility (and hence, presumably, viability) and also on oocyst growth. Mosquitoes are starved for 24–48 hr at 18°c which reduces the number of bacteria in the midgut, and are then dissected by a sterile technique after surface sterilization in 80% ethanol (Chao, 1955). However, in spite of this, very few cultures are free from contamination and it has been found necessary to include in the medium streptomycin and amphotericin B (not penicillin, to which most bacteria of the mosquito midgut are insensitive). Details of the method and a recent version of the medium used by Ball are given below. The development of the work has been summarized by Ball (1964) and by Chao & Ball (1964).

Cultivation of sporogonic stages of
Plasmodium relictum
(Chao & Ball, 1964)

MEDIUM

1   *Composition of stock solutions* (per l.)

(a)
Sodium chloride . . . . 3,500 mg
Potassium chloride . . . . 4,000 mg
Magnesium sulphate 7H$_2$O . . . . . 200 mg
Calcium chloride . . . . 100 mg

(b)
Sodium dihydrogen phosphate . 100 mg
Dipotassium hydrogen phosphate
100 mg

(c)
Sodium bicarbonate . . . . 500 mg

(d)
Glucose . . . . 800 mg
Fructose . . . . 300 mg
Sucrose . . . . 300 mg
Trehalose . . . . 400 mg
Glycerol . . . . 2 ml

(e)
α-Alanine . . . . 90 mg
β-Alanine . . . . 60 mg
L-Arginine . . . . 80 mg
L-Asparagine . . . . 50 mg
L-Aspartic acid . . . . 50 mg
L-Cysteine . . . . 40 mg

L-Cystine . . . . 20 mg
L-Glutamic acid . . . . 50 mg
L-Glutamine . . . . 80 mg
Glycine . . . . 50 mg
L-Histidine . . . . 90 mg
L-Isoleucine . . . . 50 mg
L-Leucine . . . . 50 mg
L-Lysine HCl . . . . 50 mg
L-Methionine . . . . 20 mg
L-Phenylalanine . . . . 10 mg
L-Proline . . . . 40 mg
L-Serine . . . . 50 mg
Taurine . . . . 40 mg
L-Threonine . . . . 40 mg
L-Tryptophan . . . . 20 mg
L-Tyrosine . . . . 20 mg
L-Valine . . . . 60 mg

(f)
Ca-pantothenate . . . . 2 mg
Niacin . . . . 1·5 mg
Thiamine HCl . . . . 1 mg
Riboflavin . . . . 1 mg
Pyridoxine HCl . . . . 1 mg
Folic acid . . . . 1 mg
Inositol . . . . 1 mg
Choline HCl . . . . 1 mg

Vitamin B$_{12}$	0·3 mg	(h)	
Biotin	0·2 mg	Malic acid	500 mg
p-Aminobenzoic acid	0·2 mg	α-Ketoglutaric acid	250 mg
Cholesterol	0·2 mg	Succinic acid	60 mg
		Fumaric acid	50 mg
(g)		(i)	
Guanosine	2 mg	Adenosine triphosphate	1·5 mg
Adenosine	2 mg	Coenzyme A	2·5 mg
Cytidine	2 mg	Cytochrome c	50 mg
Uridine	2 mg		
Xanthosine	2 mg	(k)	
Inosine	2 mg	Streptomycin	400 mg
Thymidine	2 mg	Amphotericin	20 mg

2 Preparation of stock solutions

The stock solutions are sterilized by filtration. Stock solution (h) is neutralized with an equimolar solution of sodium and potassium hydroxides.

3 Preparation of final medium

(a) The stock solutions are combined aseptically in equal volumes to give a final medium containing the ingredients at one-tenth of the concentration shown under 1 above.

(b) The following components are added to each 10 ml of the above mixture in the volumes shown:

(i) Chick serum, 2 ml.

(ii) Chick embryo extract (50% in a solution of 3·5 g sodium chloride and 4·0 g potassium chloride/l.: see p. 345), 0·5 ml.

(iii) Female mosquito extract (prepared by crushing whole mosquitoes in saline as in (ii) above to give 50% suspension, and then sterilizing by filtration), 0·05 ml.

(c) The pH of the complete medium is adjusted to approximately 7 with either 0·3 N hydrochloric acid or a 0·3 N equimolar solution of sodium and potassium hydroxides (sterilized presumably by filtration).

TECHNIQUE

After sterile dissection (Chao, 1955), the mosquito midgut with oocysts (or developing ookinetes) is placed in the above complete medium contained in small Petri dishes (constructed from sections of Pyrex tubing, of outside diameter 18 mm and 6 mm high for the base and outside diameter 22 mm, 4 mm high, for the lid: the top and base of the dish are made from No. 1 coverslips of suitable size, cemented to the sections of tubing with 'Sealit'* or other suitable non-toxic cement). The cultures

* Fischer Scientific Company.

are incubated at room temperature (or any temperature between 18 and 31°c) in an atmosphere of 5% carbon dioxide in air for the development of all stages excepting the sporozoites: for development of the latter, atmospheric air forms a better gaseous phase (under these conditions the pH of the medium rises from 7 to about 8). Rocking the cultures confers no detectable advantage.

NOTES: (1) Stock solutions (h), (j) and (k) are sometimes omitted: if this is done the equivalent volume of water must be added to maintain the correct concentration of the other ingredients in the final medium.

(2) Dutky (1964) has suggested that the concentration of streptomycin used in this medium could with advantage be reduced.

4. CULTIVATION OF EXOERYTHROCYTIC SCHIZONTS

More success has been achieved in this type of cultivation of malaria parasites than in any of the methods described above. The methods involved are basically tissue-culture techniques, in which the tissues concerned (almost always from chick embryos) are either established in culture and then infected with the malaria parasites, or the cultures are initiated with tissues from infected avian embryos. Among the species whose exoerythrocytic schizonts have been grown in this way are *P.gallinaceum*, *P.cathemerium*, *P.relictum*, *P.lophurae*, *P.fallax* and, with limited success, *P.elongatum*. All these are species whose exoerythrocytic schizogony occurs in cells of the reticulo-endothelial system. The exoerythrocytic stages of mammalian malaria parasites are restricted to the liver parenchyma: as this tissue has not yet been successfully grown *in vitro*, none of these species can be cultivated in this manner.

This subject has been reviewed by Pipkin & Jensen (1958) and, more recently, by Huff (1964) and Zuckerman (1966). The methods used will not be described in detail: those interested should refer to the above reviews for more information, including references.

The greatest success in the infection of already-established tissue cultures was achieved by Dubin *et al.*, (1949, 1950a, 1950b), using sporozoites of *P.gallinaceum* to infect embryonic chick spleen cells. More recently, Huff and his collaborators have used cultures of tissues from chick or turkey embryos already infected with *P.gallinaceum* or *P.fallax* to make detailed and interesting observations on the morphology and behaviour of living exoerythrocytic stages of these species (Huff *et al.*, 1960;

Davis *et al.*, 1966): cinematograph film records of their development have also been made (see Huff, 1964). Huff succeeded in maintaining individual cultures, with parasites, for as long as 5 or even 7 months in some instances: serial transfers can be continued probably indefinitely (Davis *et al.*, 1966).

II. GENERA OTHER THAN *PLASMODIUM*

The only successful cultivation *in vitro* of Sporozoa apart from malaria parasites has been the growth in tissue culture of a few species: this work is briefly mentioned here.

(i) *Eimeriidae*

Apart from the standard technique of maintaining oocysts of coccidia suspended in 2 or 2·5% aqueous potassium dichromate while they sporulate (which normally occurs outside the host), the only cultivation *in vitro* of members of this group of organisms appears to have been that of Strout *et al.* (1965). These workers obtained invasion of some cells in cultures of chick embryo kidney and fibroblasts, mouse fibroblasts, and human amnion and HeLa cells by sporozoites of the coccidian *Eimeria acervulina*, a parasite of the intestine of the chicken. Following sporozoite invasion, a few of the resulting trophozoites commenced (but did not complete) schizogony. For full details of the techniques used, including the surface sterilization of the oocysts (in an aqueous solution of chlorine, 50 parts per million, over a period of 6 days with daily changes of the solution) and the liberation from them of sporozoites by digestion with pepsin, trypsin and bile, reference should be made to the original paper (Strout *et al.*, 1965). Another, more rapid method of preparing suspensions of sporulated oocysts which are free of bacteria and most debris has been described for *E.stiedae* and *E.tenella* by Wagenbach *et al.* (1966).

(ii) *Theileriidae*

At least 3 species of this family (*T.parva*, *T.laurencei* and *T.annulata*) have been grown in tissue-culture (Brocklesby & Hawking, 1958; Hulliger, 1965). The original papers should be consulted for details.

(iii) *Toxoplasmatidae*

T.gondii has been successfully grown in tissue-culture of rat embryo heart by Lock (1953) and by a few other workers in embryonic avian tissues (see Lock, 1953 for references). Pulvertaft *et al.* (1954) grew the parasite for an unspecified time in cultures of various adult human or murine tissues (bone-marrow, lymph gland, etc.) which were maintained on a serum-agar medium in sealed chambers on microscope slides and subjected to continuous observation and cinephotomicrography. For full details of these techniques the original papers should be consulted.

REFERENCES

ANDERSON C.R. (1953). Continuous propagation of *Plasmodium gallinaceum* in chicken erythrocytes. *Am. J. trop. Med. Hyg.* **2:** 234–242.

ANFINSEN C.B., GEIMAN Q.M., McKEE R.W., ORMSBEE R.A. & BALL E.G. (1946). Studies on malarial parasites. VIII. Factors affecting the growth of *Plasmodium knowlesi in vitro. J. exp. Med.* **84:** 607–621.

BALL E.G., ANFINSEN C.B., GEIMAN Q.M., McKEE R.W. & ORMSBEE R.A. (1945). *In vitro* growth and multiplication of the malarial parasite, *Plasmodium knowlesi. Science, N.Y.* **101:** 542–544.

BALL G.H. (1947). Attempts to cultivate the mosquito phase of *Plasmodium relictum. Am. J. trop. Med.* **27:** 301–307.

BALL G.H. (1948). Extended persistence of *Plasmodium relictum* in culture. *Am. J. trop. Med.* **28:** 533–536.

BALL G.H. (1954). Prolonged contraction of mosquito digestive tract *in vitro* with partial development of oocysts of *Plasmodium relictum. Expl Parasit.* **3:** 358–367.

BALL G.H. (1964). *In vitro* culture of the mosquito phase of avian malaria. *J. Parasit.* **50:** 3–10.

BALL G.H. & CHAO J. (1957). Development *in vitro* of isolated oocysts of *Plasmodium relictum. J. Parasit.* **43:** 409–412.

BALL G.H. & CHAO J. (1960). *In vitro* development of the mosquito phase of *Plasmodium relictum. Expl Parasit.* **9:** 47–55.

BALL G.H. & CHAO J. (1961). Infectivity to canaries of sporozoites of *Plasmodium relictum* developing *in vitro. J. Parasit.* **47:** 787–790.

BASS C.C. (1911). A new conception of immunity. Its application to the cultivation of Protozoa and bacteria from the blood and to therapeutic measures. *J. Am. Med. Ass.* **57:** 1534–1535.

BASS C.C. & JOHNS F.M. (1912). The cultivation of malarial plasmodia (*Plasmodium vivax* and *Plasmodium falciparum*) *in vitro. J. exp. Med.* **16:** 567–579.

BOWMAN I.R. (1964). Comments on cultivation of erythrocytic stages. *Am. J. trop. Med. Hyg.* **13:** 167–170.

BROCKLESBY D.W. & HAWKING F. (1958). Growth of *Theileria annulata* and *T.parva* in tissue culture. *Trans. R. Soc. trop. Med. Hyg.* **52:** 414–420.

CHAO J. (1955). Sterile microdissection and isolation of malarial oocysts. *Science, N.Y.* **122:** 763.

CHAO J. & BALL G.H. (1964). Cultivation of the insect cycle of plasmodia. *Am. J. trop. Med. Hyg.* **13:** 181–192.

CLARKE, DELPHINE H. (1952). The use of phosphorus 32 in studies on *Plasmodium gallinaceum.* II. Studies on conditions affecting parasite growth in intact cells and in lysates. *J. exp. Med.* **96:** 451–463.

DAVIS A.G., HUFF C.G. & PALMER T.T. (1966). Procedures for maximum production of exoerythrocytic stages of *Plasmodium fallax* in tissue culture. *Expl Parasit.* **19**: 1–8.

DUBIN I.N., LAIRD R.L. & DRINNON V.P. (1949). The development of sporozoites of *Plasmodium gallinaceum* into cryptozoites in tissue culture. *J. natn. Malar. Soc.* **8**: 175–180.

DUBIN I.N., LAIRD R.L. & DRINNON V.P. (1950a). Further observations on the development of sporozoites of *Plasmodium gallinaceum* into cryptozoites in tissue culture. *J. natn. Malar. Soc.* **9**: 119–127.

DUBIN I.N., LAIRD R.L. & DRINNON V.P. (1950b). The infection of chicks with pre-erythrocytic stages of *Plasmodium gallinaceum* grown in tissue culture. *J. natn. Malar. Soc.* **9**: 128–131.

DUTKY S.R. (1964). Comments on cultivation of the insect cycle of Plasmodia. *Am. J. trop. Med. Hyg.* **13**: 193–194.

GEIMAN Q.M. (1949). *In vitro* methods for study and cultivation of plasmodia. In *Malariology*: 205–222. Boyd, M.F. (ed). Philadelphia & London: W.B. Saunders.

GEIMAN Q.M. (1951). The cultivation of malarial parasites. In *Parasitic infections in man*: 130–149. Most H. (ed). New York: Columbia University Press. (London: Geoffrey Cumberlege.)

GEIMAN Q.M., ANFINSEN C.B., McKEE R.W., ORMSBEE R.A. & BALL E.G. (1946). Studies on malarial parasites. VII. Methods and techniques for cultivation. *J. exp. Med.* **84**: 583–606.

GEIMAN Q.M., SIDDIQUI W.A. & SCHNELL J.V. (1966a). Plasma replacement for *in vitro* culture of *Plasmodium knowlesi*. *Science, N.Y.* **153**: 1129–1130.

GEIMAN Q.M., SIDDIQUI W.A. & SCHNELL J.V. (1966b). *In vitro* studies on erythrocytic stages of plasmodia; medium improvements and results with seven species of malarial parasites. *Milit. Med.* **131** Suppl.: 1015–1025.

GLENN S. & MANWELL R.D. (1956). Further studies on the cultivation of the avian malarial parasites: II. The effects of heterologous sera and added metabolites on growth and reproduction *in vitro*. *Expl Parasit.* **5**: 22–33.

HEWITT R. (1938). The cultivation of *Plasmodium cathemerium* for one asexual generation on inspissated egg and rabbit serum. *Am. J. Hyg.* **27**: 341–344.

HUFF C.G. (1964). Cultivation of the exoerythrocytic stages of malarial parasites. *Am. J. trop. Med. Hyg.* **13**: 171–177.

HUFF C.G., PIPKIN A.C., WEATHERSBY A.B. & JENSEN D. (1960). The morphology and behavior of living exoerythrocytic stages of *Plasmodium gallinaceum* and *P.fallax* and their host cells. *J. biophys. biochem. Cytol.* **7**: 93–102.

HULLIGER, LOTTE (1965). Cultivation of three species of *Theileria* in lymphoid cells *in vitro*. *J. Protozool.* **12**: 649–655.

LOCK J.A. (1953). Cultivation of *Toxoplasma gondii* in tissue culture in mammalian cells. *Lancet* **264**: 324–325.

LONG P.L. (1966). The growth of some species of *Eimeria* in avian embryos. *Parasitology* **56**: 575–581.

MANWELL R.D. & BRODY G. (1950). Survival and growth of four species of avian plasmodia on the Harvard culture medium. *J. natn. Malar. Soc.* **9**: 132–144.

MANWELL R.D. & GLENN S. (1953). Further studies on the cultivation of the avian malaria parasites. *Am. J. trop. Med. Hyg.* **2**: 227–233.

MANWELL R.D. & HEWITT R.I. (1937). Experiments in the cultivation of the avian malaria parasites. *Am. J. trop. Med.* **17**: 407–412.

McGhee R.B. & Trager W. (1950). The cultivation of *Plasmodium lophurae in vitro* in chicken erythrocyte suspensions and the effects of some constituents of the culture medium upon its growth and multiplication. *J. Parasit.* **36:** 123–127.

McKee R.W., Ormsbee R.A., Anfinsen C.B., Geiman Q.M. & Ball E.G. (1946). Studies on malarial parasites. VI. The chemistry and metabolism of normal and parasitized (*P.knowlesi*) monkey blood. *J. exp. Med.* **84:** 569–582.

Nydegger L. & Manwell R.D. (1962). Cultivation requirements of the avian malaria parasite *Plasmodium hexamerium*. *J. Parasit.* **48:** 142–147.

Pipkin A.C. & Jensen D.V. (1958). Avian embryos and tissue culture in the study of parasitic Protozoa. *Expl Parasit.* **7:** 491–530.

Polet H. (1966). *In vitro* cultivation of erythrocytic forms of *Plasmodium knowlesi* and *Plasmodium berghei*. *Milit. Med.* **131** Suppl.: 1026–1031.

Pulvertaft R.J.V., Valentine J.C. & Lane W.F. (1954). The behaviour of *Toxoplasma gondii* on serum-agar culture. *Parasitology* **44:** 478–484.

Row R. (1928). A simplified technique for cultivating malarial parasites aerobically. *Ind. med. Gaz.* **63:** 628–630.

Sherman I.W. (1966). *In vitro* studies of factors affecting penetration of duck erythrocytes by avian malaria (*Plasmodium lophurae*). *J. Parasit.* **52:** 17–22.

Spandorf A.A. & Manwell R.D. (1960). *In vitro* growth of *Plasmodium circumflexum* and *P.vaughani*. *Expl Parasit.* **10:** 287–292.

Strout R.G., Solis J., Smith S.C. & Dunlop W.R. (1965). *In vitro* cultivation of *Eimeria acervulina* (Coccidia). *Expl Parasit.* **17:** 241–246.

Trager W. (1941). Studies on conditions affecting the survival *in vitro* of a malarial parasite (*Plasmodium lophurae*). *J. exp. Med.* **74:** 441–461.

Trager W. (1943). Further studies on the survival and development *in vitro* of a malarial parasite. *J. exp. Med.* **77:** 411–420.

Trager W. (1947). The development of the malaria parasite *Plasmodium lophurae* in red blood cell suspensions *in vitro*. *J. Parasit.* **33:** 345–350.

Trager W. (1950). Studies on the extracellular cultivation of an intracellular parasite (avian malaria). I. Development of the organisms in erythrocyte extracts, and the favouring effect of adenosinetriphosphate. *J. exp. Med.* **92:** 349–366.

Trager W. (1952). Studies on the extracellular cultivation of an intracellular parasite (avian malaria). II. The effects of malate and of coenzyme A concentrates. *J. exp. Med.* **96:** 465–476.

Trager W. (1953). Further studies on the extracellular cultivation of an avian malaria parasite. *Ann. N.Y. Acad. Sci.* **56** (5): 1074–1080.

Trager W. (1958). Folinic acid and non-dialyzable materials in the nutrition of malaria parasites. *J. exp. Med.* **108:** 753–772.

Trager W. (1964). Cultivation and physiology of erythrocytic stages of plasmodia. *Am. J. trop. Med. Hyg.* **13:** 162–166.

Trager W. & Jernberg N.A. (1961). Apparatus for change of medium in extracellular maintenance *in vitro* of an intracellular parasite (malaria). *Proc. Soc. exp. Biol. Med.* **108:** 175–178.

Trigg P.I. (1967). *In vitro* growth of *Plasmodium knowlesi* and *P.falciparum*. *Nature, Lond.* **213:** 1019–1020.

Wagenbach G.E., Challey J.R. & Burns W.C. (1966). A method for purifying coccidian oocysts employing Clorox and sulfuric acid-dichromate solution. *J. Parasit.* **52:** 1222.

Zuckerman, Avivah (1966). Propagation of parasitic Protozoa in tissue culture and avian embryos. *Ann. N.Y. Acad. Sci.* **139:** 24–38.

CHAPTER 3

FLAGELLATES (OTHER THAN TRYPANO-SOMATIDAE) AND CILIATES

This chapter is divided into four main sections. Firstly, media used for the cultivation of the intestinal flagellates (except *Giardia*) are discussed, followed in the second section by that used for *Giardia* spp. The third section deals with the trichomonads of the human and bovine genital tracts, and the fourth with parasitic ciliates. Finally there is a short discussion on the selection of suitable media for different purposes. Some species of *Trichomonas** and *Hexamita meleagridis* have been grown in avian embryos and tissue culture: references and more details should be sought in the reviews by Pipkin (1960) and Zuckerman (1966).

I. FLAGELLATES OF THE ALIMENTARY CANAL (EXCEPT *GIARDIA*)

1. NON-AXENIC MEDIA

(i)   *Media devised for* Entamoeba *spp.*
These flagellates can usually be grown readily in any of the simple media used for parasitic amoebae (see Chapter 4). Thomson & Robertson (1925) found that *Trichomonas hominis* and *Chilomastix mesnili* flourished in Boeck & Drbohlav's (1925) diphasic LEA medium, if a piece of sterilized (i.e. boiled) human faeces 'about the size of a pea' were added to the tube of new medium at each subinoculation: Craig (1948) recommended LES medium (see Table 4.1) for the diagnosis of intestinal flagellates of man (except *Giardia*). Kofoid & McNeil (1932) also grew these 2 species, and *Enteromonas hominis*, on their LEB medium but *C.mesnili* grew rather less well. Frye & Meleney (1939) found that *T.hominis* and *C.mesnili* developed satisfactorily in their modified medium for *E.histolytica*, consisting of an egg-Ringer slope overlaid with a 0·5% solution of commercial liver extract, and Adler & Foner (1941) grew *T.hominis* in their semi-solid medium (p. 126). *T.hominis* can also be grown in the SF medium designed for *E.histolytica* by Shaffer *et al.* (1949) and, presum-

* This name is used to include *Trichomonas, Tritrichomonas* and *Pentatrichomonas.*

ably, in MS-F medium (p. 140). Balamuth (1946) found that his egg-yolk infusion medium (p. 126) supported the growth of *T.hominis* and *C.mesnili*, although not so well as it did that of *E.histolytica*. Dobell's and Laidlaw's (1926) media are also suitable for these flagellates.

(ii)   *Special media*
(a)   *With bacterial flora*
Ohira & Noguchi (1917) found that *T.tenax* (which they referred to as *T.hominis*) grew in a simple medium of diluted ascitic fluid to which a piece of fresh guinea-pig tissue (e.g. kidney) had been added. Craig & Faust (1951) and Hogue (1921) state that *T.hominis* will also grow in this medium, the latter author also obtaining growth of *T.vaginalis* in it. A medium which is easier to prepare, gives satisfactory results and is still in use today for diagnostic surveys, is that devised by Hogue (1921) (p. 80). Hogue (*loc. cit.*) also described a second medium in which growth of the flagellates was less intense.

Several authors (Boeck, 1921; Lynch, 1922; Tanabe, 1925; Cleveland, 1928; Jírovec & Rodová, 1940; Wenrich, 1946, 1947a, 1947b) have succeeded in growing intestinal trichomonads of man and other animals, as well as *C.mesnili* and *Retortamonas intestinalis*, on media which consist of fresh or dried serum diluted with varying proportions of different physiological salines. One of these recipes, modified to include a solid agar base (Craig, 1948), is described below (p. 81). Wenrich (1947a, 1947b) grew species isolated from rodents, reptiles, amphibia and insects as well as those from man. The parasites of mammals were grown at 37°c, those from the poikilotherms at room temperature. Jírovec & Rodová (1940) obtained growth of *T.vaginalis* as well as *T.hominis* and *T.tenax*, and species of *Trichomonas* from rats, pigeons and frogs; their method is given in detail below (p. 81). Hegner (1928) obtained growth of trichomonads from the intestine and vagina of rhesus monkeys on a similar medium incubated at 36°c.

The poultry pathogen *Histomonas meleagridis* was grown *in vitro* by Tyzzer (1934) in a diphasic medium which was essentially a less nutritious version of Boeck & Drbohlav's (1925) LES medium, with added rice starch and charcoal.

The growth *in vitro* of *H.meleagridis* was also studied by Bishop (1938). She found that the parasite grew well at 37°c (not lower) in Tyzzer's medium (1934), in Dobell's & Laidlaw's (1926) HSre + S (p. 128) and also in diluted horse-serum, a medium devised for *E.histolytica* by Laidlaw *et al.* (1928). Bishop also found that the presence of bacteria was probably essential for the growth of this organism. De Volt (1943) substantiated this last finding, and used a monophasic medium in which to grow the organism, similar to that of Laidlaw *et al.* (1928) (see p. 80). It seems likely that this organism would grow in many if not all of the simple media used for *Entamoeba* spp. (see Chapter 4).

Trager (1934) has cultivated the parasitic flagellate *Trichomonas termopsidis*, which inhabits the gut of the termite *Termopsis angusticollis*, monoxenically in a medium containing powdered cellulose (p. 82): certain other flagellates, parasitic in the same host but not requiring

TABLE 3.1. Some media used for the cultivation of parasitic flagellates of the alimentary canal.

Author(s)	Date	Designation	Species	Detailed description (if any)
Adler	1942	—	Most*	—
Adler & Foner	1941	—	*T.hominis*	p. 126
Balamuth	1946	—	Most*	p. 126
Boeck	1921	—	,,	—
Boeck & Drbohlav	1925	LEA	,,	—
Cleveland	1928	—	,,	—
Craig	1948	—	,,	p. 81
De Volt	1943	—	*H.meleagridis*	p. 80
Diamond	1957	TYM	Trichomonads except *T.tenax*	p. 84
Diamond	1962	TTY	*T.tenax*	p. 85
Dobell & Laidlaw	1926	HSre+S	Most*	p. 128
Frye & Meleney	1939	—	,,	—
Hegner	1928	—	,,	—
Hogue	1921	—	,,	p. 80
Honigberg	1961	—	*T.gallinae*	—
Jírovec & Rodová	1940	—	Most*	—
Karapetyan	1962	—	*G.intestinalis*	p. 91
Kofoid & McNeil	1932	LEB	Most*	—
Kott & Adler	1961	—	*T.hominis*	—
Kupferberg *et al.*	1948	STS	*T.gallinae*	—
Laidlaw *et al.*	1928	—	*H.meleagridis*	—
Lee *et al.*	1962	—⎫	Trichomonads of ⎰	p. 89
Lee *et al.*	1964	5F⎭	poikilotherms ⎱	p. 88
Ohira & Noguchi	1917	—	Most*	—
Samuels & Beil	1962	C6	Trichomonads	p. 86
Tanabe	1925	—	Trichomonads	—
Trager	1934	—	Termite symbionts	p. 82
Tyzzer	1934	—	*H.meleagridis*	—
Warren *et al.*	1961	—	*T.gallinae*	—

* Except *G.intestinalis* and possibly *H.meleagridis*.

cellulose, also grew in the same medium. By modifying the inorganic salts constitution, Trager (*loc. cit.*) obtained initial cultures of a hyper-mastigote flagellate (*Trichonympha sphaerica*) from the termite, but was unable to maintain this organism for more than one serial transfer.

Medium for
Histomonas meleagridis
(De Volt, 1943)

MEDIUM

1   Add the following to Ringer-Locke solution (p. 350), containing 0·2% w/v glucose:

> Fresh, clean turkey serum......20 ml/l.
> N/20 sodium hydroxide solution 20 ml/l.

The pH of the solution should be about 9. (Chicken serum is satisfactory, as is probably that of other species also.)

2   The solution is dispensed into test-tubes in 10 ml aliquots: the tubes are plugged with cotton and autoclaved at 120°c for 20 min. The alkalinity of the solution should prevent precipitation of the serum, no more than a slight turbidity developing occasionally.

TECHNIQUE

Before use, 1–2 mg of sterile rice starch (p. 126) is added to each tube. Transfers to fresh medium should be made twice weekly, though cultures will survive without transfer for up to 2 weeks. Although not stated by the author, the cultures are presumably incubated at 37°c.

NOTE: *H.meleagridis* will not grow in the absence of bacteria. However, if the latter become too numerous their number can be controlled by omitting the glucose from the medium and reducing the serum content to 1%.

Egg medium for intestinal flagellates
except *Giardia*
(Hogue, 1921)

MEDIUM

One whole hen's egg is thoroughly shaken in a flask using glass beads, and 200 ml of Ringer-Locke solution (p. 350) containing 0·25% w/v glucose is added. The mixture is heated over a water bath, with constant agitation, for 15 min, then filtered through cotton (using suction) and tubed in 6 ml aliquots. The tubes are plugged with cotton and autoclaved at 15 lb for 20 min.

TECHNIQUE

After inoculation (which can be achieved successfully with a single flagellate), the tubes are incubated at 35°C. Transfers to fresh medium should be made every 2–4 days, maximum growth being achieved by the second day.

Serum medium for intestinal flagellates
except *Giardia*
(Jírovec & Rodová, 1940)

MEDIUM

1   *Modified Ringer's solution:*

Sodium chloride..................6 g
Magnesium sulphate.............0·1 g
Calcium chloride ....0·1 g
Potassium dihydrogen phosphate ...3 g
Water ....1 l.
N sodium hydroxide solution to bring
pH to 7·4 (about 18–22 ml).

2   Mix 95 ml of the above solution with 5 ml serum (from man or horse): dispense in test-tubes in aliquots of 4–6 ml and sterilize (the authors recommend steaming at atmospheric pressure for 1 hr on 2 or 3 successive days to sterilize; presumably filtration could be used instead).

TECHNIQUE

Incubate at 37°C for species from mammals or birds or at room temperature for species from poikilothermic animals. Transfer to fresh medium every 7 days. If the medium is covered with a layer of paraffin, growth continues longer: obviously a degree of anaerobiosis is an advantage.

Modified Tanabe's medium for
intestinal flagellates except *Giardia*
(Craig, 1948)

MEDIUM

1   *Solid phase*

Agar ....1·5 g
Sodium chloride...............0·6 g
Water ....90 ml

This mixture is heated to melt the agar, dispensed into test-tubes in 5 ml aliquots, and autoclaved. It is allowed to set in a slant.

2   *Overlay*

Sodium chloride . . . . 0·7 g
Sodium citrate . . . . 1·0 g
Water . . . . 100 ml

This solution is autoclaved and after cooling to 50°c, 0·5 g Loeffler's dehydrated blood serum and 2 ml whipped fresh egg albumen (obtained aseptically) are added. Add to tubes containing the base in amounts sufficient to cover the slope.

TECHNIQUE

Incubate at 37°c after inoculation. The culture should be examined after 24 hr by scraping the lower part of the slant with a pipette and collecting a little of the suspended debris.

Method for *Trichomonas termopsidis*, a symbiont of termites
(Trager, 1934)

MEDIUM

1   Dissolve filter paper (Whatman No. 40) in a solution of zinc chloride (1 part by weight) in concentrated hydrochloric acid (2 parts), precipitate the cellulose with water, filter it through a Buchner funnel and wash it with water till free of chloride ions; then dry it in air and grind with a pestle and mortar to a fine powder.

2   Place 'small amounts' of the powdered cellulose and of powdered animal charcoal (Merck) into test-tubes and sterilize the cotton-plugged tubes and contents by autoclaving or dry heat.

3   Add to each tube, aseptically, about 8 ml of the following solution (sterilized by filtration):

Sodium chloride . . . . 1·169 g
Sodium bicarbonate . . . . 0·840 g
Sodium citrate $2H_2O$ . . . . 2·943 g
Sodium dihydrogen phosphate
  H_2O . . . . 0·690 g
Potassium chloride . . . . 0·745 g
Calcium chloride . . . . 0·111 g
Loeffler's dehydrated blood serum . . . 2 g
Distilled water . . . . *to* 1·0 l.

The pH should be 7·0–7·2.

4 Cover the medium in each tube with a layer of sterile petroleum jelly.

TECHNIQUE

1 For isolation, dissect aseptically the hind-gut of a termite (previously disinfected by immersion in 1:1,000 aqueous mercuric chloride solution for 15–40 min, followed by washing first in 95% ethanol and then in sterile distilled water). Place the entire gut in one tube of medium and incubate it at room temperature.

2 Serial transfers may be made every 2–4 weeks by removing about 0·3 ml of culture from the *bottom* of the tube and adding it to a tube of fresh medium.

3 The flagellates grow near the bottom of the tube: exposure of the culture to air must be avoided as far as possible. Slow multiplication occurs during the first 3 weeks, following by a stationary phase of 1 or more weeks before the cultures begin to die. Trager was unable to free the cultures of a Gram-negative bacillus, which developed with the flagellates.

2. MEDIA FOR AXENIC CULTURES

An early attempt by Cleveland (1928) to grow *Trichomonas hominis* (referred to as '*T.fecalis*') axenically *in vitro* failed, but success was later achieved by Stone & Reynolds (1939), Adler (1942) and Diamond (1957, 1962). Stone & Reynolds (1939) separated the flagellates from their bacterial concomitants by differential migration down a vertical capillary tube containing Ringer's solution and horse serum (1:8), the tube being bent into 7 S-shaped 'traps'. After about 48 hr, flagellates (without bacteria) reached the lowest trap, which was then cut off and sealed: after sterilizing its outer surface, the trap was broken with sterile forceps and dropped into a tube of culture medium.

Adler (1942) purified cultures of *T.hominis* by first limiting bacterial growth with a sulphonamide (2′:4′-diaminobenzene-4-sulphonamide), and then inoculating 1 ml of the culture (after 1 sub-passage) intra-peritoneally to a mouse. The latter was killed the next day, and its peritoneal fluid used to initiate bacteria-free cultures in a semi-solid medium to which had been added a piece of sterile mouse liver and a little ascorbic acid. Presumably antibiotics could be used instead of the sulphonamide in this procedure. Diamond (1957) succeeded in separating trichomonads of various hosts (including *T.hominis*, *T.vaginalis* and *T.foetus*) by using the V-tube migration technique of Glaser & Coria (1935b), described on p. 96. The medium, known as TYM ('trypticase, yeast, maltose'), which Diamond used to maintain axenic cultures of these organisms (and which he used in the V-tubes) is described on this page. Using a modification of this medium, Twohy (1961) was able to grow *T.augusta* in continuous culture. *T.tenax* could not be maintained axenically on medium TYM, but Diamond (1962) later succeeded in isolating and maintaining a bacteria-free strain of this species also (p. 85). This strain originated from one growing with a mixed bacterial flora in LES medium (Table 4.1): by the use of antibiotics, it was freed of bacteria and transferred to Phillips' & Rees' medium (1950) for *E.histolytica*, in which it grew in monoxenic association with *T.cruzi* (p. 139). This initial establishment in monoxenic culture was found to be essential: trichomonads taken from their natural habitat (the human mouth), or from a culture with a mixed bacterial flora, could not be established in axenic culture directly. Samuels & Beil (1962) have cultivated several species of trichomonads axenically in a serum-free medium (containing cream), which can be autoclaved (p. 86).

The avian parasite *T.gallinae* has been maintained by Warren *et al.* (1961) on modified CPLM medium, and also on commercial thioglycollate bacterial medium (obtained from Baltimore Biological Laboratory) plus 1–5% horse serum (Warren *et al., loc. cit.*; Honigberg, 1961; Honigberg *et al.*, 1964). 'STS' medium (p. 105) of Kupferberg *et al.* (1948) is also known to be suitable for *T.gallinae*. Honigberg *et al.* (1964) have grown this species in cultures of embryonic chick liver cells and found that virulent strains often invaded cells. Details of all these methods of growing *T.gallinae in vitro* should be sought in the original publications.

<h3 style="text-align:center">TYM medium for
axenic culture of trichomonads*
(Diamond, 1957)</h3>

MEDIUM

1   *Composition*

        Trypticase (Baltimore Biological
           Laboratory) ....2·0 g
        Yeast extract (Baltimore Biological
           Laboratory) ....1·0 g
        Maltose.......................0·5 g
        L-Cysteine hydrochloride........0·1 g
        L-Ascorbic acid................0·02 g
        Water to make ....90 ml

* Excepting *T.tenax*.

2 *Preparation*
(a) Dissolve the above ingredients and adjust the pH with sodium hydroxide solution to 6·8–7·0, or with hydrochloric acid to 6·0 if *T.vaginalis* is to be grown; add 0·05 g agar. (If the medium is to be used for isolation, 0·1 g of agar is used.)
(b) The solution is then autoclaved for 10 min at 15 lb/sq. in.
(c) After cooling to 48°C, 10 ml of inactivated sheep serum and 1 ml of an aqueous solution containing 100,000 units of penicillin G and 0·1 g streptomycin sulphate are added to the solution.
(d) The complete medium is dispensed in 5 ml aliquots into rubber-stoppered glass test-tubes, which can be stored at 4°C for at least 14 days.

TECHNIQUE

The tubes are incubated at 35·5°C for 1 hr before inoculation. Cultures should be transferred to fresh medium every 48–72 hr, if kept at 35·5°C. If kept at about 25°C for 5 days, and then at 35·5°C for 2 days, transfers need be made only once weekly. Large inocula are needed to initiate growth in subinoculated tubes.

TTY medium for axenic cultivation of *Trichomonas tenax*
(Diamond, 1962)

MEDIUM

1 *Composition*

Tryptose (Difco).................1·0 g
Trypticase (Baltimore Biological Laboratory) ....1·0 g
Yeast extract (Baltimore Biological Laboratory) ....1·0 g
Glucose.........................0·5 g
L-Cysteine hydrochloride........0·1 g
Ascorbic acid...................0·02 g
Sodium chloride.................0·5 g
Potassium dihydrogen phosphate.0·08 g
Dipotassium hydrogen phosphate (anhydrous) ....0·08 g
Distilled water to make........85·0 ml

2 *Preparation*
(a) Dissolve the above ingredients and adjust the pH to 7·2 with normal sodium hydroxide solution.

(b) Add the following ingredients to the above solution:

Agar (Difco) ....0·05 g
Resazurin (0·05% aq. solution)...0·2 ml

(c) Autoclave at 15 lb for 10 min.

(d) Chick embryo extract (see p. 345) is prepared as described by Diamond (1961, see p. 138), except that the embryos are homogenized in buffered saline (2 ml/g of tissue) in a Waring blender (or other suitable homogenizer) for 2 min, and afterwards refrigerated for 1 h. before being centrifuged (after removal of the froth) at 850 × g for 20 min at 0°c. It is added to the final medium just before use, in the proportion of 5% v/v.

(e) Sterile horse serum (inactivated for 30 min at 56°c) is added in the proportion of 10% v/v.

TECHNIQUE

1 The complete medium is used in 10 ml aliquots in screw-capped glass tubes (16 × 125 mm), incubated at 35°c.

2 Antibiotics can be added as follows during the establishment of a new isolation:

Penicillin G ....1,000 units/ml
Dihydrostreptomycin sulphate
1·0 mg/ml

3 Parasites must be grown monoxenically with *Trypanosoma cruzi* before establishment in this medium. The trypanosomes die out by the time of the third transfer to fresh medium. The first 15 transfers are made at intervals of 48 and 72 hr; subsequently, at intervals of 72 and 96 hr alternately. Large inocula are needed for the first 4 or 5 subinoculations.

4 Most strains increased 120-fold (from 25 to 3,000 per mm^3) after 96 hr growth.

NOTE: One strain required vitamin supplementation of the medium before adequate growth occurred: for details see the original publication (Diamond, 1962).

C6 medium for
axenic cultivation of trichomonads
(Samuels & Beil, 1962)

MEDIUM

1 *Composition* per 100 ml

Trypticase (Baltimore Biological
Laboratory) ....2·8 g

Yeast extract . . . . .300 mg
Potassium dihydrogen phosphate 7·5 mg
Glucose . . . . .150 mg
Citric acid H_2O. . . . . .8 mg
Ascorbic acid. . . . . .40 mg
Thiomalic acid . . . . .20 mg
Liver solution N.F. (Armour) . . .2·5 ml
Liver infusion (Difco; 10% solution)
. . . . 10 ml
Light cream ('single, table or coffee
cream'). . . . . .0·01 ml
Cholesterol (20 mg/ml solution
in ethanol) . . . . .0·04 ml

2 *Preparation*

Add the dry ingredients to 80 ml of distilled water, then add the liver
solution and infusion, cream and finally the cholesterol (having warmed
the solution to 50°c). Bring the pH to 6·8 with normal potassium hydroxide
solution, make up the volume to 100 ml with distilled water and autoclave. The medium can be stored in the dark for at least 3 weeks.

TECHNIQUE

Mammalian and avian forms are incubated at 32°c, others at room
temperature. Serial transfers are made weekly by transferring about
5×10^4 organisms to screw-capped tubes containing 10 ml of fresh
medium. Peak populations range from 10×10^4 to 400×10^4 organisms
per ml.

3. DEFINED MEDIA

So far, amongst the parasitic flagellates of the alimentary canal, only
certain trichomonads of poikilothermic animals (including *T.augusta* of
amphibia) have been grown in a defined medium, by Lee *et al.* (1962, 1964).
These authors used a semi-defined maintenance medium (p. 89), and
devised 3 defined media on which it was possible to maintain the flagellates (presumably axenically) at 25°c for at least a limited number of
transfers. The recipe for the latest of these defined media (Lee *et al.*, 1964).
is given below (p. 88). It is a highly complex mixture, though simpler
than the 2 earlier versions (Lee *et al.*, 1962) and obviously the use of such
a medium would be of value in nutritional and physiological studies
only.

Defined medium '5F' for certain trichomonads of poikilothermic animals
(Lee *et al.*, 1964)

MEDIUM

1 *Composition* per 100 ml

Glucose . . . . .0·5 g
'Amino acids 9T' (see below) . . . .0·25 g
Calcium pantothenate . . . . .0·004 g
Thiomalic acid . . . . .0·025 g
Disodium glycerophosphate . . . .0·150 g
TEM 4T* . . . . .0·001 g
Cholesterol . . . . .0·0005 g
'Metals no. 50'* . . . . .0·006 g
'Vitamins No. 14' (see below) . . . . .2 ml
Ascorbic acid . . . . .0·04 g
Agar . . . . .0·1 g
Trypticase (Baltimore Biological
　　Laboratory) . . . . .0·025 g†

2 *'Amino acids 9T'* (composition %):

DL-Alanine .0·05
DL-Aspartic acid . . . . .0·05
L-Glutamic acid . . . . .0·08
Glycine . . . . .0·05
L-Arginine .0·05
L-Histidine .0·04
L-Lysine . . . . .0·04
DL-Isoleucine . . . . .0·005
DL-Phenylalanine . . . . .0·004
DL-Leucine . . . . .0·005
L-Tyrosine .0·004
DL-Methionine . . . . .0·01
DL-Threonine . . . . .0·01
L-Proline . . . . .0·004
DL-Serine .0·01
DL-Valine .0·005
DL-Tryptophan . . . . .0·006

* See Maintenance Medium, below.
† If *Monocercomonas colubrorum* is being grown, use 0·2 g of Trypticase.

3 'Vitamins No. 14' (composition per ml of concentrate):

          Thiamine ....0·03 mg
          Calcium pantothenate ....0·05 mg
          Pyridoxamine ....0·01 mg
          Inositol ....0·5 mg
          Putrescine.................0·01 mg
          Folic acid ....0·025 mg
          DL-Carnitine ....0·02 mg
          Choline....................0·8 mg
          Vitamin B_{12}..................0·2 μg
          Nicotinic acid ....0·04 mg
          Riboflavin ....0·015 mg
          Pyridoxal ....0·01 mg
          p-Aminobenzoic acid ....0·005 mg
          Spermidine................0·005 mg
          Lipoic acid (=DL-thioctic acid)
                                     0·002 mg
          Betain.....................0·8 mg
          Cystamine ....0·005 mg
          Biotin......................0·5 μg

TECHNIQUE

Details of the use of this medium are not given: they are presumably similar to those of the semi-defined medium described immediately below.

Semi-defined maintenance medium for trichomonads of poikilothermic animals
(Lee et al., 1962)

MEDIUM

1 *Composition* (per 100 ml)

          Glucose.......................0·5 g
          Trypticase (Baltimore Biological
            Laboratory)....................1 g
          Yeast extract ....0·25 g
          Potassium dihydrogen phosphate 0·01 g
          Disodium glycerophosphate
            $5H_2O$ ....0·25 g
          Calcium pantothenate ....0·004 g
          Cholesterol ....0·0005 g

1   *Composition* (per 100 ml)—contd.

TEM 4T* ....0·001 g
Ascorbic acid..................0·04 g
Thiomalic acid ....0·05 g
Agar.........................0·1 g
'Metals mix No. 50'...........0·004 g
'Vitamins mix No. 12' ....1·0 ml

The pH should be adjusted to 7·5.

2   *'Metals mix No. 50'* (Lee & Pierce, 1960) contains the following metals (concentrations in mg %):

Iron, 0·1; Manganese, 1·0; Zinc, 0·5;
Copper, 0·1; Boron, 0·01; Molybdenum,
0·04; Cobalt, 0·05; Vanadium, 0·005.

3   *'Vitamin mix No. 12'* (Hutner *et al.*, 1957) contains the following substances per ml of solution:

Thiamine hydrochloride ....0·1 mg
Nicotinic acid ....0·1 mg
Calcium pantothenate ....0·1 mg
Choline dihydrogen citrate .....1·5 mg
Sodium riboflavin phosphate ..0·01 mg
Pyridoxamine dihydrochloride .0·02 mg
Pyridoxal hydrochloride ......0·02 mg
Inositol ....1·0 mg
Putrescine (1,4-diamino-butane)
    dihydrochloride............0·04 mg
p-Aminobenzoic acid ....0·01 mg
p-Hydroxybenzoic acid ....0·01 mg
Vitamin B_{12} ....0·1 μg
Biotin........................0·5 μg
Lipoic acid (*dl*-thioctic acid) ..0·004 mg
Citrovorum factor (leukovorin, the
    Ca. $5H_2O$ salt) ....0·2 μg
Folic acid ....0·004 mg

Stored at $-10°$c triturated in pentaerythritol (1:1).

TECHNIQUE

The medium is used in screw-capped tubes (125 × 20 mm), incubated at *c.* 25°c.

* 'TEM 4T' is 'a semisynthetic fat based on beef-tallow fatty acids' (Lee *et al.*, 1962) prepared as a 'diacetyl tartaric acid ester of monoglycerides from tallow' (Lee & Pierce, 1960).

Substitute ascorbyl palmitate 0·001% if *Monocercomonas colubrorum* is being grown.

II. *GIARDIA*

It is only within the present decade that organisms of this genus have been successfully cultivated *in vitro*. Karapetyan (1962), after some initial success in growing *G.intestinalis* in symbiotic relationship with the yeast-like fungus *Candida* and chick fibroblasts, succeeded in growing *G.duodenalis* of the rabbit and *G.intestinalis* of man without the presence of fibroblasts. However, axenic cultivation of the flagellates was not possible, a strain of *Saccharomyces cerevisiae* being a necessary concomitant. Often, other naturally-occurring fungi from the duodenum also developed in the cultures but this did not interfere with the growth of the flagellate. Karapetyan maintained one isolation of *G.duodenalis* for 5 months, during which time it was transferred to fresh medium 12 times.

Meyer & Pope (1965) also succeeded in growing *Giardia* spp. from the rabbit and chinchilla in Karapetyan's medium: they found that, with the strain of yeast that they were using, daily addition of fresh living yeast was essential for multiplication of the flagellates.

Method for *Giardia duodenalis*
and *G.intestinalis*
(Karapetyan, 1962)

MEDIUM

1 *Composition*

> Filtered, inactivated serum (of man,
> horse or ox) 25%
> Hottinger's tryptic meat digest
> (see below) 10%
> Chick embryo extract (p. 345) 5%
> Hanks's saline (p. 350) 60%
> Penicillin . . . . 500 units/ml
> Streptomycin. . . . . 250 units/ml

pH adjusted to 7·2–7·4 with carbon dioxide.

2 *Hottinger's digest*

Meat is boiled in twice its volume of water for 15–20 min, and minced. The pH of the water in which it has been cooked is adjusted to 8, the minced meat replaced in it and, after cooling to 40–45°c, 0·5–1% trypsin (or dried pancreatin) is added. This mixture is placed in a bottle, 2–3% of chloroform is added and, after shaking, the bottle is put in a warm (*c.* 37°c) place for digestion. Finally, the supernatant liquid is collected, autoclaved and stored for subsequent use.

3   The medium is dispensed in 2–3 ml aliquots in bottles of 5–15 ml capacity, or test-tubes, which are closed with rubber stoppers.

TECHNIQUE

After introducing the inoculum together with a wire loopful of a culture of *Saccharomyces cerevisiae*, the bottles are incubated at 37°c, at an angle of 5–7° from the horizontal.

On the second day after inoculation, 1–2 ml of fresh medium is added. Subsequently, the bottle is lightly shaken daily and about two-thirds of the fluid is removed with a pipette: an equal volume of fresh fluid is then added. Although most of the flagellates adhere to the glass during this operation, Karapetyan recommended adding the removed fluid to a bottle containing an equal volume of fresh medium and later examining that bottle also.

All bottles can be examined under a low powered microscope. Intensive growth should be seen in some bottles after 8–10 days, and subcultures can be prepared from such bottles, as follows. The bottle containing the growing culture is shaken vigorously, and all the medium in it (which may contain up to 400,000 flagellates per ml) is inoculated into 2–4 bottles of fresh medium.

NOTE: Karapetyan found that good preparations of the flagellates could be obtained by placing fragments of cover-slips in the flasks and then removing them after the flagellates had become attached (cf. Dobell, 1942).

III. TRICHOMONADS OF THE GENITAL TRACT

1. *TRICHOMONAS FOETUS*

This organism does not seem difficult to cultivate *in vitro*; it has generally been grown axenically, but will apparently multiply in some media in the presence of bacteria provided that it is not overgrown by the latter. Some of the media which have been used for its growth are listed in Table 3.2. Witte (1933) found that the organism would grow axenically at 37°c in a peptone broth containing 5–10% defibrinated blood. Gehring & Murray (1933) found that *T.foetus* would also grow in this medium in the presence of bacteria, if growth of the latter was partially suppressed by the

TABLE 3.2. Some media used for the cultivation of *Trichomonas foetus* and *T.vaginalis*.

Author(s)	Date	Designation of medium	Species	Detailed description (if any)
Andrews & Lyford*	1940	SEB	*T.foetus*	p. 95
Andrews & Lyford	1940	SDB	,,	—
Bland *et al.*	1932	RL2	*T.vaginalis*	—
Burch *et al.*	1959	TLS	,,	p. 108
De Carneri	1956b	—	*T.vaginalis*	—
Diamond†	1957	TYM	*T.vaginalis*	—
Feinberg	1953	—	,,	p. 102
Feinberg & Whittington	1957	—	,,	p. 103
Glaser & Coria	1935b	REB	*T.foetus*	—
Honigberg	1961	—	*T.vaginalis*	—
Jírovec & Rodová	1940	—	,,	—
Johnson	1942	—	,,	—
Johnson & Trussell	1943	CPLM	,,	p. 104
Kupferberg *et al.*	1948	STS	,,	p. 105
Lash	1948	FIM	,,	—
Lash	1948	FPM	,,	—
Lash	1950	—	,,	—
Lowe	1965	—	,,	p. 105
Lumsden *et al.*	1966	—	,,	p. 106
Lynch	1922	—	,,	—
McEntegart	1952	—	,,	—
Plastridge (see Fitzgerald *et al.* 1954)		—	*T.foetus*	p. 96
Rees	1937	—	,,	—
Samuels & Beil	1962	C6	,,	—
Schneider	1942	—	*T.foetus*	p. 97
Shaffer *et al.*	1949	—	*T.vaginalis*	—
Squires & McFadzean†	1962	—	,,	—
Trussell & Johnson	1941	—	,,	—
Witte	1933	—	*T.foetus*	—

* With modifications by Lyford (1941).
† See Jeffries & Harris (1967) for slight modifications of these media.

addition of 0·1 ml of a 0·1% aqueous solution of crystal violet to each culture tube (containing presumably about 10 ml of medium). Gehring & Murray obtained better growth of *T.foetus* in Kofoid & McNeil's (1932) LEB medium, again using crystal violet to reduce bacterial multiplication. Presumably antibiotics would perform this function nowadays. Glaser & Coria (1935b) separated *T.foetus* from contaminating bacteria by a method depending on the active migration of the flagellates upwards through a U- or V-shaped glass tube containing agar gel (p. 96). They obtained good axenic growth of *T.foetus* in both LEB medium and a modification of it (REB) in which Ringer's was substituted for Locke's solution. In REB medium, which had an initial pH of 7·8, growth of the flagellates became 'luxuriant' after 4–8 days at 36°c. The flagellates developed solely at the bottom of the tubes, presumably more-or-less anaerobically (as *T.vaginalis* does: see p. 99). They maintained strains by transferring flagellates to fresh culture tubes every 2–3 weeks (at 36°c). Rees (1937) substituted serum for blood in REB medium, and had some success in growing *T.foetus* axenically, using for inoculation single flagellates isolated by micromanipulation and washed free of bacteria. He found, however, that clone cultures were established more readily in the presence of bacteria. Daniel (1940) established axenic cultures in a similar medium, and found that autoclaving after the addition of the serum had no deleterious effect on longevity of the cultures. Sometimes, however, the rate of increase of the flagellates was lower in autoclaved medium, and a flocculent precipitate formed in it after several days. Serum of horse, cow or sheep was equally effective.

Andrews & Lyford (1940) and Lyford (1941), who made a detailed study of strains of *T.foetus* cultivated axenically, found that the Ringer's or Locke's solutions in the above-mentioned recipes (LEB, REB) could be replaced by plain 0·7% aqueous sodium chloride solution. The preparation of this medium (SEB) is given in detail below (p. 95). Andrews & Lyford separated the flagellates from bacteria by Glaser's & Coria's (1935b) technique (p. 96), using preferably Y-shaped tubes and 0·7% saline as diluent in the migration medium instead of Ringer's solution. They found that the viscosity of the gel in the Y-tube was critical, and the amount of agar needed might vary from batch to batch. The gel 'must be viscid enough to support red blood cells for at least 24 hr at from 20–25°c and yet thin enough to deform readily when tilted.' These conditions Andrews & Lyford found to be fulfilled by a gel consisting of 4 ml of 2% agar in saline diluted with 50 ml of saline (0·7%), slightly more concentrated than that recommended by Glaser & Coria (p. 96). Andrews & Lyford (1940) found that serum or egg albumen could be used instead of blood in the overlay of SEB medium. Growth also occurred when an overlay of beef extract or even plain 0·7% saline was used, and when Loeffler's serum slants were used instead of the coagulated egg slants of SEB. These authors also used a serum-dextrose broth medium (SDB) for some experimental work, as it supported a heavier growth of flagellates but for a shorter time.

Schneider (1942) devised a richer and more complicated buffered medium in which eggs and blood were the main nutrients, and of which all the components could be autoclaved. This medium, if sealed in airtight containers, supported cultures of *T.foetus* for 30–60 days at 37°C and for 3–4 months (or more) at 22–25°C. When kept at the lower temperatures, it was found advisable to incubate the culture at 37°C for 3–10 days before subinoculating to fresh medium. This medium (p. 97) would seem to be useful for the long-term maintenance of *T.foetus* in the laboratory.

Kupferberg *et al.* (1948) found that *T.foetus* could be maintained on their STS medium (p. 105), which was primarily designed for *T.vaginalis*, if the pH were adjusted to 7·0 instead of the 6·0 used for the latter species.

A medium devised by Plastridge (1943) was slightly modified by Fitzgerald *et al.* (1954), primarily for diagnostic cultivation of *T.foetus*. In this semisolid monophasic medium, the inoculum is placed on the surface without mixing: flagellates (if present) develop at the bottom of the tube, while contaminants tend to remain on the surface. There seems no reason why this medium (p. 96) should not be used for laboratory maintenance of *T.foetus*, once the flagellates have been separated from contaminants; indeed Plastridge used it in that way.

SEB medium
for *Trichomonas foetus*
(Andrews & Lyford, 1940 and Lyford, 1941)

MEDIUM

1   *Base*

Three whole fresh eggs are thoroughly beaten in 50 ml 0·7% saline, then distributed in 5 ml aliquots to test-tubes and heated in a water-bath to coagulate in a slant at the base of the tubes. Sterilize either by autoclaving, or by steaming without pressure on 2 successive days (the latter gives a slightly better medium).

2   *Overlay*

0·7% saline (sterilized by autoclaving), to which has been added about 2% rabbit blood (sterile, defibrinated). Five millilitres of this overlay are placed in each tube containing the base. (Alternatively, 5 ml of saline may be placed in each tube of base before autoclaving, and 2 drops of blood added aseptically after autoclaving and cooling the tubes.)

TECHNIQUE

The medium is incubated at 37°C. Transfers to fresh medium should be made at intervals of not more than 10 days, or more frequently (every 3–4 days) if it is desired to 'stimulate' growth. At room temperature, cultures have been shown to remain viable for 99 days.

Method for purifying isolations of
Trichomonas foetus
(Glaser & Coria, 1935b)

MEDIUM

1   *Composition*

Ringer's solution (p. 350)........50 ml
2% agar in Ringer's solution......3 ml

2   *Preparation*

After autoclaving the above gel and cooling to 45–50°c, add (aseptically) 1 drop of rabbit or horse blood (defibrinated), distribute the mixture in 15 ml aliquots into sterile cotton-plugged glass tubes bent into a V- or U-shape, and allow to gel.

TECHNIQUE

1   Very gently, inoculate the contaminated material to the bottom of one arm of the bent tube. About 0·25 ml of vaginal washings may be introduced; if material from a contaminated culture is being used, only 0·03 ml should be introduced.

2   Incubate the tubes at room temperature (*c.* 20°c, *not* higher) for 16–22 hr, then remove (aseptically) drops of medium from the sterile arm of the tube at different levels, starting about 2·5 cm above the base and progressing downwards. Examine these drops, and when flagellates are seen, inoculate material from that level into fresh, sterile culture medium (e.g. SEB).

Plastridge's medium for
Trichomonas foetus
(Fitzgerald *et al.*, 1954)

MEDIUM

1   *Composition*

Beef extract (Difco)...............3 g
Glucose ....10 g
Bactopeptone (Difco) ....10 g
Agar...........................0·7 g
Sodium chloride..................1 g
Distilled water ....1 l.

2   *Preparation*

(a)   Dissolve the above ingredients by boiling; adjust the pH to *c.* 7·4 with dilute sodium hydroxide solution and autoclave at 15 lb for 30 min.

(b)   When the above solution is cool, add 20 ml of bovine serum (sterile, inactivated at 56°c for 30 min).

(c)   Distribute in 10 ml aliquots to screw-capped glass bottles of 15 ml capacity. Incubate for 48 hr to check sterility: store at 4°c.

TECHNIQUE

Just before use, add penicillin (5,000–10,000 units) and streptomycin (5–10 mg) to each tube. Add the inoculum to the surface, without mixing. Incubate at 39°c for 3–5 days and examine fluid from the bottom of the tube.

Thermostable medium for prolonged cultivation of *Trichomonas foetus*
(Schneider, 1942)

MEDIUM

1   *Base*

(a)   Prepare the following solution:

>   Sodium chloride . . . . 6·5 g
>   Sodium bicarbonate . . . . 0·2 g
>   Potassium chloride . . . . 0·2 g
>   Sodium carbonate (anhydrous) . . . . 0·5 g
>   Potassium dihydrogen phosphate . . 0·5 g
>   Dipotassium hydrogen phosphate . 0·5 g
>   Glucose . . . . 2·5 g
>   Water . . . . 1 l.

(b)   Add to 50 ml of the above solution 6 whole eggs and 60 ml bovine blood (defibrinated). Beat the mixture thoroughly in a 2 l. flask, strain it through gauze and distribute in 4–5 ml aliquots in glass tubes.

(c)   Place the tubes in a sloping position in a hot autoclave, turn on the steam supply until a pressure of 10–12 lb is reached and then turn it off. Remove the tubes as soon as they are cool enough. This solidifies the base but does not sterilize it.

2 *Overlay*

(a) Prepare the following solution:

Sodium chloride	5·0 g
Magnesium sulphate	0·2 g
Ammonium dihydrogen phosphate	1·0 g
Dipotassium hydrogen phosphate	1·0 g
Sodium citrate	2·0 g
Glucose	10·0 g
Water	1 l.

(b) Add to this solution 5–7·5% bovine serum which has been centrifuged several times to remove all cells, and adjust to pH 7·2–7·4.

(c) Add 2 ml of 1·6% alcoholic solution of bromcresol purple (as an indicator of pH change during growth).

(d) Add 8 ml of an aqueous solution of haematin containing 5 mg/ml. (This solution is prepared by heating in the autoclave at 15 lb for 10 min.)

(e) Filter the solution through 2 layers of filter paper 2–3 times, until perfectly clear.

3 *Preparation of final medium*

(a) Add to each tube of base dried, crushed egg-shell to a depth of 5–10 mm and 10–12 ml of overlay.

(b) Sterilize the completed tubes by autoclaving for 30 min at 15 lb. The medium can then be stored in a refrigerator for several weeks.

TECHNIQUE

Inoculated tubes, tightly stoppered, are incubated at 37°c. Cultures survive for 1 month or more. If kept at 22–25°c they survive for 3–4 months: such cultures should be kept at 37°c for 3–10 days before sub-inoculating to fresh medium.

2. *TRICHOMONAS VAGINALIS*

(i) *Introduction*

This organism can be grown in a variety of media (see Table 3.2) in association with a mixed bacterial and fungal flora (the fungus *Candida* is a common inhabitant of the human vagina), provided growth of the contaminating organisms is not too luxuriant. A good review of the *in vitro* cultivation of *T.vaginalis* has been published by Savel (1957).

Lynch (1922) grew *T.vaginalis* in a simple saline solution of fresh serum, and Bland *et al.* (1932) grew this organism in a similar solution (using dried serum) over a base of nutrient agar. Jírovec & Rodová (1940) used a medium similar to that of Lynch to grow *T.vaginalis* and other species of the genus. In these simple media, no attempts were made to grow the flagellates monoxenically or axenically. Savel (1957) has pointed out that the presence of a *suitable* bacterial flora, or the fungus *Candida*, may enhance both the rate of multiplication of the flagellates and the length of life of individual cultures: this was shown to be true of *Candida* by Sorel (1954), who used cultures of *T.vaginalis* in a simple peptonized broth medium. Difficulties arise if the mixed bacterial flora begins to overgrow the flagellates, and for this reason most later media (including those used for diagnosis) are designed for bacteria-free cultures. *Candida*, if present in the inoculum, also develops in such media.

Johnson (1942) has studied the effect of oxygen concentration on the growth of the flagellates, and has shown that *T.vaginalis* can grow as a facultative aerobe in the presence of some oxygen, but that these conditions exert a depressing effect on the culture and strictly anaerobic conditions are best. The best pH range was between 5·5 and 6·0. Most modern media for growing this organism rely on cysteine monohydrochloride or thioglycollate as a reducing agent to remove the free oxygen, and they often incorporate methylene blue (which is decolourized under anaerobic conditions). Such media should only be used while at least the lower part of the tube is still colourless.

Wirtschafter (1954) found that, if the oxygen concentration was allowed to rise in cultures of *T.vaginalis* in CPLM medium (without agar), large multinucleate 'somatella' developed, presumably due to an inhibition of cell division: these 'somatella', if subinoculated to culture medium with a reduced oxygen tension, reverted to the normal morphology.

(ii) *Purification of isolations of* T.vaginalis

Various methods have been used to free this flagellate from contaminating bacteria and fungi. All of these involve the addition of antibiotics to the culture medium. Penicillin is almost invariably used, usually at a final concentration of 1,000 units/ml, often with streptomycin at a concentration of 0·5 mg/ml. In addition to penicillin, Adler & Pulvertaft (1944) used sulphanilamide (0·33%) and McEntegart (1952) used chloramphenicol (1,000 units/ml). Lowe (1965) used no penicillin, but chloramphenicol and streptomycin at concentrations of about 1:10,000. Thomas (1964) was able to remove the fungus *Candida albicans* by 3 passages in medium containing nystatin at a concentration of 1:10,000. Lowe (1965) used

8

nystatin in addition to neomycin, at similar concentrations, while Ivey (1961) used nystatin (25 μg/ml) for the same purpose.

De Carneri (1956a) modified Glaser's and Coria's (1935b) method of purifying *T.foetus* (p. 96) by using a tube shaped like the letter W, containing CPLM medium (with 2 insignificant modifications) plus penicillin (1,000 units/ml) and streptomycin (1 mg/ml). After 2 days' incubation at 37°c, pure *T.vaginalis* could be recovered from the limb of the tube opposite to that by which the contaminated material (including bacteria and fungi) had been introduced. It should be borne in mind that Kott & Adler (1961) found that, following bacterial contamination and subsequent antibiotic treatment *in vitro*, the antigenic type of 2 strains of *T.vaginalis* had changed, though not necessarily as a result of their treatment.

(iii) *Monoxenic culture*

De Carneri (1956b) found that cultures of *T.vaginalis* grown monoxenic-ally with *Escherischia coli* would survive for a month, routine subinocula-tion being necessary only every 2 weeks. He firstly purified the strain completely by the method described immediately above, and then mixed it with *E.coli*, growing the monoxenic culture in a diphasic serum-Ringer's medium with rice. This method has obvious advantages for the laboratory maintenance of strains. If it is desired subsequently to obtain an axenic culture from the monoxenic one, this can readily be achieved by adding penicillin (1,000 units/ml) and streptomycin (1 mg/ml) to the medium.

T.vaginalis also grows well in the presence of penicillin-inhibited but viable bacteria in the SF medium of Shaffer *et al.* (1949) and, presumably, in the modification of it known as MS-F (p. 140).

(iv) *Bacteria-free cultures*

The following media are described under this heading rather than as axenic cultures, since although the media are sterile and the introduction of contaminating bacteria is prevented by means of antibiotics, in many (possibly all) of the media the fungus *Candida* can also grow. As stated above, its presence, at least in certain media, is beneficial (Sorel, 1954): however, it can be removed, if desired, by the treatments outlined above (p. 99), and axenic growth of the flagellates is possible in all the media mentioned in this section.

Many media of this type have been described: detailed methods for preparing a few are given at the end of this section, while some of the lesser-used media are listed in Table 3.2.

Trussell & Johnson (1941) grew *T.vaginalis* in a liquid medium composed largely of peptone and serum. Johnson (1942) then grew this organism in a diphasic medium with a base of liver-infusion agar. These 2 elements were later brought together by the same authors (Johnson & Trussell, 1943; Trussell & Johnson, 1945; Johnson *et al.*, 1945) to form, with additions, the monophasic CPLM ('cysteine, peptone, liver, maltose') medium (p. 104) for axenic cultivation of *T.vaginalis*. Sprince & Kupferberg (1947) produced a rather more defined version of CPLM, which was later simplified as STS ('simplified trypticase serum') medium (Kupferberg *et al.*, 1948). Growth in this medium, from which the liver digest had been omitted (p. 105) was, however, less good than in CPLM. medium. STS medium, with added chloramphenicol, is available commercially under the name 'Trichosel Broth Kupferberg' from Baltimore Biological Laboratory (Savel, 1957).

Lash (1948) developed a medium enriched with a hydrolysate of casein which he later (1950) simplified to a recipe not unlike that of STS medium. Other modifications of CPLM medium included those of McEntegart (1952) and Feinberg (1953) (p. 102). The latter's modification was suitable for the production of *T.vaginalis* in bulk (about 1·1–1·5 g of freeze-dried parasite material were produced from each 2 l. of medium). A diagnostic medium (p. 103) developed by Feinberg & Whittington (1957) can be prepared, dispensed into test-tubes and then freeze-dried for storage: for use it is reconstituted to the original volume with distilled water. Lowe (1965) discussed the diagnostic use of Feinberg & Whittington's medium, and recommended a modification of it which, being semi-solid in consistency, can be more easily sent through the post to a diagnostic centre (p. 105).

The medium used for diagnostic purposes by the American National Institutes of Health has been described by Burch *et al.* (1959): it is known as TLS ('trypticase, liver, serum') medium (p. 108). Honigberg (1961) found a simple mixture of Baltimore Biological Laboratory's fluid thioglycollate medium with serum to be very satisfactory for the maintenance of *T.vaginalis*. Feinberg & Whittington's (1957) medium has been thoroughly analyzed by Lumsden *et al.* (1966) in such a way that the functions and optimum concentrations of its various main constituents could be determined. To do this, the medium was broken down into 6 constituent parts—salts, nutrients, reducing agent, serum, antibiotics and buffer—and isotonic solutions of each prepared. These were then mixed in appropriate proportions to produce the final modified medium (p. 106). The advantage of this is that the individual constituents can be varied experimentally without affecting the osmotic strength of the whole. Apart from being useful for isolation and routine axenic cultivation, this medium (with the addition of 10% v/v dimethyl sulphoxide) was suitable for the preservation of cultures of *T.vaginalis* by freezing at −79°c (the original paper should be consulted for details of this technique). The media used by Diamond (1957) and Samuels & Beil (1962) for axenic cultivation of *T.vaginalis* and *T.foetus* among other species, have already been referred to (Table 3.2).

(v) *Plate cultures*

Various methods have been described for growing *T.vaginalis* on agar plates containing suitable nutrients: such methods are of use in testing chemotherapeutic compounds and also for the production of clones by micromanipulation (Samuels, 1962; Cavier *et al.*, 1964). Several of these media are derived from conventional liquid media (CPLM for example), by increasing the concentration of agar. Details of these methods should be sought in papers by the following authors: Asami *et al.* (1955), Filadoro & Orsi (1958), Ivey (1961), Samuels (1962), and Cavier *et al.* (1964).

(vi) *Growth in avian embryos and tissue cultures*

T.vaginalis has been grown in this way: see reviews by Pipkin (1960) and Zuckerman (1966).

Method for bulk growth
of *T.vaginalis*
(Feinberg, 1953)

MEDIUM

1 *Composition*

> Ascorbic acid..................3·7 g
> L-Cysteine monohydrochloride...2·5 g
> Proteolysed liver (B.P.C.).......1·0 g
> Glucose......................10·0 g
> Water ....1·2 l.
> Bovine serum ....160·0 ml
> Douglas's broth* ....1·0 l.

2 *Preparation*

Dissolve the above ingredients, adjust pH to 5·8–6·0 with normal sodium hydroxide solution, and sterilize by filtration. The medium should not be stored longer than 14 days.

* This is a trypsinized digest of ox heart (0·5 kg fresh tissue per l.): for details of preparation see Fildes & McIntosh (1931).

TECHNIQUE

1 Ten millilitre aliquots in test-tubes are inoculated with 0·5 ml of an actively growing culture and incubated at 36–37°c. Transfers to fresh medium are made daily.

2 *For bulk growth*, 5 ml of a 24 hr tube culture are inoculated to 100 ml medium in a medical flat bottle of 8 oz (227 ml) capacity. After growth at 36–37°c for 24 hr, 100 ml of this culture are transferred to 2 l. warm medium contained in a narrow-neck round bottle of 80 oz (2·27 l.) capacity. Yields of 4–5 million organisms per ml can be obtained.

3 *For isolation*, this medium can be used in 10 ml aliquots, with added penicillin (1,000 units/ml) and streptomycin (500 units/ml): growth during the initial transfers is, however, slow.

Diagnostic and maintenance medium
for *T.vaginalis*
(Feinberg & Whittington, 1957)

MEDIUM

1 *Composition*

Panmede proteolysed liver powder
(Paines & Byrne Ltd) ....25·0 g
Sodium chloride................6·5 g
Glucose.......................5·0 g
Penicillin..............1,000,000 units
Streptomycin...........500,000 units
Water........................1·0 l.

2 *Preparation*

Dissolve the above ingredients, add 80 ml horse serum (inactivated) and adjust to pH 6·4 with normal sodium hydroxide solution (about 9 ml/l. are needed). Sterilize by filtration and store in screw-capped bottles at 4–5°c (for up to 3 months).

TECHNIQUE

Dispense 7 ml aliquots into $6 \times \frac{5}{8}$ in $(15 \times 1·5$ cm) test-tubes: if the diagnostic samples are small, use 2–3 ml in $3 \times \frac{1}{2}$ in $(7·5 \times 1·25$ cm) tubes. The medium in these tubes can be freeze-dried for storage, and reconstituted to the original volume with distilled water before use.

After inoculation, the tubes should be incubated at 36°c. For diagnosis, it is recommended to examine the tubes 3 times during a period of 4–5 days, preferably after centrifugation.

Thomas (1964) recommended using screw-capped bottles completely filled, instead of test-tubes, to maintain anaerobic conditions. She also recommended incubation at 34°c and found that transfers should be made every 36 hr to maintain strains at that temperature. Thomas recommended the addition of nystatin (final concentration 1:10,000) to this medium to remove the fungus *Candida albicans*, if necessary.

NOTE: A slightly modified version of this medium, containing 0·1% agar, is available commercially as 'Oxoid' Trichomonas Medium (Oxo, Ltd).

CPLM medium
for *Trichomonas vaginalis*
(Johnson & Trussell, 1943; Trussell & Johnson, 1945;
Johnson *et al.*, 1945)

MEDIUM

1 Infuse 20 g 'Bacto' liver powder (Difco) in 330 ml water for 1 hr at about 50°c. Finally raise the temperature to 80°c for 5 min, to coagulate protein, and filter through a Buchner funnel: about 320 ml infusion are obtained.

2 Mix the following ingredients:

> Cysteine monohydrochloride.....2·4 g
> Peptone......................32·0 g
> Maltose.......................1·6 g
> Agar..........................1·6 g
> Ringer's solution (p. 350).....960·0 ml
> Liver infusion (above)......*c*. 320·0 ml

3 Adjust to pH 5·8–6·0 with normal sodium hydroxide solution (about 11–13 ml): NOTE: Levine (1961) recommends pH 7·0.

4 Heat to dissolve agar and filter through cotton or coarse filter paper.

5 Add 0·7 ml of 0·5% aqueous solution of methylene blue.

6 Dispense 8 ml aliquots into test-tubes and autoclave (15 lb/15 min).

7 When cool add 2 ml sterile human serum to each tube.

8 Incubate tubes for 2–4 days at 37°c to check sterility.

TECHNIQUE

After inoculation, incubate at 35–37°c. Transfers of about 0·05 ml amounts to fresh medium should be made every 48 hr. About 2–4 million flagellates/ml should be present by this time.

Initial isolation should be made into this medium plus penicillin

(500–1,000 units/ml), followed by transfer to medium without antibiotic after about 60 hr.

NOTE: This medium may be stored at room temperature for 2–3 weeks: it must be used while there is still a colourless anaerobic zone visible in each tube (the methylene blue serves as an indicator, being decolourized under anaerobic conditions).

STS medium
for *T.vaginalis*
(Kupferberg *et al.*, 1948)

MEDIUM

1 *Composition*

Trypticase (Baltimore Biological
Laboratory)...................20 g
Cysteine monohydrochloride.....1·5 g
Maltose.......................1·0 g
Agar (Difco) ....1·0 g
Water to make ....950 ml

2 *Preparation*

(a) Mix the above ingredients, adjust to pH 6·0 (using N NaOH or N HCl), heat to dissolve the agar and filter while hot through coarse filter paper. If required, add 0·6 ml of 0·5% aqueous methylene blue solution before cooling.

(b) Cool to 46°C, readjust to pH 6·0 if necessary and make up volume to 950 ml with water.

(c) Dispense 9·5 ml aliquots in test-tubes and autoclave (15 lb/15 min).

(d) When cool, add 0·5 ml sterile human serum to each tube.

TECHNIQUE

Incubate at 37°C and transfer to fresh medium every 48 hr.

Diagnostic medium for
T.vaginalis
(Lowe, 1965)

MEDIUM

1 *Composition*

Panmede liver extract
(Paines & Byrne Ltd) ....12·5 g
Sodium chloride...............2·5 g
Maltose......................0·5 g
Water ....500 ml

2   *Preparation*

(a)   Dissolve the above ingredients by gentle heating, adjust to pH 6·2, add 1·25 g agar (see note below) and steam at 100°c for 1½ hr with intermittent mixing.

(b)   Cool to 54°c and add aseptically the following sterile ingredients:

Horse serum (inactivated)........50 ml
Oxoid Fildes extract (Oxo Ltd)...0·5 ml
1% aqueous solution of
    chloramphenicol.............5·0 ml
1% aqueous solution of
    streptomycin................5·0 ml
1% aqueous solution of neomycin 5·0 ml
0·5% aqueous solution of nystatin
    (freshly prepared)...........10·0 ml

(c)   Mix thoroughly and dispense in small screw-capped glass bottles (universal containers, 7 ml capacity), filling each to the shoulder. Incubate overnight at 37°c to check sterility.

TECHNIQUE FOR DIAGNOSIS

The head of each swab (plus suspect material) should be placed entire in a bottle of medium and sent (by post if necessary) to the laboratory. On arrival, a drop of medium close to the swab is withdrawn by means of a Pasteur pipette and examined microscopically. If flagellates are not seen, the culture is incubated at 37°c and examined daily for 3 days. (It is recommended that a second swab should be used to make a thin dried smear for subsequent staining and examination, when the culture is inoculated.)

NOTE: The quantity of agar may be varied if necessary, depending on the brand used. The resultant gel should be firm enough to remain intact if the bottle is inverted, but soft enough to break down readily on shaking.

Maintenance medium for
T.vaginalis
(Lumsden *et al.*, 1966)

MEDIUM

1   *Composition and preparation of stock solutions*
(a)   *Salts*

Sodium chloride, 0·154 M..100 volumes
Potassium chloride, 0·154 M..4 volumes
Magnesium chloride, 0·103 M 3 volumes
Calcium chloride, 0·103 M ...1 volume

(b) *Buffer* (pH 7·4)

> Sodium dihydrogen phosphate,
> 0·154 M ....1·36 volumes
> Disodium hydrogen phosphate,
> 0·103 M ....8·64 volumes
> Bromcresol purple ....15 mg/100 ml

These solutions are prepared in bulk, autoclaved and stored at 4°C.

2 *Preparation of final medium*

Mix solution (a), 392·5 ml, with solution (b), 100·0 ml, and add to this mixture the following ingredients:

(a) *Nutrients*

> Oxoid liver digest L27 (Oxo Ltd)
> 40 g/l., 300 ml
> Glucose, 0·308 M ....100 ml

(b) *Reducing agent*

> Sodium thioglycollate ....1·0 g

(c) *Serum* (calf):

> Oxoid SR34 (Oxo Ltd)....... 100 ml

(d) *Antibiotics*

> Benzylpenicillin, 1 mega unit in 5 ml
> salts solution (a) ....5·0 ml
> Streptomycin sulphate, 1 g (745,000
> units) in 5 ml salts solution (a) 2·5 ml

After dissolving and mixing all the above solutions at room temperature, the solution is sterilized by filtration and dispensed in screw–capped glass bottles (either 7 or 15 ml capacity) so as nearly to fill them. The screw caps of the bottles are centrally perforated and fitted with white rubber discs to allow inoculation and withdrawal of medium by syringe and needle without opening the bottle.

Bottles of medium may be stored at 4°C for up to 2 weeks, or longer at −20°C. The final pH is 6·1–6·4.

TECHNIQUE

The medium is incubated at 37°C after inoculation, and serial transfers (usually of 0·1 ml amounts) made to fresh medium at intervals of about 5 days.

National Institutes of Health
TLS medium for *T.vaginalis*
(Burch *et al.*, 1959)

MEDIUM

1   Prepare the following solution by heating to 100°c:

> Trypticase (Baltimore Biological
>   Laboratory)...................20 g
> Sodium chloride..................7 g
> Glucose ....10 g
> Water ....1 l.

2   Infuse 50 g Bacto-liver (Difco) in 1 l. water for 1 hr at 56°c, raise the temperature finally to 80°c, filter through coarse filter paper and restore the volume of filtrate to 1 l. with water. Then add to the infusion:

> Sodium chloride..................7 g
> Tryptone.......................5 g
> Potassium chloride ....0·4 g
> Calcium chloride ....0·4 g
> Sodium bicarbonate.............0·4 g

Heat in autoclave to dissolve, and filter.

3   Mix 600 ml solution (1 above) with 1 l. of broth (2 above) and adjust to pH 6·0 with 5 N hydrochloric acid, to make stock solution.

4   Dispense the stock medium in 8 ml aliquots in test-tubes (16 × 150 mm), autoclave and seal with paraffin wax. They may be stored at room temperature for up to 1 week. Just before use, add to each tube 0·5 ml sterile horse serum (without preservative) and incubate at 37°c for 24–72 hr to check sterility.

TECHNIQUE

After inoculating the diagnostic specimen, add the following sterile ingredients to each tube:

> 4% aqueous solution of sodium
>   thioglycollate ....0·2 ml
> Saline solution of potassium penicillin
>   G (1,000 units/ml) and dihydro-
>   streptomycin sulphate (1,000 µg/ml)
>   0·4 ml

Incubate at 37°c and examine sediment daily for 4–5 days.

IV. PARASITIC CILIATES

Relatively little work has been done on the cultivation of these organisms (Table 3.3): it may conveniently be discussed under two headings, firstly *Balantidium coli* (the only ciliate parasite of man) and secondly the ciliates which inhabit the rumen of ruminants. In addition to these two groups, Nelson (1943b) has cultivated *Nyctotherus cordiformis*, a parasite of the rectum of frogs, in an extract of frog rectal contents in 'frog-Ringer' (a modification of Ringer's solution, isotonic with the blood of amphibia: p. 350). He (Nelson, 1943a) has also grown *N.cordiformis* in a medium prepared from ground-up alcohol-preserved tissues (preferably stomach, or liver) of frogs. After evaporation of the alcohol, the residue is re-suspended in 'frog-Ringer' solution.

TABLE 3.3. Some media used for the cultivation of parasitic ciliates.

Author(s)	Date	Designation of medium	Species	Detailed description (if any)
Adler & Foner	1941	—	*Bal. coli*	p. 126
Atchley	1935	—	,,	—
Barrett & Yarbrough	1921	—	,,	—
Dobell & Laidlaw	1926	HSre+S	,,	p. 128
Glaser & Coria	1935a	'Purification'	,,	—
	1935a	'Maintenance'	,,	—
Hungate	1942, 1943	—	Spirotrichs of rumen	p. 111
Lamy & Lamy	1951	—	*Bal. coli*	—
Levine	1961	RSS	,,	—
Nelson	1943a	—	*Nyctotherus*	—
	1943b	—	,,	—
Rees	1927	—	*Bal. coli*	—
Schumaker	1931	—	,,	—
Sugden & Oxford	1952	—	Holotrichs	p. 112
Tanabe (modified: see Craig 1948)		—	*Bal. coli*	p. 81

(i) *Balantidium coli*

This organism, first cultivated by Barret & Yarbrough (1921), will grow in a variety of undefined media. Apparently no attempt has been made to cultivate this organism either axenically or in a defined medium. The best temperature range for the growth of *Bal.coli* was investigated by Cox (1961), who found that growth would occur only between 20° and

43°c. Within this range growth was slower, and consequently each individual culture lasted longer, the lower the ambient temperature. At 25°c, cultures survived for 10 days, with a maximum growth (5,000 ciliates/ml) on the fourth and fifth days: at 40°c, culture life was only 3 days but the maximum growth (on the second day) was 17,000/ml. Cox used the HSre+S medium of Dobell & Laidlaw (1926), which was first shown to be suitable for *Bal.coli* by Jameson (1927). For routine growth in this medium, Cox's results suggest that a temperature of 37°c, with subinoculation to fresh medium every 48 or 72 hr, would be effective.

Many authors (Barret & Yarbrough, 1921; Rees, 1927; Schumaker 1931; Atchley, 1935; Glaser & Coria, 1935a; Lamy & Lamy, 1951; Levine, 1961) have used simple saline solutions of serum (pig, ox, horse or human), usually with added starch (which Schumaker found to be essential), at temperatures of about 37°c: however, Craig (1948) recommended a diphasic version of Tanabe's (1925) medium, without added starch (p. 81). Transfers to fresh media were made usually 2 or 3 times a week. Schumaker (1931) showed *Bal.coli* to be a facultative anaerobe, but found that oxygen had no inhibitory effect upon its growth. Jameson (1927) and Lamy & Lamy (1951) observed conjugation *in vitro* at 37°c, but not at 25°c. Barret & Yarbrough (1921) reported encystment, possibly because their medium, being devoid of starch, was less nutritious. Other media which have been used are listed in Table 3.3. Glaser & Coria (1935a) achieved monoxenic cultivation of *Bal.coli* by using their V-tube technique, repeated 5 times, for the partial 'purification' of the ciliate (p. 96). For cultivation after purification, they used a liquid medium (5% serum in Ringer's solution, plus starch). The semi-solid medium of Adler & Foner (1941) (p. 126) is also suitable. Nelson (1940) used a method rather similar to Glaser's & Coria's (1935a) to separate *Bal.coli* from faecal debris, and then grew the ciliates in a 10% solution in Ringer's saline of pig's caecal contents (filtered through cotton but not sterilized), with added starch. As Kirby (1950) pointed out, corresponding media, prepared from the intestinal contents of the appropriate hosts, might prove useful for the cultivation of ciliates of other vertebrates. Nelson himself (1943b) modified this technique for the growth of a ciliate parasitizing the rectum of frogs (see above, p. 109).

(ii) *Rumen ciliates*

This group of specialized organisms consists of members of 2 ciliate groups, the Spirotricha and Holotricha. The former (*Diplodinium* and *Entodinium* spp.) have been successfully cultivated *in vitro* by Hungate (1942, 1943) (p. 111) and the latter (*Isotricha* and *Dasytricha* spp.) have been grown with partial success by Sugden & Oxford (1952) (p. 112). Serial transfers were not achieved with the holotrichs, but they could be maintained alive *in vitro* for periods up to about 1 month. The subject has been reviewed by Hungate (1955) and Oxford (1955). The spirotrichs are obligate anaerobes (Hungate, 1955) and rapidly die in the presence of oxygen: the holotrichs are facultatively anaerobic, though much less sensitive to the presence of dissolved oxygen than the spirotrichs (Sugden & Oxford, 1952).

Heald *et al.* (1952) used streptomycin in order to render the holotrichs 'virtually' bacteria-free (below). In these conditions the organisms do not reproduce and only survive *in vitro* for a short time, but they can be used for certain experimental procedures. The organisms of both groups may be collected repeatedly from an animal (such as a sheep) with a surgical fistula of the rumen: a method for separating the (less-numerous) holotrichs was described by Heald *et al.* (1952).

Method for preparing suspensions
of holotrich ciliates
from rumen contents
(Heald *et al.*, 1952)

1   Collect rumen liquid (1 l.) from a 'fistulated' sheep: strain, add 0·5% glucose and incubate in a separating funnel at 40°c for 3 hr.
2   The ciliates sink to the bottom of the funnel to form a white layer: this is run off into sterile acetate-phosphate buffer without bicarbonate, pH 7·2 (see Sugden & Oxford's medium, p. 112) in test-tubes of 50 ml capacity. Allow the ciliates to sediment (at 40°c) and wash with warm (40°c) buffer by decantation several times.
3   The ciliates can now be used to inoculate Sugden's and Oxford's medium (p. 112): any contaminating spirotrichs rapidly die. Alternatively, 'virtually' bacteria-free suspensions of living holotrichs can be prepared by incubating for 20–24 hr in buffer plus 0·0008M streptomycin, and repeating with fresh buffer and streptomycin for a further 20–24 hr. (Such bacteria-free ciliates will not grow in culture.)

Medium for spirotrich
ciliates of the rumen
(Hungate, 1942, 1943)

MEDIUM

1   Prepare the following inorganic salt solution, in distilled water:

Sodium bicarbonate.............0·1%
Potassium dihydrogen phosphate .0·1%
Magnesium sulphate (anhyd.)....0·01%
Calcium chloride (anhyd.) ......0·01%
Sodium chloride................0·6%

2   A mixture of nitrogen (95%) and carbon dioxide (5%) is bubbled through the above solution for 15 min. The solution is then dispensed in 20 ml aliquots into 50 ml conical (Erlenmeyer) flasks.

3   To each flask is added 16 mg powdered dried grass and 16 mg powdered cellulose. (The latter is prepared by treating absorbent cotton wool with concentrated hydrochloric acid for several days, then filtering, washing and drying the product and grinding it in a mortar.)

TECHNIQUE

The medium is inoculated with either 0·5 ml rumen contents (if a primary isolation) or with 20 ml of a vigorous culture, and the nitrogen-carbon dioxide gas mixture is again bubbled through. The flask is then tightly stoppered, and incubated at 38–39°c. Transfers to fresh medium should be made at intervals of 2 days.

NOTES: (1) As described above, the medium is suitable for *Diplodinium neglectum*: with the following slight modifications, it can be used also for other species.

For *D.maggii*: transfer to fresh medium every 24 hr; added cellulose is not necessary, but grass powder (15 mg/20 ml) should be included.

For *D.multivesiculatum*: added ground wheat, as well as grass and cellulose, is beneficial.

For *D.denticulatum*: transfers should be made daily.

For *Entodinium caudatum*: ground wheat is beneficial; when added, grass and cellulose may be omitted.

(2) Clone cultures could be obtained with all the above species except *D.multivesiculatum*. Axenic growth is *not* possible.

Medium for holotrich ciliates
of the rumen
(Sugden & Oxford, 1952)

MEDIUM

1   Prepare the following aqueous solution (see note below):

Sodium chloride................0·5%
Sodium acetate ....0·15%

Potassium dihydrogen phosphate. .0·1%
Sodium bicarbonate............0·1%
Magnesium sulphate 7H$_2$O .....0·01%
Calcium chloride 2H$_2$O ....0·01%

pH = 6·8–7·0

2 Add 0·1% cellobiose and *either* 10% (v/v) centrifuged sterile (filtered) rumen liquor *or* 5% (v/v) of centrifuged, boiled and strained grass extract (prepared by squeezing minced, fresh grass in a gauze bag).

TECHNIQUE

1 One hundred millilitres conical (Erlenmeyer) flasks are filled completely with this medium plus a fairly heavy inoculum of washed ciliates (prepared by the method described on p. 111), about one-fifth of the total yield from 1 l. of rumen contents. The flask is closed by a bung with a Bunsen outlet valve, and incubated at 39°C. (Any spirotrichs contaminating the inoculum die rapidly due to the oxygen content of the medium.)
2 The medium should be removed by careful decantation, and fresh medium added, every 24 hr.

NOTE: A simpler basic salt solution is described by Oxford (1955) to replace solution (1) above:

Sodium chloride................0·5%
Sodium acetate................0·13%
Potassium dihydrogen phosphate 0·03%
Dipotassium hydrogen phosphate.0·1%
Magnesium sulphate 7H$_2$O......0·01%

pH = 7·2

This can be sterilized by autoclaving, but subsequently carbon dioxide should be bubbled through to lower the pH to about 6·8.

V. SELECTION OF SUITABLE MEDIA

For the cultivation of ordinary intestinal flagellates (excluding *Giardia*), choosing a medium is almost a problem of 'embarras de richesse'. As a matter of convenience for diagnostic purposes or routine maintenance in the laboratory, it is often best to use a medium which is also suitable for the intestinal amoebae, such as Dobell's HSre + S (p. 128): this is also the medium of choice for the ciliate *Bal.coli*. Adler's & Foner's (1941) semisolid medium (p. 126) is also suitable for parasites of all these groups if it is desired to use a medium with increased viscosity. If one is interested in diagnosing or maintaining flagellates alone, Hogue's (1921) medium is simple to prepare and reliable to use. For axenic cultivation of flagellates, if this is required for special purposes, the 2 media devised by Diamond (1957, 1962) may be used. The only defined medium available for growth of intestinal flagellates is that devised by Lee *et al.* (1964), on which only certain trichomonads of poikilothermic animals can be grown (p. 88).

The choice of media for cultivating either *Giardia intestinalis*, or the spirotrich and holotrich rumen ciliates is easy, since only one satisfactory recipe has been devised for organisms of each of these 3 groups: that of Karapetyan (1962) for *G.intestinalis* (p. 91), and those of Hungate (1942, 1943) and Sugden & Oxford (1952) for the 2 groups of rumen ciliates (pp. 111–112).

For diagnosis of *T.foetus*, there seems to be little to choose between the medium devised by Andrews & Lyford (1940) (p. 95) and that of Plastridge (1943) (p. 96). Both of these media are also suitable for routine maintenance in the laboratory.

Of the several diagnostic media which have been described for *T.vaginalis*, any of the following should prove satisfactory: CPLM (p. 104), Feinberg's & Whittington's (1957) (p. 103), or the modifications of it devised by Lowe (1965) (p. 105) and Lumsden *et al.* (1966) (p. 106), and the TLS medium used by the American National Institutes of Health (p. 108). Any of these media should also be suitable for routine maintenance of cultures.

REFERENCES

ADLER S. (1942). A note on bacteria-free cultures of *Trichomonas hominis. Trans. R. Soc. trop. Med. Hyg.* **35**: 219–221.

ADLER S. & FONER, ANNIE (1941). Culture of intestinal protozoa. *Lancet* **240**: 243–244.

ADLER S. & PULVERTAFT R.J.V. (1944). The use of penicillin for obtaining bacteria-free cultures of *Trichomonas vaginalis* Donné 1837. *Ann. trop. Med. Parasit.* **38**: 188–189.

ANDREWS J. & LYFORD, HELEN S. (1940). Cultural observations on *Trichomonas foetus. Am. J. Hyg.* **31** C: 43–50.

ASAMI K., NODAKE Y. & UENO T. (1955). Cultivation of *Trichomonas vaginalis* on solid medium. *Expl Parasit.* **4**: 34–39.

ATCHLEY F.O. (1935). Effects of environmental changes on growth and multiplication in populations of *Balantidium. Am. J. Hyg.* **21**: 151–166.

BALAMUTH W. (1946). Improved egg yolk infusion for cultivation of *Entamoeba histolytica* and other intestinal protozoa. *Am. J. clin. Path.* **16**: 380–384.

BARRET H.P. & YARBROUGH, NANCY (1921). A method for the cultivation of *Balantidium coli. Am. J. trop. Med.* **1**: 161–164.

BISHOP, ANN (1938). *Histomonas meleagridis* in domestic fowls (*Gallus gallus*). Cultivation and experimental infection. *Parasitology* **30**: 181–194.

BLAND P.B., GOLDSTEIN L., WENRICH D.H. & WEINER, ELEANOR (1932). Studies on the biology of *Trichomonas vaginalis*. *Am. J. Hyg.* **16**: 492–512.

BOECK W.C. (1921). *Chilomastix mesnili* and a method for its culture. *J. exp. Med.* **33**: 147–175.

BOECK W.C. & DRBOHLAV J. (1925). The cultivation of *Endamoeba histolytica*. *Am. J. Hyg.* **5**: 371–407.

BURCH T.A., REES C.W. & REARDON, LUCY (1959). Diagnosis of *Trichomonas vaginalis* vaginitis. *Am. J. Obstet. Gynec.* **77**: 309–313.

CAVIER R., GEORGES P. & SAVEL J. (1964). La culture de *Trichomonas vaginalis* sur plaques de milieux gélosés. *Expl Parasit.* **15**: 556–560.

CLEVELAND L.R. (1928). The separation of a *Tritrichomonas* of man from bacteria; its failure to grow in media free of living bacteria; measurement of its growth and division rate in pure cultures of various bacteria. *Am. J. Hyg.* **8**: 256–278.

COX F.E.G. (1961). The cultivation of *Balantidium coli* throughout its viable temperature range. *Ann. trop. Med. Parasit.* **55**: 305–308.

CRAIG C.F. (1948). *Laboratory diagnosis of protozoan diseases.* Ed. 2. London: Henry Kimpton.

CRAIG C.F. & FAUST E.C. (1951). *Clinical parasitology.* Ed. 5. London: Henry Kimpton.

DANIEL G.E. (1940). Note on cultivation of *Trichomonas foetus*. *J. Parasit.* **26**: 85.

DE CARNERI I. (1956a). Isolation of *Trichomonas vaginalis* from fungi and bacteria. *Am. J. trop. Med. Hyg.* **5**: 210–212.

DE CARNERI I. (1956b). Conservation of *Trichomonas* in monobacterial cultures. *Am. J. trop. Med. Hyg.* **5**: 677–680.

DE VOLT H.M. (1943). A new medium for the cultivation of *Histomonas meleagridis*. *J. Parasit.* **29**: 353–355.

DIAMOND L.S. (1957). The establishment of various trichomonads of animals and man in axenic cultures. *J. Parasit.* **43**: 488–490.

DIAMOND L.S. (1961). Axenic cultivation of *Entamoeba histolytica*. *Science, N.Y.* **134**: 336–337.

DIAMOND L.S. (1962). Axenic cultivation of *Trichomonas tenax*, the oral flagellate of man. I. Establishment of cultures. *J. Protozool.* **9**: 442–444.

DOBELL C. (1942). Some new methods for studying intestinal amoebae and other Protozoa. *Parasitology* **34**: 101–112.

DOBELL C. & LAIDLAW P.P. (1926). On the cultivation of *Entamoeba histolytica* and some other entozoic amoebae. *Parasitology* **18**: 283–318.

FEINBERG J.G. (1953). A method for the bulk growth of a parasitic Protozoan. *Nature, Lond.* **171**: 1165–1166.

FEINBERG J.G. & WHITTINGTON M. JOAN (1957). A culture medium for *Trichomonas vaginalis* Donné and species of *Candida*. *J. clin. Path.* **10**: 327–329.

FILADORO F. & ORSI N. (1958). Cultivation of *Trichomonas vaginalis* on a solid medium and its application to the assay of Trichomycin potency. *Antibiotica Chemother.* **8**: 561–563.

FILDES P. & MCINTOSH J. (1931). The preparation of culture media. In *A system of bacteriology in relation to medicine* **9**: 48–75 Fildes P. & Ledingham J.C.G. (eds) for the Medical Research Council). London: His Majesty's Stationery Office.

FITZGERALD P.R., HAMMOND D.M. & SHUPE J. LE G. (1954). The role of cultures in immediate and delayed examinations of preputial samples for *Trichomonas foetus*. *Vet. Med.* **49**: 409–412 & 445.

9

FRYE W.W. & MELENEY H.E. (1939). Liver extract as a substitute for serum in the culture medium for *Endamoeba histolytica*. *Science, N.Y.* **89**: 564–565.

GEHRING K. & MURRAY C. (1933). Cultivation of *Trichomonas bovis*. *Cornell Vet.* **23**: 335–343.

GLASER R.W. & CORIA N.A. (1935a). The partial purification of *Balantidium coli* from swine. *J. Parasit.* **21**: 190–193.

GLASER R.W. & CORIA N.A. (1935b). Purification and culture of *Tritrichomonas foetus* (Riedmüller) from cows. *Am. J. Hyg.* **22**: 221–226.

HEALD P.J., OXFORD A.E. & SUGDEN, BRENDA (1952). A convenient method for preparing massive suspensions of virtually bacteria-free ciliate Protozoa of the genera *Isotricha* and *Dasytricha* for manometric studies. *Nature, Lond.* **169**: 1055–1056.

HEGNER R. (1928). Experimental transmission of trichomonads from the intestine and vagina of monkeys to the vagina of monkeys (*Macacus rhesus*). *J. Parasit.* **14**: 261–264.

HOGUE, MARY JANE (1921). The cultivation of *Trichomonas hominis*. *Am. J. trop. Med.* **1**: 211–214.

HONIGBERG B.M. (1961). Comparative pathogenicity of *Trichomonas vaginalis* and *Trichomonas gallinae* to mice. I. Gross pathology, quantitative evaluation of virulence, and some factors affecting pathogenicity. *J. Parasit.* **47**: 545–571.

HONIGBERG B.M., BECKER R. DI M., LIVINGSTON M.C. & McCLURE M.T. (1964). The behavior and pathogenicity of two strains of *Trichomonas gallinae* in cell cultures. *J. Protozool.* **11**: 447–465.

HUNGATE R.E. (1942). The culture of *Eudiplodinium neglectum*, with experiments on the digestion of cellulose. *Biol. Bull. mar. biol. Lab., Woods Hole* **83**: 303–319.

HUNGATE R.E. (1943). Further experiments on cellulose digestion by the Protozoa in the rumen of cattle. *Biol. Bull. mar. biol. Lab., Woods Hole* **84**: 157–163.

HUNGATE R.E. (1955). Mutualistic intestinal Protozoa. In *Biochemistry and physiology of Protozoa* **2**: 159–199. Hutner S.H. & Lwoff A. (eds.) New York and London: Academic Press.

HUTNER S.H., BAKER H., AARONSON S., NATHAN, HELENE A., RODRIGUEZ E., LOCKWOOD, SALLY, SANDERS M. & PETERSEN R.A. (1957). Growing *Ochromonas malhamensis* above 35°C. *J. Protozool.* **4**: 259–269.

IVEY M.H. (1961). Growth characteristics of clones of *Trichomonas vaginalis* in solid medium. *J. Parasit.* **47**: 539–544.

JAMESON A.P. (1927). The behaviour of *Balantidium coli* Malm. in cultures. *Parasitology* **19**: 411–419.

JEFFRIES L. & HARRIS, MARGARET (1967). Observations on the maintenance of *Trichomonas vaginalis* and *Trichomonas foetus*; the effects of cortisone and agar on enhancement of severity of subcutaneous lesions in mice. *Parasitology* **57**: 321–334.

JÍROVEC O. & RODOVÁ, HELENA (1940). Ueber die Züchtung der Trichomonaden. *Zentbl. Bakt. ParasitKde.*, I. Abt., Orig. **145**: 351–360.

JOHNSON G. (1942). Physiology of a bacteria-free culture of *Trichomonas vaginalis*. IV. Effect of hydrogen-ion concentration and oxygen tension on population. *J. Parasit.* **28**: 369–379.

JOHNSON G. & TRUSSELL R.E. (1943). Experimental basis for the chemotherapy of *Trichomonas vaginalis* infections. I. *Proc. Soc. exp. Biol. Med.* **54**: 245–249.

JOHNSON G., TRUSSELL, MARGARET & JAHN, FRANCES (1945). Isolation of *Trichomonas vaginalis* with penicillin. *Science, N.Y.* **102**: 126–128.

KARAPETYAN A. (1962). *In vitro* cultivation of *Giardia duodenalis. J. Parasit.* **48**: 337–340.

KIRBY H. (1950). *Materials and methods in the study of Protozoa.* Berkeley & Los Angeles: University of California Press. London: Cambridge University Press.

KOFOID C.A. & MCNEIL, ETHEL (1932). The advantages of Locke's blood medium in the culture of parasitic protozoa of the digestive tract. *Am. J. Hyg.* **15**: 315–317.

KOTT, HANNAH & ADLER S. (1961). A serological study of *Trichomonas* sp. parasitic in man. *Trans. R. Soc. trop. Med. Hyg.* **55**: 333–344.

KUPFERBERG A.B., JOHNSON G. & SPRINCE H. (1948). Nutritional requirements of *Trichomonas vaginalis. Proc. Soc. exp. Biol. Med.* **67**: 304–308.

LAIDLAW P.P., DOBELL C. & BISHOP, ANN (1928). Further experiments on the action of emetine in cultures of *Entamoeba histolytica. Parasitology* **20**: 207–220.

LAMY L. & LAMY H. (1951). Determinisme de la zygose chez *Balantidium coli*, en culture. Action de la température. *C.r. Séanc. Soc. Biol.* **145**: 994–996.

LASH J.J. (1948). Protein hydrolysate-enriched media for the propagation of *Trichomonas vaginalis* (Donné). *Am. J. trop. Med.* **28**: 111–119.

LASH J.J. (1950). A simplified casein hydrolysate-serum medium for the cultivation of *Trichomonas vaginalis. Am. J. trop. Med.* **30**: 641–642.

LEE J.J., AST T.G., HUTNER S. & ALLEN J. (1964). A defined medium for Trichomonads. *J. Parasit.* **50** Suppl.: 20. [Abstract only.]

LEE J.J. & PIERCE S. (1960). *Hypotrichomonas acosta* (Moskowitz) from reptiles. II. Physiology. *J. Protozool.* **7**: 402–409.

LEE J.J., PIERCE S., HUTNER S.H., SMITH B.J. & GURSKI D.R. (1962). Trichomonads from poikilotherms: nutritional and physiological notes. *J. Protozool.* **9**: 445–450.

LEVINE N. (1961). *Protozoan parasites of domestic animals and man.* Minneapolis: Burgess Publishing Company.

LOWE G.H. (1965). A comparison of current laboratory methods and a new semi-solid culture medium for the detection of *Trichomonas vaginalis. J. clin. Path.* **18**: 432–434.

LUMSDEN W.H.R., ROBERTSON D.H.H. & MCNEILLAGE, GILLIAN J.C. (1966). Isolation, cultivation, low temperature preservation and infectivity titration of *Trichomonas vaginalis. Br. J. vener. Dis.* **42**: 145–154.

LYFORD, HELEN S. (1941). Some reactions of a pathogenic flagellate, *Trichomonas foetus*, to environmental changes in bacteria-free cultures. *Am. J. Hyg.* **33** C: 69–87.

LYNCH K.M. (1922). Cultivation of *Trichomonas* from the human mouth, vagina and urine. *Am. J. trop. Med.* **2**: 531–538.

MCENTEGART M.G. (1952). The application of a haemagglutination technique to the study of *Trichomonas vaginalis* infections. *J. clin. Path.* **5**: 275–280.

MEYER E.A. & POPE, BETTY L. (1965). Culture *in vitro* of *Giardia* trophozoites from the rabbit and chinchilla. *Nature, Lond.* **207**: 1417–1418.

NELSON E.C. (1940). An intestinal content culture medium. I. Methods of preparation and use and data obtained in the cultivation of *Balantidium coli* from the pig. *Am. J. trop. Med.* **20**: 731–745.

NELSON E.C. (1943a). Alcohol-preserved tissue-cultivation medium. Methods of preparation and use and results obtained in the cultivation of *Nyctotherus cordiformis. Am. J. Hyg.* **38**: 185–192.

NELSON E.C. (1943b). Cultivation of *Nyctotherus cordiformis. J. Parasit.* **29**: 292–297.

OHIRA T. & NOGUCHI H. (1917). The cultivation of *Trichomonas* of the human mouth (*Tetratrichomonas hominis*). *J. exp. Med.* **25**: 341–347.

OXFORD A.E. (1955). The rumen ciliate Protozoa: their chemical composition, metabolism, requirements for maintenance and culture, and physiological significance for the host. *Expl Parasit.* **4**: 569–605.

PHILLIPS B.P. & REES C.W. (1950). The growth of *Endamoeba histolytica* with live and heat-treated *Trypanosoma cruzi*. *Am. J. trop. Med.* **30**: 185–191.

PIPKIN A.C. (1960). Avian embryos and tissue culture in the study of parasitic Protozoa. II. Protozoa other than *Plasmodium*. *Expl Parasit.* **9**: 167–203.

PLASTRIDGE W.N. (1943). Cultivation of a bacteria-free strain of *Trichomonas foetus*. *J. Bact.* **45**: 196–197. [Abstract only.]

REES C.W. (1927). Balantidia from pigs and guinea-pigs: their viability, cyst production and cultivation. *Science, N.Y.* **66**: 89–91.

REES C.W. (1937). Obtaining bacteria-free pure lines of *Trichomonas foetus* by means of microisolation. *Am. J. Hyg.* **26**: 283–291.

SAMUELS R. (1962). Agar techniques for colonising and cloning trichomonads. *J. Protozool.* **9**: 103–107.

SAMUELS R. & BEIL, ELIZABETH A. (1962). Serum-free medium for axenic culture of trichomonads. *J. Protozool.* **9** Suppl.: 19. [Abstract only.]

SAVEL M.J. (1957). La culture de *Trichomonas vaginalis* Donné, 1837. *C.r. Soc. fr. Gynéc.* **27**: 159–172.

SCHNEIDER M.D. (1942). A new thermostabile medium for the prolonged bacteria-free cultivation of *Trichomonas foetus*. *J. Parasit.* **28**: 428–429.

SCHUMAKER E. (1931). The cultivation of *Balantidium coli*. *Am. J. Hyg.* **13**: 281–295.

SHAFFER J.G., RYDEN F.W. & FRYE W.W. (1949). Studies on the growth requirements of *Endamoeba histolytica*. IV. Further observations on the cultivation of *E.histolytica* and other intestinal protozoa in a clear medium without demonstrable bacterial multiplication. Some modifications and simplifications of the medium. *Am. J. Hyg.* **49**: 127–133.

SPRINCE H. & KUPFERBERG A.B. (1947). The nutrition of Protozoa. I. A simplified medium for the investigation of unknown factors in blood serum essential for the sustained growth of *Trichomonas vaginalis*. *J. Bact.* **53**: 435–439.

SOREL C. (1954). Trois techniques de recherche du *Trichomonas vaginalis*: leur valeurs comparées. *Presse méd.* **62**: 602–604.

SQUIRES S. & MCFADZEAN J.A. (1962). Strain sensitivity of *Trichomonas vaginalis* to Metronidazole. *Br. J. vener. Dis.* **38**: 218–219.

STONE W.S. & REYNOLDS F.H.K. (1939). A practical method of obtaining bacteria-free cultures of *Trichomonas hominis*. *Science, N.Y.* **90**: 91–92.

SUGDEN, BRENDA & OXFORD A.E. (1952). Some cultural studies with holotrich ciliate Protozoa of the sheep's rumen. *J. gen. Microbiol.* **7**: 145–153.

TANABE M. (1925). The cultivation of trichomonads from man, rat and owl. *J. Parasit.* **12**: 101–104.

THOMAS, PATRICIA M. (1964). Some laboratory aspects of *Trichomonas vaginalis*. *J. med. Lab. Technol.* **21**: 46–50.

THOMSON J.G. & ROBERTSON A. (1925). Notes on the cultivation of certain amoebae and flagellates of man, using the technique of Boeck & Drbohlav. *J. trop. Med. Hyg.* **28**: 345–349.

TRAGER W. (1934). The cultivation of a cellulose-digesting flagellate, *Trichomonas termopsidis*, and of certain other termite Protozoa. *Biol. Bull. mar. biol. Lab., Woods Hole* **66**: 182–190.

TRUSSELL R.E. & JOHNSON G. (1941). Physiology of pure culture of *Trichomonas vaginalis*: III. Fermentation of carbohydrates and related compounds. *Proc. Soc. exp. Biol.* **47:** 176–178.

TRUSSELL R.E. & JOHNSON G. (1945). *Trichomonas vaginalis* Donné. Recent experimental advances. *Puerto Rico J. publ. Hlth trop. Med.* **20:** 289–321.

TWOHY D.W. (1961). A continuous flow cultural system for *Tritrichomonas augusta*. *J. Protozool.* 8 Suppl.: 5. [Abstract only.]

TYZZER E.E. (1934). Studies on histomoniasis, or 'blackhead' infection, in the chicken and the turkey. *Proc. Am. Acad. Arts Sci.* **69:** 191–264.

WARREN L.G., KITZMAN W.B. & HAKE, EVELYN (1961). Induced resistance of mice to subcutaneous infection with *Trichomonas gallinae* (Rivolta, 1878). *J. Parasit.* **47:** 533–537.

WENRICH D.H. (1946). Culture experiments on intestinal flagellates. I. Trichomonad and other flagellates obtained from man and certain rodents. *J. Parasit.* **32:** 40–53.

WENRICH D.H. (1947a). Culture experiments on intestinal flagellates. II. Additional observations on flagellates from man, rodents and insect larvae. *J. Parasit.* **33:** 25–28.

WENRICH D.H. (1947b). Culture experiments on intestinal flagellates. III. Species from amphibians and reptiles. *J. Parasit.* **33:** 62–70.

WIRTSCHAFTER S.K. (1954). Giant multinucleated cells in cultures of *Trichomonas vaginalis*. *J. Parasit.* **40:** 100–101.

WITTE J. (1933). Bakterienfreie Züchtung von Trichomonaden aus dem Uterus des Rindes in einfachen Nährböden. *Zentbl. Bakt. ParasitKde.* 1 Abt., Orig. **128:** 188–195.

ZUCKERMAN, AVIVAH (1966). Propagation of parasitic Protozoa in tissue culture and avian embryos. *Ann. N.Y. Acad. Sci.* **139:** 24–38.

CHAPTER 4

AMOEBAE

I. *ENTAMOEBA HISTOLYTICA*

Most of the effort aimed at cultivating intestinal amoebae has been directed at the only pathogen of the group, *Entamoeba histolytica* and a considerable degree of success has been achieved, provided that one is content to allow a population of bacteria to develop alongside the amoebae. Axenic cultures of these amoebae have fairly recently been established, but the process is not easy. For diagnostic purposes, the presence of a mixed bacterial flora does not matter, and the usual practice is to prepare the medium aseptically and then to inoculate a small piece of faecal matter. In this way an assortment of bacterial species is introduced into the medium: if these become so numerous that they threaten to overgrow any amoebae present, a narrow-spectrum antibiotic such as penicillin or streptomycin may be added to control but not eliminate the bacterial flora. Spingarn & Edelman (1952) found that the addition of penicillin G (1,000–2,000 units/ml) or, preferably, streptomycin sulphate (1–2 mg/ml) to the liquid phase helped in the isolation of *E.histolytica* from faeces: Al-Dabagh (1965) used only 532 units/ml of penicillin G. For some research purposes, however, the presence of a motley assortment of bacteria as well as the amoebae cannot be tolerated: if this is so, the amoebae can either be grown in monoxenic culture in association with one known species of bacterium (or sometimes flagellate or tissue cells: see below), or, with some difficulty and in a complex medium, entirely on their own (axenic culture). Methods for both these procedures will be given later in this chapter (pp. 131–141).

In monoxenic cultures of this nature, the effect of various bacterial species upon the amoebae can be studied. It has been found that this effect is considerable—some floras are more conducive to encystment of the amoebae than others, while not all bacterial species are capable of supporting the growth of the rhizopods at all (see Jacobs, 1950b and Dobell, 1952).

Axenic cultures would be, theoretically, the most suitable for studies on the metabolism and physiology of the amoebae, but it is perhaps dubious whether such studies (on amoebae or other organisms) can be regarded as giving a completely true picture of what occurs under natural conditions, since it seems that the process of establishing such cultures may involve considerable selection of the population: consequently, the strain finally established may consist of individuals whose physiology differs considerably from that of the majority of individuals found in a 'wild' strain. This situation arises to a greater or lesser extent in any *in vitro* cultivation technique (and in many *in vivo* ones) and, provided it is borne in mind, by no means negates the value of the results obtained from such studies.

Recently, Neal (1967) has reviewed the whole subject of the *in vitro* cultivation of *E.histolytica* and other species: cultivation in chick embryos and tissue cultures has also been reviewed by Pipkin (1960) and Zuckerman (1966).

1. CLASSICAL METHODS OF CULTIVATING *E.HISTOLYTICA*

Among the earliest media to be used successfully for the cultivation of *E.histolytica* were those based on hen's eggs as a source of protein and other nutrients, often together with serum. *E.histolytica* was first cultivated by Cutler (1918) in an infusion of egg, or of blood, and later Boeck & Drbohlav (1925) obtained growth of *E.histolytica* by accident in a diphasic medium which they were using to cultivate intestinal flagellates. None of these media is in use nowadays.

Dobell & Laidlaw (1926) made a very full study of the different types of egg-serum media which could be produced, using different combinations of slopes made from coagulated horse serum (HS) or from coagulated whole egg in 50 ml Ringer's solution (E) with overlays of horse serum diluted 1:8 with Ringer's solution (hs), or a solution of the albumen from four eggs in 1 l. of Ringer's solution (re). The resulting media were known by the appropriate combinations of the initial letters shown in parentheses above (capital letters refer to the solid slope and lower-case letters to the overlay).

Dobell & Laidlaw found that all 3 species of *Entamoeba* which parasitize man grew much better if a little sterile solid starch was added to the overlay: this is indicated in the 'coded' name of the medium by the addition of the symbols '+S' after the other letters. Rice starch was the best, since the grain size was most suitable. This starch is actively ingested by the amoebae in culture. The presence of a bacterial flora (usually mixed) is essential to growth in this type of medium. These authors obtained the best growth of the 3 'human' species of *Entamoeba* in the medium with a serum slope overlaid with albumen solution containing starch (HSre + S). *E.histolytica* and *E.coli* grew equally well in egg-slope media overlaid with either diluted horse serum or diluted egg albumen, containing starch (Ehs + S and Ere + S). On the other hand *Endolimax nana* was found to grow best in media without starch, notably in egg-slope media with either serum or egg-albumen overlays (Ehs or Ere): Ehs is virtually the same as Boeck & Drbohlav's (1925) LES medium, except that Ringer's solution is used as diluent instead of Locke's (see p. 146 for a detailed description of Ehs).

For general purposes the most suitable medium of those studied by Dobell & Laidlaw seems to be HSre + S (p. 128). *E.histolytica* from man (and *E.invadens* from the snake) grow readily in this medium. Although *E.coli* will also grow in it, this parasite is much more difficult to maintain through serial transfers and under ordinary diagnostic conditions, it is probable that only *E.histolytica* will be present after a few days (this diagnosis should, however, be checked by the examination of stained microscopic preparations of any amoebae found). Neal (1953) successfully grew the free-living *E.moshkovskii* in this medium at 24°c (p. 148).

Dobell & Laidlaw (1926) and later workers have obtained encystment of *E.histolytica* in medium HSre + S: this is apparently dependent on the nature of the bacterial flora present. The subject is a complicated one and those interested are referred to Dobell (1952). The amoebae develop anaerobically in this medium; although the medium is open to the air, the aerobic bacteria present rapidly reduce all the available oxygen (Dobell, 1952: see also Jacobs, 1950a). Dobell & Laidlaw (1926) were able to initiate HSre + S cultures with either trophozoites or cysts, but found that the latter will develop only if they have been allowed to cool from 37°c to room temperature before being inoculated to the warm (37°c) medium.

Dobell & Laidlaw's medium has stood the test of time, and HSre + S is still commonly in use today for routine maintenance of amoebae and for clinical diagnosis. Coupled with one of the 'sterilization' techniques outlined below (p. 136), it can be used to grow *E.histolytica* monoxenically in the presence of a suitable aerobic bacterium: but amoebae will not grow axenically in this medium. Dobell (1942) has described a method for making permanent preparations of amoebae growing in tubes of his media which produces excellent results, and would probably be applicable to other types of media also.

Various modifications of, and additions to, the original media of Boeck & Drbohlav (1925) and Dobell & Laidlaw (1926) have appeared over the years. Most of these are listed in Table 4.1; some are discussed below.

TABLE 4.1. Some media which have been used for the cultivation of
*Entamoeba histolytica**

Author(s)	Date	Designation of medium	Type of medium	Detailed description (if any)
Adler & Foner	1941	—	Monophasic, semi-solid	p. 126
Balamuth	1946	—	Monophasic	p. 126
Boeck & Drbohlav	1925	LES	Diphasic	—
Boeck & Drbohlav	1925	LEA	,,	—
Boeck & Drbohlav	1925	—	,,	—
Cleveland & Collier	1930	Liver infusion	,,	p. 127
Craig	1926	—	Monophasic	—
Cutler	1918	—	,,	—
Cutler	1918	—	Diphasic	—
Diamond	1961	—	Diphasic, axenic	p. 137
Dobell & Laidlaw	1926	HSre+S	Diphasic	p. 128
Drbohlav	1925	—	,,	—
Faust & Russell	1964	—	Diphasic	—
Frye & Meleney	1939	—	,,	—
Hansen & Anderson	1948	—	Monophasic, monoxenic	—
Jones	1946	—	Monophasic	p. 129
Kofoid & McNeil	1932	LEB	,,	—
Nelson	1947	—	Monophasic	p. 130
Pavlova	1938	—	,,	—
Phillips & Rees	1950	—	Monophasic, monoxenic	p. 139
Reeves et al.	1957a	MS-F	,, ,,	p. 140
Sadun et al.	1952	—	,, ,,	—
Shaffer et al.	1949	S-F	,, ,,	—
Shaffer et al.	1953	—	,, axenic	—
Singh et al.	1963	—	Diphasic	—
St John	1932	—	Monophasic	—
Tanabe & Chiba	1928	—	Diphasic	—
Tsuchiya	1934, 1942	SC	Monophasic	—

* Many of these media are suitable for other parasitic amoebae also: see text p. 142.

Cleveland & Collier (1930) found that simple saline solutions of serum (as devised by Craig, 1926) were satisfactory in isolating *E.histolytica* from only a very small proportion of known infected persons (less than 10%). They found that LES was successful in about 25% of cases, and that HSre+S succeeded in about 70% of attempts. They devised a liver infusion-agar medium in which, they claimed, only one failure to isolate occurred in 200 trials (p. 127).

Adler & Foner (1941) developed a semi-solid monophasic medium, analogous to the Noguchi-Wenyon medium for trypanosomatids (p. 22), in which cultures lasted for about 2 weeks, though the population maximum occurred after about 1 week, when subinoculations should preferably be made (p. 126). They (Adler & Foner, 1941) referred to a convenient method of separating *E.histolytica* from *E.coli*, if the 2 are growing together in culture. The culture is inoculated subcutaneously to a rabbit and, when an abscess develops, the amoebae are recovered from it and returned to culture: only *E.histolytica* will have survived. (Presumably antibiotics may be needed to prevent death of the rabbit from septicaemia.)

Balamuth (1946) used a monophasic medium made of egg yolk and liver extract, with added rice starch (p. 126). Initially (Balamuth & Sandza, 1944) egg yolk infusion alone was used, but the addition of liver extract was found to increase growth and to be useful when the medium was used for diagnosis. Hitchcock & Rawson (1946) obtained satisfactory results from this medium containing only 1·6% of dehydrated egg yolk: this is one-ninth of the concentration used by Balamuth.

Jones (1946) obtained satisfactory growth in a medium based on that of Pavlova (1938), but enriched with a proprietary autolysed yeast extract (p. 129).

Nelson (1947) developed a means of preparing media suitable for *E.histolytica* from alcoholic extracts of various fresh tissues (p. 130) or hen's egg yolks. As the extracts may be kept for 2 years or more, it seems that this method might be useful under certain conditions when access to fresh materials such as liver, egg or serum is impossible. Nelson found this medium very good for both isolation of *E.histolytica* (for which purpose he found it better than liver-infusion agar) and for strain maintenance. For isolation, he recommended subinoculating fresh tubes after 24–48 hr, whether or not amoebae were seen in the first tube. For routine maintenance, he recommended making serial transfers after 4–10 days: individual tubes will continue to support amoebae for up to 17 days. All the human parasitic amoebae grew in the first tube inoculated with faeces, but Nelson found that only *E.histolytica* can be successfully transferred to subcultures.

There have been few experimental attempts to identify substances which are essential for, or beneficial to, the amoebae. Andrews *et al.* (1933) found that the numbers of amoebae growing in various diphasic media could be doubled by infusing faecal matter in the overlay of the medium, followed by sterilization by filtration. Dopter & Deschiens (1937, 1938) and Deschiens (1938) thought that human serum was better than horse serum as a constituent of the overlay of diphasic media (in contradiction to Boeck & Drbohlav's observations). They also found that serum from jaundiced patients was better than normal human serum, due to its bilirubin content. DeLamater & Hallman (1947) attempted to produce as simple a medium as possible. They found that deproteinized serum (or a double volume of its dialyzate) diluted with an equal volume of M/15 phosphate buffer (pH 6·8) with added rice starch would support growth in the presence of a mixed bacterial flora: if the amoebae were grown monoxenically this medium was inadequate and partially deproteinized serum (i.e. heated to 100°c for 20 min) had to be substituted. DeLamater & Hallman concluded, therefore, that in the conditions of their cultures there were one or more heat-stable dialyzable components of human serum which were necessary for the growth of E.histolytica.

Nakayama (1958), using a simple basal medium consisting of a slant of 2% agar in Ringer's solution overlaid with 1% sodium citrate in Ringer's solution containing starch, investigated the effect of adding certain substances to the overlay. He found that amoebae (associated with bacteria) could grow in this medium plus any one of the following substances: albumen, glucosamine (a constituent of albumen), gelatin, glycoproteid, phosphoproteid, proteose-peptone and glutathione. These results are somewhat at variance with those reported by Robinson (personal communication*), who found that protein or metaprotein was an essential constituent, without which sustained growth of amoebae (E.histolytica or other species) did not occur. Robinson concluded that the amoebae did not utilize the protein directly, but by the ingestion of bacteria metabolizing the protein: although the bacteria would grow in a medium lacking protein, such bacteria did not provide a suitable substrate for the amoebae. It is possible that the difference between Nakayama's & Robinson's conclusions is due to the different bacteria with which each author was working (cf. the conclusions of Shaffer, Schuler & Key (1958), recorded on p. 133 below).

Latour & Reeves (1965) have shown the need for iron in the diet of E.histolytica, and a study of the effect of various factors in the growth and induction of encystation and excystation of E.histolytica, in culture, including hydrogen-ion concentration and oxidation-reduction potential, has been made by Chang (1942, 1943, 1946).

Geiman & Becker (1953) have devised a method of growing E.histolytica in the presence of bacteria in a perfusion jar; the amoebae and bacteria are

* I am very grateful to Dr G.L. Robinson for allowing me to refer to his unpublished observations.

contained within a small volume (1·75 ml) of medium, separated by a cellophane membrane from a larger volume (70 ml) of the same medium. Details of this method should be sought in the original publication.

Semi-solid medium for
parasitic amoebae
(Adler & Foner, 1941)

MEDIUM

1   Prepare, sterilize and mix aseptically the following in the proportions indicated (by volume):

> 3% agar......................................1 part
> Locke's solution (with 0·1% of glucose, p. 350)....8 parts
> Serum (inactivated; horse, cow, goat or human)....1 part

2   Dispense (aseptically) 5 ml aliquots in test-tubes and add sterile rice starch (see note 2).

TECHNIQUE

The medium should be inoculated with a culture of *Bacillus prodigiosus* a day or two before the amoebae are introduced.

NOTES: (1) *Trichomonas hominis* also grew well in this medium preconditioned by the prior inoculation of *B.prodigiosus*.

(2) Rice starch is added to each tube by means of a sterile wire loop as used for the examination of cultures, dipping the loop first into the overlay and then into the starch: one loopful is enough for each tube. The rice starch is previously spread out in a thin layer in a flat dish, dried in an incubator or dessicator, then placed in small cotton-plugged glass tubes and sterilized by dry heat at 160° (or 180°) c for 1 hr.

Egg yolk-liver extract
medium for parasitic amoebae
(Balamuth, 1946)

MEDIUM

1   Mix 36 g dehydrated egg yolk (see note) with an equal amount of water, add 125 ml 0·8% sodium chloride solution and mix well.

2   Boil the mixture with constant stirring (the presence of some glass

beads in the flask is recommended) or steam it at 80°c for 20 min. Add water if necessary to restore the original volume.

3   Filter through a double layer of muslin or gauze and add 0·8% saline to restore the volume to 125 ml.

4   Autoclave the liquid (15 lb, 20 min).

5   Cool the liquid to below 10°c and filter if it is required to give a clear solution (this is not essential).

6   Add 125 ml M/15 phosphate buffer at pH 7·5*.

7   Make a 5% solution of powdered liver concentrate (e.g. No. 408 of Eli Lilly & Co.) by boiling in water, filtering and autoclaving the solution: add 1 volume of this solution to 9 volumes of the egg yolk solution. (This can be omitted if the medium is not being used for diagnosis.)

8   Autoclave the mixture: it may be stored at 4°c for several months.

TECHNIQUE

Dispense 7–10 ml aliquots in test-tubes and add a loopful of sterile powdered whole rice or rice starch (see note on p. 126). Inoculate and incubate at 37°c; the population of amoebae reaches a maximum after 2–4 days.

NOTE: Fresh egg yolks may be used in preparing this medium in the proportion of 4 hard-boiled yolks suspended in 125 ml of 0·8% saline.

Liver infusion agar medium for parasitic amoebae
(Cleveland & Collier, 1930)

MEDIUM

1   *Composition of base*

> Difco Liver infusion agar (containing an infusion of beef liver, 500 g; peptone, 10 g; sodium chloride, 5 g; and agar, 20 g per pound) . . . . .30 g
> Disodium hydrogen phosphate . . . . .3 g
> Water . . . . .1 l.

2   *Preparation of base*

Dissolve the above by heating in a water-bath, or steaming; dispense into test-tubes, autoclave and allow to set in a slant.

* KH_2PO_4 soln. (9·08 g/l.), 20·5 ml:
  $Na_2HPO_4.2H_2O$ soln. (11·88 g/l.), 104·5 ml.

3 Preparation of overlay

Fresh horse serum is diluted 1:6 with 0·8% saline or Ringer's solution (p. 350).

4 Preparation of final medium

Cover the slopes with overlay and add a loopful of sterile rice starch (see note on p. 126) to each tube.

TECHNIQUE

Inoculate, incubate at 37°c and subinoculate after 48 hr.

NOTES: (1) Cleveland & Collier obtained profuse growth in this medium: encystation of the amoebae occurred. They found it to be almost specific for E.histolytica, other species (except E.gingivalis) failing to survive more than a few transfers (Cleveland & Sanders, 1930).

(2) Kofoid & McNeil (1932) found this medium so rich that overgrowth by Blastocystis and bacteria frequently obliterated the population of amoebae; nowadays the latter hazard could be prevented by the use of narrow-spectrum antibiotics (see p. 120 above).

(3) This medium is available commercially from Difco Laboratories under the name of 'Bacto-Entamoeba medium'.

HSre + S medium for
parasitic amoebae
(Dobell & Laidlaw, 1926)

MEDIUM

1 Base

Horse serum (sterile, inactivated) is poured into sterile cotton-plugged test-tubes to produce a slant about 3–4 cm in length. These tubes are then heated at 80°c in a water bath for 60–70 min, to coagulate the serum: during this process the tubes should be sloped at such an angle that the serum does not cover the whole of the base of the tube. The completed tubes may be incubated at 37°c for 24–48 hr to check their sterility.

2 Overlay

Fresh hen's eggs are cleaned and sterilized and a small hole cut with sterile scissors in the blunt end of the egg: each egg is then inverted over a flask containing sterile Ringer's solution (p. 350) and, by puncturing the narrow end of the egg, the albumen is allowed to run out of the hole and into the flask. The proportion of egg albumen to Ringer's solution is the contents of 4 eggs to 1 l. (If necessary this solution can be sterilized by means of filtration.)

3 Preparation of complete medium

The albumen-Ringer solution is added to the test-tubes containing the coagulated serum in sufficient quantity just to cover the slant. The completed tubes (referred to by Dobell & Laidlaw as 'Boeck tubes') should be incubated at 37°c for 24–48 hr to check their sterility, and may be stored in a refrigerator for a few days (up to 1 week) before use. Just before use, a small amount of sterile rice starch (see note on p. 126) is added to each tube.

TECHNIQUE

For inoculation, a wire loopful of faecal matter is introduced to the bottom of the overlay. The tubes should be warmed to 37°c before inoculation. Incubate at 37°c and examine and subinoculate daily for the first few days: established cultures need be subinoculated only every 2–4 days. Subinoculations are usually made with a pipette: the base of the slope is scraped to dislodge any amoebae, and then 0·5–1 ml of the sediment at the bottom of the tube is transferred to a new tube.

If this medium is being used for diagnosis, it is advisable to subinoculate for 2 or 3 days even if no amoebae are seen, since it may take a few days for reasonable numbers of trophozoites to develop.

'Marmite' medium for
parasitic amoebae
(Jones, 1946)

MEDIUM

1 Buffered saline solution (pH 7·2)
Prepare and mix the following in the proportions indicated:

> Disodium hydrogen phosphate (0·9476% w/v) ......375 ml
> Potassium dihydrogen phosphate (0·9078% w/v)....125 ml
> Sodium chloride (0·9% w/v) ....2,250 ml

Presumably any isotonic phosphate-buffered saline at pH 7·2 would be satisfactory.

2 *Preparation of final medium*
Mix the following proportions by volume:

Buffered saline (1 above)............................8·5
Horse serum ....0·5
'Marmite'* solution (1%)............................1·0

Dispense medium in 10 ml aliquots in test-tubes and add 30 mg rice starch (see note on p. 126) *or* dispense in 300 ml aliquots in Roux culture bottles and add 0·9 g starch. Presumably the medium should be sterilized by filtration: details are not given by the author.

TECHNIQUE

After inoculation, incubate at 37°c.

**Alcoholic extract medium
for parasitic amoebae**
(Nelson, 1947)

MEDIUM

1 Prepare alcoholic extract by adding 100 ml of chopped liver (human, calf, ox, guinea-pig or cat), cat intestine, or hen's egg-yolk, to 900 ml ethanol: the tissues need not be in very small pieces. Allow to infuse for at least 48 hr, shaking the mixture at intervals. These extracts may be stored in stoppered bottles for at least 2 years, and used as required.
2 To prepare 10 culture tubes, take 10 ml of extract and heat it over a water bath to drive off the ethanol. Redissolve the sediment in 20 ml molten 2% agar in 0·5% saline buffered with M/30 phosphate buffer to pH 7·4 (for tissue extract) or 7·6 (egg yolk extract)† and dispense in 2 ml aliquots in test-tubes: these can be autoclaved but if sterile tubes and sterile saline are used and all procedures done aseptically, autoclaving will not be necessary. Allow the agar to set in a sloping position. These slants may be stored in a refrigerator for up to 2 weeks.
3 Add to each tube enough sterile (autoclaved) buffered saline (see above), preferably with 0·025% agar added, to cover the slant of agar.

* 'Marmite' is an autolysed yeast extract made by Marmite Ltd.
† M/30 phosphate buffer: disodium hydrogen phosphate solution, 4·75 g/l. and potassium dihydrogen phosphate solution, 4·53 g/l. Mix in proportions of sodium salt, 82 ml and potassium salt, 18 ml for pH 7·4: 88 ml and 12 ml respectively for pH 7·6.

TECHNIQUE

After inoculation, incubate at 37°C.

2. METHODS FOR THE PRODUCTION OF MONOXENIC AND AXENIC CULTURES OF E. HISTOLYTICA

The earlier methods for producing monoxenic cultures depended upon the destruction of aerobic bacterial contaminants, so that the amoebae grew in association with anaerobes only, followed by the introduction of a single species of aerobic bacterium and the elimination of the anaerobes.

Various methods have been described for destroying aerobic bacteria associated with cysts of *E.histolytica* (see Rao, 1951, for a review): three such techniques are those of Rao (p. 137), Dobell (1952) (p. 136) and Singh *et al.* (1963) (p. 137). In order to complete the sterilization of cysts by removing any anaerobic bacteria which may be present, Dobell (1952) found that it was necessary to cultivate the amoebae for some time in a suitable medium (e.g. Dobell's Ehs + S, see p. 122) to which had been added gentian violet in the proportion of about 0·5 ml of 0·2% sterile aqueous solution to 1 ml of the liquid overlay in the culture tube (Neal, 1952: Dobell used 1 ml of 0·1% solution). Repeated subinoculation of the cultures to fresh medium, containing gentian violet, is necessary for complete sterility to be achieved—perhaps for 20 or more passages. Neal (1952) stressed that subinoculation must be done daily, or the solid phase of the medium absorbs the dye from solution. Similarly, freshly-prepared culture tubes must be used in which the solid slope has not shrunk away from the glass: if this occurs, fluid will flow into the gap and the concentration of dye in it will be reduced rapidly by absorption below the level at which it is effective. Since the amoebae will not grow in simple media without the presence of bacteria, a suitable strain of aerobic bacterium must be added to the culture before the gentian-violet procedure is begun: at the concentration recommended, the gentian-violet will not interfere with the development of the aerobes.

More recently, antibiotics (usually penicillin and streptomycin) have been used in the production of monoxenic strains of *E.histolytica* (see below, modified Shaffer-Frye technique, p. 140). However, the increasing occurrence of antibiotic-resistant strains of bacteria makes it likely that the classical methods may sometimes be essential to success. Also if it is intended to grow the amoebae in the presence of various bacterial strains which are sensitive to antibiotics, the latter cannot be used to remove other undesirable bacteria unless the isolation is carried out in a medium such as that of Shaffer *et al.* (1949).

Hansen & Anderson (1948) reported monoxenic growth of *E.histolytica* and an unidentified bacterium ('organism T') in a medium composed almost entirely of synthetic substances including various minerals, amino-acids, vitamins and cholesterol; yeast nucleic acids and rice starch were included. Praiseworthy as was this attempt to produce a defined medium, since the amoebae were cultivated in the presence of viable, multiplying bacteria, it is uncertain whether in fact these authors were producing a medium which was partially defined with respect to the amoebae or the bacteria. Monoxenic cultures of *E.histolytica* have been grown in conjunction with trypanosomatids as well as bacteria. Cultivated forms of *Trypanosoma cruzi* have been used (Phillips, 1950; Phillips & Rees, 1950: see p. 139), as has an unidentified species of the genus *Crithidia* (Diamond, 1961). Phillips (1950) initiated his cultures with amoebae grown in Shaffer-Frye medium (p. 133) in association with a penicillin-inhibited streptobacillus. He found that, after 4 serial transfers in his medium with added penicillin, the antibiotic could be discontinued without any evidence of the presence of viable bacteria.

The population of amoebae increased approximately 6-fold during 48 hr in Phillips' medium. No multiplication of amoebae occurred in the absence of flagellates, nor in the presence of concentrations of the latter as low as 1 million per ml. Fifty million trypanosomes per ml were adequate, and there was little or no advantage in using richer cultures. Multiplication did occur (to a somewhat smaller extent) in cultures in which the flagellates had been heated to 48°c for 10 min before introducing the amoebae. The flagellates in such cultures were non-motile and incapable of initiating cultures in standard trypanosome media. A slightly higher temperature (50°c for 10 min) destroyed the growth-promoting properties of the suspension.

Phillips (1950) and Phillips & Rees (1950) succeeded in initiating cultures in microtubes (4 × 50 mm) with inoculations of single amoebae: in some cases, up to 200 progeny were present after 72 hours' incubation. Serial transfers from these microtube cultures were not attempted. Such cultures have proved very useful in studying the effect of various agents on the rates of multiplication of the amoebae (see Baernstein, Rees & Bartgis, 1957).

Jacobs (1947) had occasional success in obtaining growth of *E.histolytica* in monoxenic (bacterial) cultures in which the bacterial growth had been suppressed by the use of antibiotics. This approach was further extended by Shaffer and various co-workers in a series of papers (Shaffer & Frye,

1948; Shaffer, Walton & Frye, 1948; Shaffer, Ryden & Frye, 1948 and 1949) which culminated in the development of the Shaffer-Frye (S-F) technique (Shaffer, Ryden & Frye, *loc. cit.* and Shaffer, 1953). This method was then slightly simplified by Reeves *et al.* (1957a), in that 'preconditioning' of their medium (MS-F) by the prior growth in it of bacteria was omitted: amoebae, bacteria and penicillin were all introduced to the medium simultaneously (p. 140). Although the penicillin inhibits the multiplication of the bacilli in this medium, Reeves *et al.* (1957a) found that the presence of viable organisms was essential to the growth of the amoebae: if the bacilli were killed by exposure to air, chemicals or heat (*c.* 60°C), the medium was not suitable. Shaffer, Schuler & Key (1958) further investigated the role of the bacteria in this medium, and concluded that the essential factor was the ingestion by the amoebae of small round bodies excreted or secreted from the bacterium's surface: the production of these bodies was probably induced by the antibiotic present in the medium.

Shaffer (1953), when initiating cultures on the original S-F medium (which he stressed was not intended to be a diagnostic medium) from stools containing either cysts or trophozoites of *E.histolytica*, or from cultures grown with a mixed bacterial flora, recommended the addition of streptomycin (1,500 units/ml) during the first 2 or 3 transfers. Reeves *et al.* (1957a) found that counts of about 100,000 to 500,000 amoebae per tube were obtained after 48–72 hr growth, representing an increase of the order of 10–100 times. They also showed that maltose may be substituted for glucose in MS-F medium, but that most other sugars were unsuitable.

Trypticase is the only suitable peptone for use in S-F (and presumably MS-F) medium, but McDade & Shaffer (1959) modified the bacterial medium so that other peptones could be used.

The MS-F technique was used by Swart & Warren (1962) for the large-scale growth of *E.histolytica*. They used the medium in either 120 ml aliquots in 6 oz screw-capped medical flat (prescription) bottles or aliquots of 600 ml in 32 oz bottles, and obtained yields of about 1.8×10^6 organisms per 6 oz bottle or 19.2×10^6 per 32 oz bottle. Swart & Warren found it preferable to adjust the pH of the medium to 6·5 instead of 7·0.

Subsequently Reeves & Ward (1965) further modified the MS-F technique for use in bulk to produce large numbers of amoebae. The method of bacterial (*Bacteroides symbiosus*) cultivation is the same as that given for MS-F medium (p. 140); the bacteria are harvested by the bulk storage method. The final medium is prepared substantially as before, except that to the basal medium has been added 0·79 g/l. L-cysteine monohydrochloride*, the proportion of horse serum increased to about 13%, and more penicillin (100,000 units/28 ml) used.

The medium was used in aliquots of either 28 ml as a thin layer (c. 3 mm deep) in a Petri dish of 90 mm diameter, or 280 ml in a sterile domestic baking dish of Pyrex glass, measuring 7×11 in. (c. 18×28 cm) and covered with aluminium foil. Chlortetracycline (final concentration 3–4 μg/ml) was sometimes needed to suppress the growth of contaminating *Mycoplasma*.

The dishes, after inoculation with amoebae (about 0·5–2·0 million active trophozoites per Petri dish), were incubated at 36–37°c in a positive pressure anaerobic incubator (constructed from a modified sterilizing oven: details are given in the original paper) under pre-purified commercial nitrogen. The incubator, which contained a beaker of 30% sodium hydroxide to absorb oxygen, etc., was evacuated to about 28 in. (c. 71 cm) of mercury and then filled to 3–5 lb/sq.in. (c. 300 g/cm²) positive pressure with nitrogen: this was repeated twice before the final filling with nitrogen. After 24 or 48 hr incubation, a second similar volume of bacterial suspension, horse serum and penicillin was added to each dish, and the amoebae harvested 24 hr later by centrifugation at $225 \times g$ for 5 min. It was found that all the bacteria could be removed from the amoebae by suitable washing in a mixture of 0·1 M sodium thiomalate (pH 7·0), 1 part and 0·15 M potassium chloride, 9 parts.

Reeves & Ward (1965) obtained from 20–90 million amoebae per Petri dish, representing about 0·6–2·6 million/ml of culture fluid. Production of trophozoites, which can be washed free of the accompanying bacteria, on this scale holds out great promise for the making of biochemical or serological analyses, etc., of the trophozoites, which these authors have already commenced.

An approach to the problem of growing axenic cultures of *E.histolytica* was made by Shaffer, Sienkiewicz & Washington (1953) Reeves, *et al.* (1957b), Baernstein *et al.* (1957) and Diamond (1961), all of whom succeeded in growing *E.histolytica* in media containing either whole, living chick embryo tissue cells or various fractions of such cells. The method used by Shaffer *et al.* is given on p. 141. Reeves *et al.* (1957b), using a modification of the Shaffer-Frye medium (see p. 133), succeeded in growing *E.histolytica* in the presence of a centrifuged ($700 \times g$ for 15 min), but not frozen, 50% extract of 10-day-old chick embryo without added cells: the extract itself did, however, contain a few intact erythrocytes and

---

* Reeves *et al.* (1959) had reported that cysteine (0·79 g/l.) added to the basal medium in the MS-F technique, had no significant effect upon the growth of the amoebae.

other cells which resembled leucocytes and so the culture could not conclusively be stated (as the authors pointed out) to be axenic. The active principle in the chick embryo extract was somewhat reduced in potency, though not destroyed, by freezing and thawing. It was completely destroyed or removed by heating to 70°c for 10 min and by high-speed centrifugation at 3,000 × g for 15 min. In the same year, Baernstein *et al.* (1957) obtained cultures of *E.histolytica* in a medium resembling that of Shaffer, Sienkiewicz & Washington (1953) but without the addition of whole chick embryo cells. They were unable to detect any intact cells in their chick embryo extract after centrifugation for 2–3 min at 200 × g. Since, however, Reeves *et al.* (1957b) had found that centrifugation for 15 min at 700 × g failed to remove all intact cells from their chick embryo extract, it is perhaps doubtful whether the medium of Baernstein *et al.* was in fact entirely free from cells. Baernstein and his colleagues used microcultures in tubes measuring about 2 × 55 mm, inoculated with a single trophozoite isolated by micromanipulation. Best results were obtained from a mixture of equal parts of horse serum, water and the supernatant fluid from a suspension of six 9–10-day-old chick embryos ground up in 9 ml Hanks's saline and centrifuged as above: growth rates of around 11·5 generations in 100 hr were obtained in these microcultures. Baernstein *et al.* experimented with the addition of various substances to this medium: their original paper (1957) should be consulted for details of these experiments.

The first unequivocally axenic culture of a species of *Entamoeba* seems to have been obtained by Stoll (1957a, b), who succeeded in growing *Entamoeba invadens*, a pathogenic parasite of snakes, in a medium which was undoubtedly free of any intact cells except the amoebae themselves. As its natural host is a poikilothermic vertebrate, *E.invadens* can be cultivated at room temperature. Stoll initiated his cultures with *E.invadens* which was growing in a serum-saline mixture containing a piece of sterile, fresh liver (p. 149). Stoll maintained strains in this cell-free medium for over 5 years by transferring the amoebae to fresh tubes on average every 23 days (range 4–55 days).

Diamond (1960) has extended this work and developed a medium based on that in which he (Diamond, 1957) cultivated trichomonads. In this medium he has successfully grown *E.invadens* and *E.terrapinae* (also a parasite of reptiles). Diamond initiated these cultures from monoxenic cultures of the amoebae in the presence of *T.cruzi* (Phillips' method, see p. 139). The flagellates disappeared from the culture between the second and third transfers. He also succeeded in establishing clones of *E.invadens* in culture by inoculating single trophozoites to micro-cultures of the above medium (including agar) and transferring their progeny to ordinary, macrocultures (with agar) after 1 week: subsequently, these clone cultures were handled by his standard method (p. 139).

A slightly simpler medium for axenic growth of *E.invadens* was developed by McConnachie (1962): in this a dried ox-liver digest is used instead of serum, and the whole medium can be autoclaved.

E.histolytica is more demanding in its nutritional requirements than either *E.invadens* or *E.terrapinae*, and cannot be grown axenically in the media mentioned above. Diamond (1961) has, however, succeeded in growing *E.histolytica* axenically in a diphasic medium supplemented with chick embryo extract which, since it is centrifuged at $1,000 \times g$ for 30 min and frozen (or, in some cases, boiled), is unlikely to contain any viable, intact cells (p. 137). Diamond initiated these cultures with cysts collected from cultures of *E.histolytica* grown on Phillips' medium (p. 139) in association with a species of *Crithidia* and washed in dilute hydrochloric acid to kill the flagellates.

Diamond (1961) found that the amoebae multiplied 3- or 4-fold during 72 hr, and Jackson & Stoll (1964), using this medium, reported 5- to 10-fold increases after 1 week's growth. Diamond found that heated embryo extract was equally satisfactory, thus demonstrating conclusively that the presence of viable intact chick embryo cells was not a prerequisite of successful growth of the amoebae in this medium. Jackson & Stoll (1964) reported that, although embryo extract and the vitamin mixture were beneficial, neither was essential.

Jackson & Stoll (1964) attempted to obtain axenic cultures of *E.histolytica* in an enriched version of Stoll's medium for axenic growth of *E.invadens* (p. 149), but attained only limited success: *E.histolytica* rarely survived more than 1 or 2 weekly subcultures, the longest survival obtained being for 7 subcultures with population increases of about 2- or 3-fold.

Methods for 'sterilizing' cysts of *E.histolytica*
Dobell (1952)

1   The cysts are washed several times in sterile half-strength Ringer's solution (p. 350): sterile water can also be used.

2   The cysts are then suspended in sterile acriflavine solution (0·1% in either water or Ringer's solution) and placed in a refrigerator at 2–10°c (preferably the former) for at least 1 week and preferably 2.

3   Finally, the cysts are washed several times, as above. Dobell conducted the washing procedures by allowing the cysts to settle from the solution

under the influence of gravity alone. The mature cysts are resistant to acriflavine under these conditions, but immature cysts (and, of course, trophozoites) are killed.

Rao (1951)

1 Cysts are concentrated and washed in sterile water three times, with centrifugation at 1,500 rev/min for 10 min.
2 The cysts are suspended in 10 ml sterile mercuric chloride solution (0·002% aq.) for 45 min.
3 After washing again in sterile water, the cysts are suspended in sterile potassium permanganate solution (0·02% aq.) for 15 min.
4 After 2 further washes in water, the cysts are suspended in sterile acriflavine solution (0·02% aq.) overnight (for about 16 hr).
5 Finally, the cysts are washed twice in sterile normal saline.

All these procedures are performed at room temperature. Rao claimed that this freed the cysts of all bacterial contaminants but Neal (1952) found that the spores of anaerobes were not destroyed.

Singh et al. (1963)

1 Wash about 1 g faeces repeatedly (by centrifugation and resuspension) in sterile water.
2 Re-suspend the final deposit in 2% hydrochloric acid solution and leave at room temperature for 48 hr (Robinson, personal communication, used 24 hr).
3 Wash the deposit several times in 0·85% sodium chloride solution. The cysts can then be inoculated to culture tubes or stored in saline at 4°c for up to 10 days.

Axenic cultivation of *E.histolytica*
(Diamond, 1961; Jackson & Stoll, 1964)

MEDIUM

1 *Nutrient broth*

Tryptose (Difco) . . . . .1·0 g
Trypticase (Baltimore Biological Laboratory) . . . . .1·0 g
Yeast extract (Baltimore Biological Laboratory) . . .1·0 g
Glucose . . . . .0·5 g
L-Cysteine hydrochloride . . . . .0·1 g
L-Ascorbic acid . . . . .0·02 g
Sodium chloride . . . . .0·5 g

Potassium dihydrogen phosphate...............0·08 g
Dipotassium hydrogen phosphate (anhyd.).......0·08 g
Water ....80 ml
Resazurin (0·05% aqueous) ....0·02 ml

Adjust pH to 7·2 with N NaOH solution.

2   *Base*

Nutrient broth (as above) with agar 2% (w/v): boil to dissolve, place 4 ml aliquots in screw-capped 16×125 mm tubes, autoclave (15 lb, 10 min). This base can be stored in a refrigerator.

3   *Chick embryo extract* (see also p. 345)

Eleven to twelve-day-old embryos are collected aseptically and, after removing the eyes and beak, cut into 2 or 3 pieces and weighed. The pieces are then quickly frozen by immersion, in a suitable container, in a dry ice-alcohol mixture and placed in a refrigerator for 1 hr. After this, 3 ml sterile, chilled buffered saline* are added per gram of tissue and allowed to act for 96 hr at 3°C.

The extract is then filtered through cheesecloth and centrifuged at 0°C for 30 min at $1,000 \times g$. The supernatant liquid is collected, distributed in 10 ml aliquots in screw-capped tubes, quickly frozen in a dry ice-alcohol bath and stored at -22°C. This is referred to as $CEEM_{25}$ (chick embryo extract mild, 25%).

Alternatively, prepare an extract by pouring boiling buffered saline on to the weighed pieces of embryo (3 ml/g), boil them for 2 min, cool and refrigerate at 3°C for 24 hr. Subsequently collect and store the supernatant as outlined above. This is referred to as $CEEH_{25}$ (H=heated).

4   *Overlay*

Nutrient broth.............1 volume
Water ....3 volumes
Agar........................0·05%

Autoclave (15 lb, 10 min).

5   *Vitamin mixture* from tissue-culture medium NCTC 109 (p. 351).

* Buffered saline, pH 6·8:

Sodium chloride...........................5 g/l.
KH_2PO_4...................................1·6 g/l.
Na_2HPO_4 (anhyd.).........................1·6 g/l.

6   *Preparation of final medium*
One week before the medium is required, melt the base in each tube, add to it 1 ml horse serum (sterile and inactivated at 56°c for 30 min) and allow to reset in a slope. Then add to each tube 3·25 ml overlay and replace in the refrigerator for 1 week.

TECHNIQUE

Immediately before use, add to each tube (after allowing it to reach room temperature) 1·5 ml chick embryo extract (3 above) and 0·25 ml vitamin mixture (5 above). Bring to 37°c to remove air and inoculate: incubate at 37°c (Jackson & Stoll: Diamond recommended 35°c).

Penicillin G (250 units/ml overlay) and dihydrostreptomycin sulphate (0·25 mg/ml overlay) can be used if necessary to free cultures of bacterial concomitants. Initially, subinoculations should be made at varying intervals of from 1–7 days depending on the rate of multiplication of the amoebae: when the cultures become established, subinoculations are made alternately at intervals of 72 and 96 hr, by transferring 0·5–1·5 ml amounts from the lower part of the culture tube.

Monoxenic cultivation of
E.histolytica with *T.cruzi*
(Phillips & Rees, 1950)

MEDIUM

1   *T.cruzi* is cultivated at 24–25°c in Johnson's diphasic medium (an earlier version of the medium of Tobie *et al.* described on p. 32; the latter would certainly be equally suitable. See Table 1.2 for reference to Johnson's medium).
2   A heavy growth of flagellates (*c.* 50 million per ml) in the overlay of Johnson's medium is mixed with a 0·3% solution of sodium thioglycollate in physiological saline in the proportion of 4 parts of trypanosome culture to one part of thioglycollate and dispensed in test-tubes.

TECHNIQUE

The tubes of medium are inoculated with amoebae (with bacterial associates suitably removed), sealed with petroleum jelly and incubated at 37°c. Subinoculations are made after 48 hr.

Modified Shaffer–Frye technique (MS-F)
for monoxenic culture of *E.histolytica*
(Reeves *et al.*, 1957a)

MEDIUM

1 *Basal medium*

Trypticase (Baltimore Biological Laboratory)........20 g/l.
Glucose ....10 g/l.
Sodium chloride...............................2·5 g/l.
Dipotassium hydrogen phosphate 3H₂O..........2·0 g/l.
Thiomalic acid (= mercaptosuccinic acid, Eastman)...1·5 g/l.

The thiomalic acid is dissolved in water and approximately neutralized with sodium hydroxide solution before adding the other ingredients (a 10-fold concentrated solution of thiomalic acid and the salts can be prepared and stored in a refrigerator for several weeks).

This medium is dispensed in 12 ml aliquots in screw-capped 16 × 125 mm tubes and autoclaved (15 lb, 10 min). With the caps tightly closed, such tubes may be stored in the refrigerator for up to 1 week.

2 *Bacterial culture*

Bacteroides symbiosus* is grown at 37°C in the basal medium (1 above) *plus* 0·2% yeast extract: this medium must be freshly made twice weekly. Cultures can either be grown in test-tubes and subinoculated daily with 0·6 ml amounts from the previous day's culture, or they can be grown in large volume and the bacteria harvested and stored, as follows. Flasks containing from 400 to 800 ml of basal medium plus 0·2% yeast extract are inoculated with 2–5% of their volume of a flourishing 24 hr-old bacterial culture which has been transferred daily for several days. Sixteen to eighteen hours later, the bacteria are harvested by centrifugation, washed twice with normal saline containing 0·02 M sodium thiomalate and stored under 0·1 M sodium thiomalate in a refrigerator for up to 3 months: exposure to air must be avoided. For use, the bacteria are re-suspended in the thiomalate solution and an appropriate amount (see below) added to the amoebic culture.

TECHNIQUE

To each screw-capped tube containing 12 ml basal medium, is added 0·1–0·5 ml sterile horse serum, 5,000 units of penicillin in a small volume

---

* This Gram-negative anaerobic streptobacillus is available from the American Type Culture Collection, 209 M. Street, N.W., Washington 6, D.C., U.S.A. (Reeves *et al.*, 1957a).

of saline, 2 ml of *B.symbiosus* culture or an equivalent amount of washed stored bacteria (see 2 above) and an inoculum containing *E.histolytica*. The tubes are incubated in a slanted position at 37°c for 48–72 hr, when subinoculation of about 5,000–10,000 amoebae (about 0·5 ml) should be made to fresh tubes.

Monoxenic culture of *E.histolytica* with chick embryo cells
(Shaffer, Sienkiewicz & Washington, 1953)

MEDIUM

1 *Composition*

Hanks's saline (p. 350) without bicarbonate.....22·5 ml
Normal horse serum ....25·0 ml
Chick embryo extract (2a below) ....1·5 ml
Penicillin G....................2,500 units in 1·0 ml
Phenol red TC (Difco Laboratories)............0·1 ml
Chick embryo cells (2b below) ....5·0 ml

2 *Preparation of components*

(a) The chick embryo extract (EE 50) is prepared from crushed 10-day-old embryos, extracted for 1 hr in an equal volume of Hanks's saline at 4°c, and centrifuged. The supernatant is then deep-frozen, thawed and recentrifuged before storage in a deep-freeze (see p. 345).

(b) Just before use, sufficient ground-up 9–11-day-old chick embryo to give a 10% suspension is added to the medium. Various chick embryo tissues were used instead of ground whole embryo; embryonic liver cells were found to be the most active: using them, amoebae multiplied approximately 13-fold in 72 hr. (These authors obtained no multiplication of amoebae in the absence of fresh intact chick tissue cells.)

TECHNIQUE

Two millilitres aliquots of medium in test-tubes are incubated in an anaerobic jar at 37°c. (Rubber-stoppered tubes can be used without an anaerobic jar, but are less satisfactory.) Subinoculations to fresh medium are made every 48–72 hr, by transferring about 0·2–0·25 ml from the positive cultures.

II. OTHER SPECIES OF AMOEBAE

1. PARASITES OF MAN

Many of the media already described as suitable for *E.histolytica* will also support the growth of other parasitic amoebae (Table 4.2). In many cases where other species are not specifically mentioned, it is likely that they might grow but have not been tried. The non-pathogenic amoebae parasitizing man are, in general, less readily cultivated than is *E.histolytica*, on the media presently available. Media which have been mentioned as being able to support growth of these amoebae for more than a few serial transfers are listed below (for the purpose of this chapter, *Dientamoeba fragilis* is regarded as an amoeba).

TABLE 4.2. Some media which have been used for the cultivation of parasitic amoebae of man other than *Entamoeba histolytica*.

Author(s)	Date	Designation of medium	Species	Type of medium	Detailed description (if any)
Balamuth	1946	—	*D.fragilis, E.nana, I.buetschlii*	Monophasic	p. 126
Boeck & Drbohlav	1925	LES	*D.fragilis, E.coli, E.nana, I.buetschlii*	Diphasic	—
Cleveland & Collier	1930	—	*D.fragilis*	Diphasic	p. 144
Cleveland & Collier	1930	Liver infusion	*E.gingivalis*	,,	p. 127
Culbertson *et al.*	1965	—	*Hartmanella*	Plate	p. 145
Dobell & Laidlaw	1926	Ehs	*E.nana*	Diphasic	p. 146
Dobell & Laidlaw	1926	Ehs+S	*D.fragilis, E.coli*	,,	—
Dobell & Laidlaw	1926	Ere	*E.nana*	,,	—
Dobell & Laidlaw	1926	HSre+S	*E.coli* (?), *E.gingivalis, D.fragilis*	,,	p. 128
Drbohlav	1925	—	*E.coli, E.gingivalis*	,,	—
Jacobs	1953	LER	*D.fragilis*	,,	—
Kofoid & McNeil	1932	LEB	*E.nana, I.buetschlii*	,,	—
Shaffer, Ryden & Frye	1949	S-F	*E.coli*	Monophasic, monoxenic	—

(1) Boeck & Drbohlav's LES can support *Iodamoeba buetschlii*, *Endolimax nana* and *Dientamoeba fragilis* ('easily maintained' according to St John, 1926). Kasprzak (1965) found that *E.coli* also grew in it.

(2) Drbohlav's modifications of Boeck & Drbohlav's media supported growth of *E.coli* and *E.gingivalis* (the latter grew particularly well on Drbohlav's heated blood-agar base with albumen-Ringer's solution overlay).

(3) HSre + S (p. 128) supported *E.coli*, *E.gingivalis* and *Dientamoeba fragilis* (see Dobell, 1940): *E.coli*, at least, grows in it less readily than does *E.histolytica* (see also Dobell, 1936).

(4) Cleveland's liver infusion agar (p. 127) supported *E.gingivalis*, but less well than *E.histolytica* (Cleveland & Sanders, 1930).

(5) Kofoid & McNeil's LEB is said to support growth of *I.buetschlii* and *E.nana* (at least for short periods).

(6) Balamuth's egg yolk–liver extract medium (p. 126) supported growth of *E.nana*, *I.buetschlii* and *D.fragilis*, but they grew less well than *E.histolytica* did. *E.coli* could sometimes be grown in this medium.

(7) Shaffer & Frye's S-F medium (p. 133). According to Shaffer, Ryden & Frye (1949), this medium is capable of supporting the growth of *E.coli* in addition to *E.histolytica* but not *E.nana*: presumably this is true also of MS-F medium (p. 140).

Some media have been designed or used more-or-less specifically for amoebae of man other than *E.histolytica*: these are described below.

Dobell & Laidlaw (1926) found that, unlike the three species of *Entamoeba* which parasitize man, *Endolimax nana* grew better in media to which no starch was added. They obtained best growth of *E.nana* in 2 media referred to as Ehs and Ere, following Dobell's scheme outlined earlier (p. 121). Details of the preparation of Ehs are given on p. 146: these can readily be adapted to the production of Ere if required by substituting the overlay described on p. 128 for Hsre + S. The medium is essentially similar to Boeck & Drbohlav's LES.

Dientamoeba fragilis was found by Cleveland & Collier (1930) to grow well in a diphasic medium described on p. 144 below. Brug (1936) cultivated this amoeba in Dobell's HShs (p. 121), and found that the addition of a few milligrams of calcium carbonate to each tube improved growth, presumably because of its effect in reducing acidity.

Dobell (1940) grew this amoeba-flagellate readily in his HSre + S (p. 128) or Ehs + S (i.e. Ehs as described on p. 146, with the addition of solid rice starch to the overlay). Dobell maintained the cultures at 37–38°c, and subinoculated to fresh tubes at weekly intervals. He found that *D.fragilis* did not survive in the presence of *Blastocystis*.

Jacobs (1953) established *D.fragilis* in monoxenic culture in a medium which he refers to as Locke-egg-rice (LER) medium. The details of the medium are not given: presumably it was a modification of LES (Table 4.1) in which the overlay was simply Locke's solution with added rice starch. The anaerobic bacterium *Clostridium perfringens* was inoculated into this medium and allowed to develop for 24 hr before introducing the amoeba-flagellates. Penicillin (200 units), streptomycin (2 mg) and sodium sulpha-diazine (0·1 mg) were added per ml of overlay for the first 7 serial transfers to inhibit the development of bacteria other than *Cl.perfringens*. After the seventh transfer, these substances were omitted and the culture was continued monoxenically. *D.fragilis* would not grow in the presence of certain other single strains of bacterium, nor in strictly axenic cultures. The normally free-living amoeba *Hartmanella* (=*Acanthamoeba*) has recently been suspected of being occasionally an accidental but pathogenic parasite of man (Fowler & Carter, 1965). Culbertson *et al.* (1965) have described a culture medium suitable for isolating this amoeba from mammalian tissues or tissue fluids as well as from soil samples, throat swabs, etc. Details of this medium are given below (p. 145), together with details of their 'maintenance media'. The latter are richer, and heavier growth of the amoebae is obtained: they cannot, however, be used for isolation since contaminating bacteria, usually present in the suspect material, might overgrow the amoebae in spite of the use of antibiotics. Two such maintenance media have been described, one solid and one liquid. The solid medium the authors found 'desirable particularly to facilitate recovery of bacteria-free amoebae.'

Medium for *Dientamoeba fragilis*
(Cleveland & Collier, 1930)

MEDIUM

1 *Base*

> Loeffler's dehydrated beef serum (beef blood serum, 3 parts
>   and gluose broth, 1 part) ....80 g
> Water ....1 l.

Dispense in test-tubes and heat to 80°c (in a water-bath) to coagulate.

2 *Overlay*

> Horse serum...................................1 volume
> Ringer's solution (p. 350) or 0·8% saline ....6 volumes

This medium must be prepared aseptically.

Method for parasitic *Hartmanella*
(Culbertson *et al.*, 1965)

MEDIUM FOR ISOLATION

1 *Composition of base*

> Agar...........................3 g
> Sodium chloride...............1·7 g
> Water ....100 ml

2 *Bacterial culture*

Aerobacter aerogenes is grown on slopes of Trypticase Soy Agar (Baltimore Biological Laboratory). After 16–20 hr growth, the bacteria are washed from the surface of the agar with, and collected in, Trypticase Soy Broth (Baltimore Biological Laboratory). The suspension is adjusted to contain about 18×10^9 bacteria per ml. Part of the bacterial suspension is placed in a sealed ampoule and immersed in a water bath at 65°c for 30 min to kill the bacteria. The killed suspension may be stored at 4°c.

3 *Antibiotics*

Neomycin sulphate (Merck, Sharp & Dohme), 0·56% aqueous solution; Nystatin (Squibb), aqueous suspension of 1,500 units/ml.

4 *Preparation of complete isolation medium*

The agar (1 above) is melted and allowed to cool in a water bath to 56°c. The other ingredients (2 and 3 above) are heated to 56°c and the following mixture prepared:

> 3% Agar in 1·7% saline........100 ml
> Killed bacterial suspension ....5 ml ⎫
> Neomycin.....................5 ml ⎬ Mixed before
> Nystatin suspension.............5 ml ⎪ addition
> Water ....85 ml ⎭

Eight millilitres aliquots of the complete medium are poured into Petri dishes (100 mm diameter). After setting, the dish is inverted with one edge slightly raised to allow evaporation of excess water (this must be done aseptically). The plates are then inoculated with about 0·05 ml of living bacterial suspension: this is spread over an area of about 25–40 mm diameter in the centre of the plate. The plate surface is again allowed to dry at room temperature (or overnight at 4°c). Such plates may be stored for up to 3 days.

TECHNIQUE FOR ISOLATION

Small drops of fluid or pieces of tissue are placed in the centre of the bacterial area. The temperature of incubation is not given but is presumably between 20°c and 30°c (see Neff, 1957). The plates are examined microscopically through the cover of the dish with a 5× or 10× objective for the following 4–5 days, or until amoebae are seen migrating radially outwards on the surface of the agar. They can then be transferred by means of a wire loop to one of the richer maintenance media described below.

MEDIA FOR MAINTENANCE

1 *Preparation of solid maintenance medium*

This consists of double-strength Trypticase Soy Agar (Baltimore Biological Laboratory) to which is added an equal volume of solution containing antibiotics in the concentrations recommended above (4): killed *Ae.aerogenes* suspension is spread on the solid agar in Petri dishes (this is more satisfactory than incorporating the killed bacteria in the agar). Cultures have been initiated on this medium with a single amoeba isolated from a plate of the same medium.

2 *Preparation of liquid maintenance medium*

This is prepared from double-strength Trypticase Soy Broth (Baltimore Biological Laboratory), dispensed in 40 ml aliquots in 125 ml Erlenmeyer (conical) flasks to which is added an equal volume of solution containing the antibiotics and killed bacteria (in the same concentrations as before—4 above).

TECHNIQUE FOR MAINTENANCE

After a few transfers, antibiotics can be omitted if the cultures are now free of viable bacteria. Some strains of *Hartmanella* are able to grow without the presence of dead bacteria, others are not: encystment may occur in the maintenance media, particularly with strains of the latter type.

Ehs medium for *Endolimax nana*
(Dobell & Laidlaw, 1926)

MEDIUM

1 *Base*

Sterilize the outside of 4 hen's eggs and break them aseptically into a sterile flask containing 50 ml of Ringer's solution (p. 350) and some glass beads. Shake the mixture and dispense it into sterile cotton-plugged test-tubes, filling each to about one-third of its capacity. Place the tubes in a water bath at an angle to produce a suitable slant about 3–4 cm long and heat at 80°c for 60–70 min to coagulate the mixture. The completed tubes may be incubated at 37°c for 24–48 hr to check their sterility.

2 *Overlay*

Horse serum (inactivated) is diluted with 8 times its volume of Ringer's solution. If necessary, this mixture may be sterilized by filtration, but if the Ringer's solution has been previously autoclaved and the serum collected and handled aseptically, this should not be necessary.

3 *Preparation of final medium*

Add the horse serum-Ringer's solution mixture to the tubes in sufficient quantity just to cover the slope and incubate to check sterility. These tubes may be stored in a refrigerator for up to 1 week before use.

TECHNIQUE

Allow the tubes to warm up to 37°c before inoculation and incubate them at 37°c. Examination, subinoculation, etc., are carried out as described under HSre + S medium (p. 128).

2. PARASITES OF ANIMALS OTHER THAN MAN

Very little work has been done on the cultivation of parasitic amoebae which do not infect man (Table 4.3), with the exception of axenic cultivation of *Entamoeba invadens* by Stoll (1957a, b) and Jackson & Stoll (1964), and of that species and *E.terrapinae* by Diamond (1960). This work has been discussed above (p. 135). *E.invadens* grows readily in Dobell & Laidlaw's (1926) HSre + S medium (p. 128). Cleveland & Sanders (1930) reported that a species of *Entamoeba* from the tortoise grew in their liver-infusion agar (p. 127).

Barret & Smith (1924, 1926) and Smith & Barret (1928) cultivated a variety of parasitic amoebae from reptiles, amphibia and insects in simple dilutions of inactivated human serum (usually 10%) in 0·5% saline. Warhurst (1967) has grown *Endolimax blattae* of the cockroach in a di-phasic medium consisting of a horse serum slant overlaid with 0·5% saline or with 5% horse serum in 0·5% saline: better growth was obtained when starch was added. All amoebae of poikilothermic animals should,

TABLE 4.3. Some media which have been used for the cultivation of parasitic amoebae of animals other than man.

Author(s)	Date	Designation of medium	Species	Type of medium	Detailed description (if any)
Barret & Smith	1924, 1926	⎱—	Various, from poikilotherms	Monophasic	—
Smith & Barret	1928	⎰			
Diamond	1960	—	*E.invadens, E.terrapinae*	Monophasic, axenic	p. 149
Dobell & Laidlaw	1926	HSre+S	*E.moshkovskii*	Diphasic	p. 128
Dobell & Laidlaw	1926	HSr+S	,,	,,	—
Jones	1946	—	,,	Monophasic	p. 129
McConnachie	1962	—	*E.invadens*	Monophasic, axenic	—
Neal	1953	—	*E.moshkovskii*	Monophasic	—
Stoll	1957a, b	—	*E.invadens*	Monophasic, axenic	p. 149
Warhurst	1967	—	*Endolimax blattae*	Diphasic	—

of course, be cultivated at temperatures in the region of 25–28°c, though Warhurst (1967) found that *Endolimax blattae* grew also at 37°C.

The free-living *Entamoeba moshkovskii* has been cultivated by Neal (1953) in horse serum (1 volume) and Ringer's solution buffered to pH 7·2 (8 volumes), with added starch; in Dobell & Laidlaw's (1926) HSr+S medium, a slope of coagulated horse serum overlaid with Ringer's solution and added starch; and in Jones' (1946) 'Marmite' medium (p. 129), including starch. All cultures should be kept at about 24°C. Neal found that *E.moshkovskii* would also grow in richer media such as Dobell & Laidlaw's (1926) Ehs+S and HSre+S (p. 128), but encystment occurred more frequently in the poorer media. For isolation, the 'Marmite' medium was best.

It is probable that other species of parasitic amoebae would grow in many of the media described in this chapter. This is particularly likely to be true of the species of *Entamoeba* living in various animals other than man, which belong to the same morphological type as *E.histolytica*.

E.invadens has been grown in chick embryos: see the reviews by Pipkin (1960) and Zuckerman (1966). Particularly interesting is the work of Meerovitch (1961), who infected isolated chick embryo intestine, growing *in vitro*, with *E.invadens*: the amoebae invaded the intestinal wall but did not give rise to characteristic lesions because, Meerovitch suggested, of the absence of bacteria.

Medium for axenic
E.invadens and *E.terrapinae*
(Diamond, 1960; Jackson & Stoll, 1964)

MEDIUM

1 *Composition*

Trypticase (Baltimore Biological Laboratory).....2·0 g
Yeast extract (Baltimore Biological Laboratory)...1·0 g
Maltose.......................................0·5 g
L–Cysteine hydrochloride ....0·1 g
L–Ascorbic acid..............................0·02 g
Potassium dihydrogen phosphate..............0·08 g
Dipotassium hydrogen phosphate (anhyd.).......0·08 g
Water to make...............................90 ml

2 *Preparation*

Dissolve the above ingredients in the water, adjust the pH to 7·0–7·2 with
N NaOH solution, autoclave (15 lb, 10 min): when cool, add 10 ml
horse or sheep serum (inactivated at 56°c for 30 min). Dispense in 10 ml
aliquots in screw-capped tubes and store at 4°c until used.

TECHNIQUE

For initial isolation the medium must be used with the addition of 0·05%
agar for at least the first 7 transfers (at fortnightly intervals): subsequently,
transfers are made weekly by subinoculating 1 ml amounts to new tubes.
Incubation is at room temperature.

E.invadens
(Stoll, 1957a, b; Jackson & Stoll, 1964)

MEDIUM

1 *Heat-stable portion* (A)

Liver infusion broth (50% w/v) ....36·0 ml
Mucin, 1701-W (Wilson) granular: supernatant
   solution of 0·5% suspension................27·0 ml
Trypticase (Baltimore Biological Laboratory), 2%
   solution ....22·5 ml
Sodium chloride, 10% solution...............4·5 ml

Adjust pH to 7·2–7·3 with N sodium hydroxide solution, and autoclave.

2 *Heat-labile portion* (B)

Raw liver extract (chilled acid infusion sterilized
by Seitz filtration: p. 257) ....25% w/v

3 *Preparation of final medium*

Place aliquots of 7·0 ml of portion A and 1·0 ml of portion B in 16 ×
150 mm test-tubes, heat to 56°c to remove air and then cool.

TECHNIQUE

Inoculate and incubate at room temperature, sealing the tubes with
petroleum jelly.

NOTES: (1) Stoll found that screw-capped tubes could be used instead of
open tubes sealed with petroleum jelly, but were perhaps less satisfactory.
(2) Commercially frozen raw chicken livers were a suitable source of
both the broth and the raw liver extract.

III. CHOICE OF A SUITABLE MEDIUM

Several media have been described in detail in this chapter for use with
E.histolytica; it remains only to consider their respective uses.

For routine diagnosis and maintenance of strains as teaching material,
there is probably little to choose between Dobell's HSre + S (p. 128) and
Cleveland's liver-infusion agar media (p. 127). Cleveland & Collier (1930)
claimed that the latter was the more sensitive for diagnosis, but Kofoid
& McNeil (1932) found it so rich that amoebae were often overgrown by
the flourishing bacterial population.

The main use of Adler's & Foner's semi-solid medium (p. 126) would
seem to be in transporting cultures through the post. The increased
viscosity of the medium should tend to reduce damage to the amoebae
through the shaking of the tube.

Balamuth's medium (p. 126) will appeal to those wishing to grow
amoebae in a simple, monophasic medium. It can also be stored at 4°c
for several months.

The 'Marmite' medium of Jones probably has few if any advantages
over the earlier media mentioned above. Nelson's alcoholic extract
medium (p. 130) is included because it can be made entirely from preserved ingredients, which could be very useful in particular circumstances.

The methods described for growing monoxenic or axenic cultures are all rather specialized and would not, of course, be used for routine diagnosis or strain maintenance for teaching purposes.

In conclusion, it may be noted that the fungus *Blastocystis hominis*, commonly present in human faeces, grows so readily in many (if not all) of the media mentioned in this chapter that it may smother the species of amoebae which one is trying to grow. Smedley (1956) has described a method of removing *Blastocystis* from such cultures by removing the fluid phase and diluting it approximately 10-fold with distilled water: after standing for 20 min at room temperature, the mixture is inoculated into several fresh culture tubes. *E.histolytica* (and probably other amoebae, although this should be investigated) can survive this treatment, while *Blastocystis* does not: although a few individuals may be seen in the inoculated cultures, they do not become established. Robinson (personal communication) has modified this method somewhat. He collected the sediment from the contaminated culture, diluted it 10-fold with decinormal hydrochloric acid, and allowed it to sediment for 1–1½ min. He then discarded the supernatant fluid and the finer particles still suspended in it, and resuspended the sediment in culture fluid before inoculating it to fresh medium. He recommended that such cultures be examined daily and, as soon as amoebae were seen, they should be transferred to fresh medium, before any surviving *Blastocystis* had begun to multiply: in spite of this, the treatment with hydrochloric acid might need to be repeated.

REFERENCES

ADLER S. & FONER, ANNIE (1941). Culture of intestinal Protozoa. *Lancet* **240**: 243–244.

AL-DABAGH M.A. (1965). The pathogenicity of the small race of *Entamoeba histolytica* to splenectomized rats. *Trans. R. Soc. trop. Med. Hyg.* **59**: 545–549.

ANDREWS J., JOHNSON C.M. & SCHWARTZ S.C. (1933). The use of fecal extracts in the cultivation of *Endamoeba histolytica*. *Am. J. trop. Med.* **13**: 591–593.

BAERNSTEIN H.D., REES C.W. & BARTGIS I.L. (1957). The rate of reproduction of *Entamoeba histolytica* in microcultures from inocula of single trophozoites in cell-free medium prepared from embryos of the chick. *J. Parasit.* **43**: 143–152.

BALAMUTH W. (1946). Improved egg yolk infusion for cultivation of *Entamoeba histolytica* and other intestinal Protozoa. *Am. J. clin. Path.* **16**: 380–384.

BALAMUTH W. & SANDZA J.G. (1944). Simple standardized culture medium for physiological studies on *Entamoeba histolytica*. *Proc. Soc. exp. Biol. Med.* **57**: 161–163.

BARRET H.P. & SMITH, NANNIE M. (1924). The cultivation of an *Endamoeba* from the turtle *Chelydra serpentina*. *Am. J. Hyg.* **4**: 155–159.

BARRET H.P. & SMITH, NANNIE M. (1926). The cultivation of *Endamoeba ranarum*. *Ann. trop. Med. Parasit.* **20**: 85–88.

BOECK W.C. & DRBOHLAV J. (1925). The cultivation of *Endamoeba histolytica*. *Am. J. Hyg.* **5**: 371–407.

BRUG S.L. (1936). Observations on *Dientamoeba fragilis. Ann. trop. Med. Parasit.* **30**: 441–452.

CHANG S.L. (1942). Studies on *Entamoeba histolytica.* I. Effect of hydrogen-ion concentration on encystation of *E.histolytica. Am. J. trop. Med.* **22**: 471–485.

CHANG S.L. (1943). Studies on *Endamoeba histolytica.* II. Observation concerning encystation, maturation and excystation of *E.histolytica* and on the longevity of culture-induced cysts in various fluids and at different temperatures. *J. infect. Dis.* **72**: 232–241.

CHANG S.L. (1946). Studies on *Entamoeba histolytica.* IV. The relation of oxidation-reduction potentials to the growth, encystation and excystation of *Entamoeba histolytica* in culture. *Parasitology* **37**: 101–112.

CLEVELAND L.R. & COLLIER, JANE (1930). Various improvements in the cultivation of *Entamoeba histolytica. Am. J. Hyg.* **12**: 606–613.

CLEVELAND L.R. & SANDERS, ELIZABETH P. (1930). Encystation, multiple fission without encystment, excystation, metacystic development and variation in a pure line and nine strains of *Entamoeba histolytica. Arch. Protistenk.* **70**: 223–266.

CRAIG C.F. (1926). Observations upon the cultivation of *Endamoeba histolytica. Am. J. trop. Med.* **6**: 461–464.

CULBERTSON C.G., ENSMINGER P.W. & OVERTON W.M. (1965). The isolation of additional strains of pathogenic *Hartmanella* sp. (*Acanthamoeba*). Proposed culture method for application to biological material. *Am. J. clin. Path.* **43**: 383–387.

CUTLER D.W. (1918). A method for the cultivation of *Entamoeba histolytica. J. Path. Bact.* **22**: 22–27.

DELAMATER J.N. & HALLMAN F.A. (1947). Studies on the culture of *Endamoeba histolytica. Proc. Soc. exp. Biol. Med.* **65**: 26–29.

DESCHIENS R. (1938). Action de la bilirubine et de la bile totale sur les amibes dysentériques. *C.r. Séanc. Soc. Biol.* **129**: 626–628.

DIAMOND L.S. (1957). The establishment of various trichomonads of animals and man in axenic cultures. *J. Parasit.* **43**: 488–490.

DIAMOND L.S. (1960). The axenic cultivation of two reptilian parasites, *Entamoeba terrapinae* Sanders & Cleveland, 1930, and *Entamoeba invadens* Rodhain, 1934. *J. Parasit.* **46**: 484.

DIAMOND L.S. (1961). Axenic cultivation of *Entamoeba histolytica. Science, N.Y.* **134**: 336–337.

DOBELL C. (1936). Researches on the intestinal Protozoa of monkeys and man. *Parasitology* **28**: 541–593.

DOBELL C. (1940). Researches on the intestinal Protozoa of monkeys and man. X. The life-history of *Dientamoeba fragilis*: observations, experiments and speculations. *Parasitology* **32**: 417–461.

DOBELL C. (1942). Some new methods for studying intestinal amoebae and other Protozoa. *Parasitology* **34**: 101–112.

DOBELL C. (1952). [Completed by R.A. Neal and edited by C.A. Hoare.] Researches on the intestinal Protozoa of monkeys and man. XII. Bacterial factors influencing the life history of *Entamoeba histolytica* in cultures. *Parasitology* **42**: 16–39.

DOBELL C. & LAIDLAW P.P. (1926). On the cultivation of *Entamoeba histolytica* and some other entozoic amoebae. *Parasitology* **18**: 283–318.

DOPTER C. & DESCHIENS R. (1937). Action comparée du sérum humain normal et du sérum humain ictérique sur les cultures d'amibes dysentérique. *C.r. Séanc. Soc. Biol.* **126**: 969–972.

DOPTER C. & DESCHIENS R. (1938). Action des sels biliaires et due cholestérol sur les cultures d'amibes dysentériques. *C.r. Séanc. Soc. Biol.* **129:** 628–632.

DRBOHLAV J.J. (1925). Une nouvelle preuve de la possibilité de cultiver *Entamoeba dysenteriae* type *histolytica*. *Annls Parasit. hum. comp.* **3:** 349–357.

FAUST E.C. & RUSSELL P.F. (1964). *Craig and Faust's clinical parasitology:* 995–996. Ed. 7. London: Henry Kimpton.

FOWLER M. & CARTER R.F. (1965). Acute pyogenic meningitis probably due to *Acanthamoeba* sp.: a preliminary report. *Br. med. J.* **1965 2** (5464): 740–742.

FRYE W.W. & MELENEY H.E. (1939). Liver extract as a substitute for serum in the culture medium for *Endamoeba histolytica*. *Science, N.Y.* **89:** 564–565.

GEIMAN Q.M. & BECKER C.E. (1953). *In vitro* growth and metabolism of *Endamoeba histolytica*. *Ann. N.Y. Acad. Sci.* **56:** 1048–1056.

HANSEN E.L. & ANDERSON H.H. (1948). An essentially synthetic liquid medium for *Entamoeba histolytica*. *Parasitology* **39:** 69–72.

HITCHCOCK D.J. & RAWSON G.W. (1946). The use of dehydrated, coagulated egg yolk in the preparation of a medium for culturing *Endamoeba histolytica*. *J. Parasit.* **32:** 170–174.

JACKSON G.J. & STOLL N.R. (1964). Axenic culture studies of *Entamoeba* species. *Am. J. trop. Med. Hyg.* **13:** 520–524.

JACOBS L. (1947). The elimination of viable bacteria from cultures of *Endamoeba histolytica* and the subsequent maintenance of such cultures. *Am. J. Hyg.* **46:** 172–176.

JACOBS L. (1950a). Oxidation-reduction potentials in the cultivation of *Endamoeba histolytica*. *Am. J. trop. Med.* **30:** 803–815.

JACOBS L. (1950b). The substitution of bacteria in cultures of *Endamoeba histolytica*. *J. Parasit.* **36:** 128–130.

JACOBS L. (1953). The cultivation of *Dientamoeba fragilis*. *Ann. N.Y. Acad. Sci.* **56:** 1057–1061.

JONES W.R. (1946). The experimental infection of rats with *Entamoeba histolytica*; with a method for evaluating the anti-amoebic properties of new compounds. *Ann. trop. Med. Parasit.* **40:** 130–140.

KASPRZAK W. (1965). Probleme der Kultivierung von Darmprotozoen *in vitro*. *Angew. Parasit.* **6:** 166–170.

KOFOID C.A. & McNEIL, ETHEL (1932). The advantages of Locke's blood medium in the culture of parasitic Protozoa of the digestive tract. *Am. J. Hyg.* **15:** 315–317.

LATOUR N.G. & REEVES R.E. (1965). An iron-requirement for growth of *Entamoeba histolytica* in culture, and the antiamoebal activity of 7-iodo-8-hydroxy-quinoline-5-sulfonic acid. *Expl Parasit.* **17:** 203–209.

McCONNACHIE, ELSPETH W. (1962). A medium for the axenic culture of *Entamoeba invadens*. *Nature, Lond.* **194:** 603–604.

McDADE J.J. & SHAFFER J.G. (1959). Studies on the growth requirements of *Entamoeba histolytica*. VI. A modification of the S-F technic which makes possible the utilization of peptones other than trypticase. *Am. J. trop. Med. Hyg.* **8:** 540–545.

MEEROVITCH E. (1961). Growth of *Entamoeba invadens* in organotypic cultures of embryonic chick intestine. *Can. J. Microbiol.* **7:** 685–695.

NAKAYAMA A. (1958). Studies on the culture medium of *Entamoeba histolytica*. *Yokohama Med. Bull.* **9:** 290–296.

NEAL R.A. (1952). Experimental production of pure mixed strains of *Entamoeba histolytica*. *Parasitology* **42:** 40–42.

NEAL R.A. (1953). Studies on the morphology and biology of *Entamoeba moshkovskii* Tshalaia, 1941. *Parasitology* **43**: 253–268.

NEAL R.A. (1967). The *in vitro* cultivation of *Entamoeba*. *Symp. Br. Soc. Parasit.* No. 5: 9–26.

NEFF R.J. (1957). Purification, axenic cultivation and description of a soil amoeba, *Acanthamoeba* sp. *J. Protozool.* **4**: 176–182.

NELSON E.C. (1947). Alcoholic extract medium for the diagnosis and cultivation of *Endamoeba histolytica*. *Am. J. trop. Med.* **27**: 545–552.

PAVLOVA E.A. (1938). [Culture methods for *Entamoeba histolytica*.] *Medskaya Parazit.* **7**: 224–227.

PHILLIPS B.P. (1950). Cultivation of *Endamoeba histolytica* with *Trypanosoma cruzi*. *Science, N.Y.* **111**: 8–9.

PHILLIPS B.P. & REES C.W. (1950). The growth of *Endamoeba histolytica* with live and heat-treated *Trypanosoma cruzi*. *Am. J. trop. Med.* **30**: 185–191.

PIPKIN A.C. (1960). Avian embryos and tissue culture in the study of parasitic Protozoa. II. Protozoa other than *Plasmodium*. *Expl Parasit.* **9**: 167–203.

RAO V.G. (1951). Sterilization of cysts of *Entamoeba histolytica* by chemical disinfectants, and initiation and maintenance of pure cultures in association with single species of bacteria. *Trans. R. Soc. trop. Med. Hyg.* **44**: 593–604.

REEVES R.E., MELENEY H.E. & FRYE W.W. (1957a). A modified Shaffer-Frye technique for the cultivation of *Entamoeba histolytica* and some observations on its carbohydrate requirements. *Am. J. Hyg.* **66**: 56–62.

REEVES R.E., MELENEY H.E. & FRYE W.W. (1957b). Bacteria-free cultures of *Entamoeba histolytica* with chick embryo tissue juice. *Z. Tropenmed. Parasitol.* **8**: 213–218.

REEVES R.E., MELENEY H.E. & FRYE W.W. (1959). The cultivation of *Entamoeba histolytica* with penicillin-inhibited *Bacteroides symbiosus* cells. I. A pyridoxine requirement. *Am. J. Hyg.* **69**: 25–31.

REEVES R.E. & WARD, ANNE B. (1965). Large lot cultivation of *Entamoeba histolytica*. *J. Parasit.* **51**: 321–324.

SADUN E.H., KRUPP, IRIS M. & EVERRITT, MARTHA G. (1952). Cultivation of *Endamoeba histolytica* in embryonic fluids. *Proc. Soc. exp. Biol. Med.* **80**: 272–275.

SHAFFER J.G. (1953). Factors affecting the propagation of *Endamoeba histolytica in vitro* in the S-F medium and in tissue bearing substrate. *Ann. N.Y. Acad. Sci.* **56**: 1033–1047.

SHAFFER J.G. & FRYE W.W. (1948). Studies on the growth requirements of *Endamoeba histolytica*. I. Maintenance of a strain of *E.histolytica* through one hundred transplants in the absence of an actively multiplying bacterial flora. *Am. J. Hyg.* **47**: 214–221.

SHAFFER J.G., RYDEN F.W. & FRYE W.W. (1948). Studies on the growth requirements of *Endamoeba histolytica*. III. The growth and multiplication of two strains of *E.histolytica* in a transparent medium without the addition of rice flour or other particulate matter and without demonstrable bacterial growth. *Am. J. Hyg.* **47**: 345–350.

SHAFFER J.G., RYDEN F.W. & FRYE W.W. (1949). Studies on the growth requirements of *Endamoeba histolytica*. IV. Further observations on the cultivation of *E.histolytica* and other intestinal Protozoa in a clear medium without demonstrable bacterial multiplication. Some modifications and simplifications of the medium. *Am. J. Hyg.* **49**: 127–133.

SHAFFER J.G., SCHULER R.W. & KEY, IRIS D. (1958). Studies on the growth requirements of *Entamoeba histolytica*. The ingestion of altered bacterial structures by *E.histolytica* in the Shaffer-Frye medium. *Am. J. trop. Med. Hyg.* **7:** 302–308.

SHAFFER J.G., SIENKIEWICZ H.S. & WASHINGTON J.E. (1953). The propagation of *Endamoeba histolytica* in tissue-bearing culture without accompanying bacteria or other micro-organisms. *Am. J. Hyg.* **57:** 366–379.

SHAFFER J.G., WALTON J.G. & FRYE W.W. (1948). Studies on the growth requirements of *Endamoeba histolytica*. II. Preliminary observations on the cultivation of *E.histolytica* in a modified thioglycollate medium. *Am. J. Hyg.* **47:** 222–225.

SINGH B.N., DAS S.R. & SAXENA U. (1963). A simple and reliable method for obtaining viable sterile cysts of *Entamoeba histolytica* from human faeces for monobacterial culture. *Ann. Biochem. exp. Med.* **23:** 51–56.

SMEDLEY S.R. (1956). A method of freeing cultures of *Entamoeba histolytica* from contamination with *Blastocystis*. *Trans. R. Soc. trop. Med. Hyg.* **50:** 232–233.

SMITH, NANNIE M. & BARRET H.P. (1928). The cultivation of a parasitic amoeba from the cockroach. *J. Parasit.* **14:** 272–273.

SPINGARN C.L. & EDELMAN M.H. (1952). Further observations on the use of streptomycin and penicillin in the cultivation of *Endamoeba histolytica* from stools. *Am. J. trop. Med. Hyg.* **1:** 412–416.

ST. JOHN J.H. (1926). Differential characteristics of the amoebae of man in culture. *Am. J. trop. Med.* **6:** 319–325.

ST. JOHN J.H. (1932). A new medium for the cultivation of *Endamoeba histolytica*. *Am. J. trop. Med.* **12:** 301–305.

STOLL N.R. (1957a). Axenic culture of *Entamoeba invadens* in the absence of tissue. *J. Protozool.* **4** Suppl.: 6. [Abstract only.]

STOLL N.R. (1957b). Axenic serial culture in cell-free medium of *Entamoeba invadens*, a pathogenic amoeba of snakes. *Science, N.Y.* **126:** 1236. [Abstract only.]

SWART, DOROTHEA L. & WARREN L.G. (1962). The origin of antigenic substances in *Entamoeba histolytica* Schaudinn, 1903, and serologic manifestations of their antibody-inducing properties. *J. Parasit.* **48:** 124–130.

TANABE M. & CHIBA E. (1928). A new culture medium for *Entamoeba histolytica*. *Acta medicin. Keijo* **11:** 221–224.

TSUCHIYA H. (1934). Further studies on the cultivation of *Endameba histolytica* and a complement fixation test for amebiasis. *J. lab. Clin. Med.* **19:** 495–504.

TSUCHIYA H. (1942). Evaluation of a culture method as an aid in the diagnosis of amebiasis. *Am. J. trop. Med.* **22:** 147–151.

WARHURST D.C. (1967). Cultivation *in vitro* of *Endolimax blattae* Lucas, 1927, from the cockroach hind gut. *Parasitology* **57:** 181–186.

ZUCKERMAN, AVIVAH (1966). Propagation of parasitic Protozoa in tissue culture and avian embryos. *Ann. N.Y. Acad. Sci.* **139:** 24–38.

PART TWO

CULTIVATION OF HELMINTHS

PART TWO

CULTIVATION OF HELMINTHS

INTRODUCTION

Recently the cultivation of helminths *in vitro* has received much attention (Berntzen, 1966; von Brand, 1966; Clegg & Smyth, 1967; Read & Simmons, 1963; Silverman, 1965; Smyth, 1962, 1966; Weinstein 1958, 1960, 1966; Woodruff, 1963) but it presents several major difficulties. Many helminths have complex life-cycles involving the development of larval stages in one or more intermediate host. Each stage in development may thus require different physico–chemical conditions and may possess different nutritional requirements. Frequently these are imperfectly known and difficult to reproduce *in vitro*, particularly considering the complex nature of the biological materials that parasites feed on, such as bile, blood, tissue exudates, intestinal contents etc. Also rapid diffusion of metabolic waste products from the parasite is usually possible *in vivo* and thus the accumulation of toxic waste products around the parasite seldom occurs. When culturing parasites *in vitro* suitable conditions must be provided to permit the removal of waste materials.

Many parasites live in a non-sterile habitat (e.g. gastro-intestinal parasites) so that antiseptic procedures are necessary before they can be axenically cultivated *in vitro*. The choice of larval forms derived from a sterile environment for the initial stages of cultivation may overcome such difficulties. The use of larvae is a further advantage when the adult is of considerable size (e.g. in the case of very long adult cestodes) so that technical difficulties could be avoided. Exsheathment or hatching of larvae is frequently necessary before helminths will develop *in vitro*; Rogers (1966) has reviewed the techniques in current use.

With regard to assessing the results of *in vitro* cultivation, it is first necessary to have detailed knowledge of the life-cycle of the parasite under study. Not only should the broader aspects of the life-cycle be known, but detailed pictures of the entire process of maturation and development should be available both from the histological and biochemical points of view. In particular Bell & Smyth (1958) have correlated mitotic activity of platyhelminths (*in vitro* and *in vivo*) with their phase of development, thus providing a useful technique for estimating growth of worms *in vitro*. Unfortunately such details are only available for a few parasitic worms and therefore before attempting cultivation *in vitro*, the normal picture should be obtained.

In addition to this many parasitic species possess food reserves (mainly glycogen) with the result that when they are placed in an isotonic medium (either simple or complex) and incubated at the body temperature of the host, endogenous energy sources are available which allow the organisms merely to survive *in vitro* for considerable periods of time. In most early experiments such survival was adjudged by movement. It is now recognized that survival *per se* as a criterion is of little value in culture work unless it is considered together with the normal physiological and morphological condition of the organism. Prolonged survival may merely indicate abnormal culture conditions, for the metabolism of the worms may be so depressed by the cultural conditions that prolonged periods of survival become possible. All these points must be borne in mind when attempting to cultivate helminths *in vitro*.

HELMINTHS REVIEW REFERENCES

BELL E.J. & SMYTH J.D. (1958). Cytological and histochemical criteria for evaluating development of trematodes and pseudophyllidean cestodes *in vivo* and *in vitro*. *Parasitology*, **48**: 131–148.

BERNTZEN A.K. (1966). *In vitro* cultivation of parasites. *Ann. N.Y. Acad. Sci.* **139**: 176–189.

BRAND T. VON (1966). *Biochemistry of parasites*. New York: Academic Press Inc.

CLEGG J.A. & SMYTH J.D. (1967). Growth, development and culture methods: parasitic platyhelminths. In *Chemical Zoology* I. New York: Academic Press.

READ C.P. & SIMMONS J.E. JR. (1963). Biochemistry and physiology of tapeworms. *Phys. Revs.* **43**: 263.

ROGERS W.P. (1966). Exsheathing and hatching mechanisms in helminths. In *Biology of parasites*: 33–40. E.J.L. Soulsby (ed.). London and New York: Academic Press.

SILVERMAN P.H. (1965). *In vitro* cultivation procedures for parasitic helminths. In *Advances in Parasitology* **3**: 159. B. Dawes (ed.). London: Academic Press.

SMYTH J.D. (1962). *Introduction to animal parasitology*. London: English Universities Press.

SMYTH J.D. (1966). *The physiology of trematodes*. Edinburgh: Oliver and Boyd Ltd.

WEINSTEIN P.P. (1958). Some projected uses for the cultivation of helminths. *Am. J. trop. Med. Hyg.* **7**: 1–3.

WEINSTEIN P.P. (1960). Culture of parasites (review of a discussion). *Proc. helminth. Soc. Wash.* **27**: 233.

WEINSTEIN P.P. (1966). The *in vitro* cultivation of helminths with reference to morphogenesis. In *Biology of parasites* 143–157. E.J.L. Soulsby (ed.). London: Academic Press.

WOODRUFF A.W. (1963). Interrelationships between physiology and biochemistry of parasite and host. *W.H.O. Publ. Hlth Paper* No. 66: 1–13.

CHAPTER 5

TREMATODA

I. SCHISTOSOMATIDAE

The human blood flukes are parasites of medical importance and as such have received considerable attention. Many workers have attempted in the past to maintain the adults *in vitro*, often for the purpose of testing anthelminthic drugs, but only very recently have attempts been made to culture the larval stages.

(i) *Eggs*

Very few attempts have been made to maintain the eggs of schistosomes and these have in the main been directed towards immunological tests rather than *in vitro* culture. The eggs of *Schistosoma japonicum* have been known to survive for up to 6 months in wet faeces at 8°c (Ito, 1955). Newsome (1957) reported some success in the storage of live *S.mansoni* eggs for use in the circumoval precipitin test.

(ii) *Miracidia*

Recently some success has been obtained in the cultivation of this stage in the life-cycle by Targett & Robinson (1964). Using a medium consisting of equal parts of snail blood and 3% agar containing 1% glucose, they maintained miracidia at 26·7°c for 51 hr when blood from *Limnaea* sp. or *Helix pomatia* was used. Only 18 hr survival was obtained with the blood of the natural host, *Australorbis glabratus*; it is interesting to note therefore that serum or blood taken from the natural host is not as good for *in vitro* culture as blood from other unrelated hosts.

(iii) *Rediae*

This stage in the life-cycle has been studied by Chernin (1963, 1964) who maintained portions of the digestive gland and gonad of *Australorbis glabratus* infected 40 days previously. The tissues were minced and explanted in flasks under sterile conditions. Chernin found that the best medium was a balanced salt solution containing glucose and trehalose maintained at 26–28°c (p. 167). During the first week of culture normal cercariae emerged from the rediae (these were infective for the first 4 days only) but the numbers of cercariae produced decreased during the next 2 weeks *in vitro*. Sugars were important for the production of cercariae because if they were omitted, fewer cercariae were produced. On the other hand the addition of amino acid mixtures to the cultures did not increase the numbers of cercariae produced.

(iv) *Cercariae*
An interesting technique for the culture of cercariae has been devised by Jensen and his colleagues (Jensen & Stirewalt, 1963; Jensen *et al.*, 1965). They grew cercariae in Rose multipurpose dialysis chambers containing explants of chick or mouse tissues. These chambers were bathed on one side with medium 199 and on the other side with 199 containing 20% serum (horse, human, rabbit or calf seemed to be equally successful). The cercariae cast their tails, evacuated their acetabular glands and increased in length, thus approaching the next stage in the life-cycle, i.e. the schisto-somule found in the lungs of an infected animal.

(v) *Schistosomules*
One of the first attempts at growing schistosomules *in vitro* was that of Senft and Weller (1956) who used both 6–10 days and 16 days old schistosomules (*S.mansoni*) recovered from mice. They used a medium consisting of 45% bovine amniotic fluid, 45% Hanks's balanced salt solution, 5% inactivated horse serum and 5% beef embryo extract plus antibiotics, and maintained their cultures at 37°c. The culture medium was adjusted to pH 7·4 by gassing with 5% carbon dioxide in air every 2–4 days. The older schistosomules survived the longest (35 days) and during this time increased in length up to 360%; even those worms damaged before culture regenerated their lost tissues *in vitro*. The addition of red blood cells to the cultures stimulated the activity and growth of the schistosomules but no significant internal development occurred in the worms, in spite of such prolonged activity and substantial increase in size.

Somewhat longer periods of survival were obtained by Robinson (1957) when he cultured schistosomules recovered from hamsters 11 days after infection (*S.mansoni*). He maintained the juvenile worms for periods up to 58 days in 1 part horse serum to 2 parts Tyrode's solution containing 0·2% glucose. Although numerous substances were added and the worms were very active, only a few of them doubled in size. The same year Mao & Lyu (1957) achieved similar results with *S.japonicum*; the worms survived 6 days in Tyrode's solution containing glucose and high concentrations of water soluble vitamins but almost doubled their length when reared in serum media.

The following year, Cheever & Weller (1958) reported on a complex series of experiments designed to evaluate the effect of different nutrient factors on the growth of *S.mansoni* which had been obtained previously in experiments by Senft & Weller (1956). Growth of these worms was investigated in media designed for the culture of human tissues, in a variety of media containing horse or human serum and in defined media with and without supplements of various kinds.

Schistosomules were recovered from the livers of white mice, 16–18 days after infection, by the perfusion technique of Yolles *et al.* (1947). The worms survived almost indefinitely (i.e. more than 6 months) in media used for growth studies, when the medium was changed weekly (Senft & Weller, 1956); but Cheever & Weller (1958) only observed the growth of worms over a 4-week period when evaluating the various media under test.

No growth occurred in the defined media (medium 199 alone or supplemented with 0·2% crystalline serum albumin or 0·3% purified globulin) but the worms survived from 12–49 days. When medium 199 was supplemented with an equal volume of human serum, a 600% increase in size was obtained in 3 weeks, compared with only 300% increase when Hanks's saline was used with human serum (horse serum was not as beneficial as human serum). In spite of such substantial growth *in vitro* the worms did not attain complete sexual maturity as judged by their lack of ability to produce sperm or ova, although they readily copulated and maintained this posture for considerable periods.

Clegg (1959, 1961, 1965) improved on the results of earlier workers in that he induced male schistosomules (*S. mansoni*), recovered from the lungs of white mice, to develop sperm *in vitro*; the females underwent gametogeny and a few produced ova. Initially (1959) he obtained rapid growth in a basic culture medium consisting of serum, Hanks's balanced saline, red blood cells and 0·25% lactalbumin hydrolysate. Later (1965) he improved his cultures by using a different basic culture medium (equal volumes of inactivated rabbit serum and Earle's saline plus 0·5% lactalbumin hydrolysate, 0·1% glucose, 1% rabbit red cells and antibiotics) contained in screw-cap culture tubes. The pH of the medium was maintained at 7·4 with carbon dioxide (p. 168). Development *in vitro* compared favourably with that *in vivo* (Fig. 5.1) during the early stages, but lagged behind during the later stages in that the worms required 6 weeks *in vitro* to reach the stages which would have taken only 4 weeks *in vivo*.

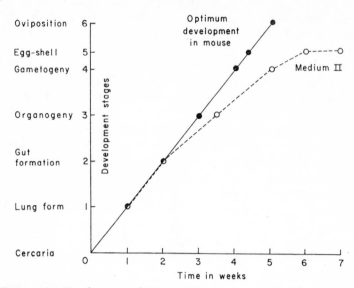

Figure 5.1 Development of *S.mansoni in vitro* compared with optimum development in the white mouse. (Clegg, 1965.)

A few females contained developed eggs but the majority only showed signs of gametogeny and egg shell development.

Further improvement in development was obtained by introducing young schistosomules, recovered from mice 7 days after infection, into a cellulose sac containing some red blood cells and immersing the whole in an improved basic culture medium (additional components were 0·4% glucose and 10% chick embryo extract), the pH of which was maintained at 7·4 as previously (Clegg, 1965). The culture tubes were agitated in a 37°c water bath to ensure dispersal of the metabolites and in addition they were spun at intervals to deposit the red blood cells and make them available to the schistosomules. In one experiment a single female matured completely in 24 days and in another a male worm reached maturity in 30 days but in several experiments with this technique growth was severely inhibited; no improvement was obtained when Clegg supplemented the basic medium with concentrated liver extract or 0·1% purified liver extract.

Further success was obtained when he applied his technique to the cercarial stage. Cercariae from the snail did not respond to the above culture treatment but when they were allowed to penetrate the skin of a mouse and recovered 30 min later, they developed at the same rate *in vitro* as did the schistosomules recovered from the lungs.

Adults

The earliest successful *in vitro* experiments on adult schistosomes were those of Lee & Chu (1935) who maintained *Schistosoma japonicum* from rabbits for many weeks under sterile conditions. They found that almost any animal serum (horse, sheep or rabbit) or even human ascitic fluid would serve as a satisfactory medium. They noted that it was essential to change the medium periodically (every 1–2 weeks) to obtain good survival. The maximum suvival period (2½ months) was obtained in rabbit serum contained in Carrel flasks; the addition of Locke's solution or glucose to the medium did not prolong survival time. Chu (1938) later described egg-laying and copulation *in vitro* by *S.japonicum*.

Somewhat better results were obtained in a series of experiments initiated by Newsome & Robinson (1954) and continued by Robinson (1956, 1958, 1960). These workers devised a continuous flow apparatus for the maintenance of adult *S.mansoni* and later used *S.japonicum*. Serum was again the medium of choice and the best results were obtained with worms recovered from hamsters 8 weeks after infection (p. 170). Various sera (rat, rabbit, human, baboon, cotton-rat, horse and guinea-pig) were tried and the best survival (28 days, occasionally 2 months) was obtained with horse serum containing 0·1% glucose. However guinea-pig serum was found to be the most suitable for maximum egg production. In fact Robinson demonstrated that more eggs were laid in sera from animals which are poor hosts than were laid in sera from good hosts. Egg laying appeared to be associated with copulation and Robinson deduced that the stimulus for egg-laying was a tactile one. The optimum temperature for cultivation was found to be 37°c (cf. 28°c reported to be optimum by Lee & Chu, 1935); higher temperatures resulted in the death of the worms.

Attempts to use a defined culture medium were made by Ross & Bueding (1950). They used *S.mansoni* recovered from mice 6–8 weeks after infection, and compared the worms' survival in whole serum with that in serum ultrafiltrate, or a chemically defined medium consisting of a buffered balanced salt solution plus amino acids, vitamins and glucose. The worms survived for 14–18 days in whole serum and almost as long (10–12 days) in serum ultrafiltrate thus indicating that the non–dialysable components (e.g. proteins) were of little significance to the survival of the worms. Disappointing results were obtained with the chemically defined medium for in it these worms survived only a number of hours (12–18). By adding the various components of the defined medium to serum and obtaining no inhibition of survival, Ross & Bueding demonstrated that such poor survival in the chemically defined medium was due to its nutritional inadequancy rather than direct toxicity.

Further studies on the maintenance of adult schistosomes in chemically defined media were carried out by Ito and his colleagues in Japan (Ito, 1955; Ito *et al.*, 1955; Ito & Komiya, 1955). They used adult *S.japonicum* recovered from rabbits and guinea-pigs 6–11 weeks after infection and maintained them in static Carrel flasks; motility of the worms was their only criterion of survival. They compared survival in various chemically defined media with that in natural media (whole or defibrinated horse blood, horse red blood cells, or horse serum). Undiluted horse serum at 28°c supported the worms for the longest time and it is interesting to note that changing of the medium was demonstrated as being directly beneficial to the worms (33 days survival in unchanged serum; 64 days survival in serum changed regularly). Although the adult worms did not survive as long in chemically defined media as they did in serum alone, these workers obtained considerably longer survival periods than had Ross and Bueding five years earlier. Ito & Komiyo (1955) compared physiological saline, Locke's, Tyrode's, and Ringer's solutions. Ringer's solution was the most effective and when used together with 0·5% glucose and 1% asparagine, female worms survived for 5–12 days and male worms for 2–4 days. The addition of bovine serum albumin did not prolong survival and the optimum cultivation temperature was found to be 28°c (range tested was 8, 18, 28, 38°c).

More recently the Senfts (Senft & Senft, 1962; Senft 1963, 1965) have maintained adult *S.mansoni* from mice in the chemically defined medium NCTC 109 and have also begun to define the amino acid requirements of the worms (p. 171). Whole worms or fragments appeared to survive equally well (the criterion of survival was motility, especially of the gut). However, great variation in survival periods was obtained (8–45 days), the majority surviving between 15 and 25 days: it is possible that this variation may have been due to differences in the age of the worms as this was not indicated. Further indication of the efficacy of this medium was the fact that egg-laying continued in these worms to the 24th day of culture. An initial acclimatization period of 2–3 days was required by the worms before continuous egg-laying resulted (maximum number produced was 100 eggs/day on days 4–6 *in vitro*). However the medium was far from optimal since the eggs were all non-viable and had abnormal cell organization; flame-cell movements were seen in only a few eggs.

The changes in amino acid composition of a fully defined medium during culture of *S.mansoni* have been extensively studied (Senft & Senft, 1962; Senft, 1963) and in 1965 Senft reviewed the existing knowledge of the amino acid and protein metabolism of these worms. Schistosomes require carbohydrates both as a source of energy and as a pool from which to manufacture amino acids, particularly alanine. Histidine, tryptophan, arginine and possibly aspartic acid are the amino acids most readily used by schistosomes *in vitro*.

Schistosoma mansoni Larval stages
(Chernin, 1963, 1964)

MEDIUM

	g/l.
NaCl	2·8
KCl	0·15
Na_2HPO_4 (anh.)	0·07
$MgSO_4.7H_2O$	0·45
$CaCl_2.2H_2O$	0·53
$NaHCO_3$	0·05
Glucose	1·0
Trehalose	1·0
Penicillin G	200 units/ml
Streptomycin sulphate	200 μg/ml
Phenol red (0·4%)	5·0 ml/l.

1 Dissolve all the above ingredients *except* $CaCl_2.2H_2O$ in 800 ml double distilled water.
2 Dissolve the $CaCl_2.2H_2O$ in 200 ml double distilled water.
3 Combine parts 1 and 2 whilst stirring.
4 Sterilize medium by filtration (Millipore 'H' filters, 0·45 μ pore size were used by Chernin but would not have removed the smallest bacteria).
5 Store medium at 5°c in rubber stoppered vessels until used.

TECHNIQUE

Infected snails are blotted dry, wiped with 70% alcohol and kept temporarily between alcohol-moistened gauze pads. Each snail is gently crushed between glass slides in a Petri dish (the operation being carried out in a sterile room or cabinet). The body is then transected with iris scissors just distal to the loop of the mid-intestine, revealing the sporocyst laden digestive gland and ovotestis. These are dissected out and transferred to a 50 mm Petri dish containing 10 ml culture medium. The tissue is cut into 1–2 mm³ fragments and the dish agitated gently at intervals for 20 min. The fluid is replaced by a further 10 ml of medium and left for 20 min. The tissue fragments are then transferred to a 50 ml Erlenmeyer culture flask, the transfer fluid removed and replaced with 5 ml fresh culture medium. Each flask is closed with a rubber stopper and should contain the tissue fragments from a single snail. Cultures should be maintained at 26–28°c in the dark (exposure to light induces emergence of cercariae from the tissues and should be carried out, usually for 1 hr, before a cercarial count is made on the medium) and the culture medium changed daily.

Cultures may be evaluated by counting the emerged cercariae and by histological study of the tissues.

Chernin found that cercarial emergence from tissues (40 days after infection) was normal during the first week but decreased during weeks 2 and 3; the majority of these cercariae were infective to white mice. Also, cercarial embryos matured *in vitro* (tissues used 19 days after infection) after a lag period of 8–13 days.

Schistosoma mansoni Schistosomules
(Clegg, 1965)

MEDIUM

1 *Preparation of Serum*

Adult rabbit serum (sterilized by filtration and used directly or stored at −20°c) should be inactivated at 56°c for 30 min before use.

2 *Preparation of Red Blood Cells*

Rabbit red blood cells in freshly drawn blood are washed rapidly at 37°c in Earle's saline (p. 350) containing 1% serum and 0·1 mg heparin/ml followed by Earle's-serum alone. After appropriate dilution in Earle's saline, 1% red blood cells are immediately added to the culture media. The longevity of red cells in culture following this treatment is very high and negligible haemolysis occurs during periods of more than 14 days. However the cells should usually be replaced at intervals of 7 days.

3 *Medium (II) Constituents*

> Earle's saline (modified—see p. 350 and note below) . .1 part
> Inactivated rabbit serum. . . . . .1 part
> Glucose . . . . .0·1%
> Lactalbumin hydrolysate (Nutritional Biochemical
> Corporation. Enzymic hydrolysate) . . . . .0·5%
> Rabbit red cells 1%
> Penicillin . . . . .100 i.u./ml
> Streptomycin . . . . .100 µg/ml

N.B. Earle's saline: to maintain isotonicity the NaCl content of Earle's saline is reduced by 0·18 g for every gram of lactalbumin hydrolysate used in the medium (5% w/v aqueous lactalbumin hydrolysate is isotonic).

1   Recovery of Schistosomules

White mice are exposed either to 500–5,000 cercariae when large numbers of young, 7 day old, schistosomules are required for culture or to 200 cercariae when older schistosomules and adults are required. At the appropriate time after infection the mice are killed and either the lungs or liver perfused as follows.

(a)   *Lungs.* 10 ml Earle's saline containing 0·1 mg heparin/ml are injected into the right ventricle to perfuse the lungs. The left ventricle is punctured to allow the perfusate to flow away with the blood from the lung capillaries (schistosomules are held firmly in the lungs and do not escape with the perfusate).

The perfused lungs are then chopped into small fragments (1 mm^3) with fine scissors and transferred to a 20 ml screw-capped bottle. After addition of 10 ml Earle's saline containing heparin (0·1 mg/ml), the lung fragments are incubated for 1 hr at 37°C, pH 7·4. The escaped schistosomules can then be separated from the lung fragments by passing the suspension through a stainless steel wire mesh (mesh 60) attached to a metal tube. The filtrate is centrifuged slowly for 1 min and most of the supernatant discarded. The remaining supernatant (about 0·5 ml) containing the schistosomules is transferred to a sterile slide and examined under a dissecting microscope in a sterile cabinet. Individual schistosomules are picked up with a micropipette and a given number transferred to a culture tube.

(b)   *Liver.* 15–30 minutes after the subcutaneous injection of heparin (4 mg in 0·4 ml water) the mouse is killed and the abdominal cavity opened whilst maintaining sterile conditions. The liver is perfused with Earle's saline containing 5% horse serum as follows: the hepatic vein, inferior vena cava and portal vein are tied and cut distal to the ties. After cutting the oesophagus and freeing the diaphragm from its insertion, the liver and diaphragm are transferred to a sterile Petri dish. The tie is removed from the portal vein and a number 22 needle inserted into the hepatic venous sinus. Thirty to 60 ml of perfusate are forced through the liver at a rate sufficient to keep it slightly distended. The schistosomules can be recovered from the perfusate in the same manner as described above (see 1a). Mature schistosomes can be recovered from the mesenteric veins with mounted needles and similarly treated.

2 *Cultivation of Schistosomules*

The recommended culture tube is a 20 ml screw-top tube with a flat internal base and a rubber liner. Each tube contains 4–5 ml of medium and is incubated at 37°c. The pH of each culture is adjusted to 7·4 by gassing with 8·8% carbon dioxide in air 3 times, at intervals of 10 min, prior to culture. During culture the 1% red blood cells sediment to form a thin layer in which the schistosomules develop. The medium should be replaced every 3–4 days by aspirating all the medium except for approximately 0·5 ml containing the red cells and worms. Nearly all the red cells can be replaced when required by suspending them in the medium before aspiration. The relatively heavy schistosomules sediment in a few seconds and can easily be left in the tube when the culture medium is drawn off.

Clegg showed that development of schistosomules occurred to stage 5 (see Fig. 5.1) within 42 days.

Schistosoma japonicum and *S.mansoni* Adults
(Robinson, 1956, 1960)

MEDIUM

Horse serum supplemented with glucose (0·1%) or guinea-pig serum diluted 1:1 with Tyrode's solution (p. 350).

TECHNIQUE

Adult worms are dissected aseptically from the hepatic portal veins of infected hamsters 8 weeks after infection. The worms are obtained in pairs and disturbed *as little as possible* during the transfer from hamster to culture. They should be washed once in Tyrode's solution before being inserted into the apparatus (Fig. 5.2). They are induced to travel to the observation chamber by withdrawing sufficient medium through the withdrawal arm by means of a syringe and needle; the apparatus should be maintained at 37°c and the medium changed daily.

Horse Serum

Robinson showed that worms will survive up to 2 months in horse serum supplemented with glucose.

Guinea-Pig Serum

Robinson found that with a gaseous phase of air, worms survive and continue to lay eggs for at least 14 days in guinea-pig serum diluted

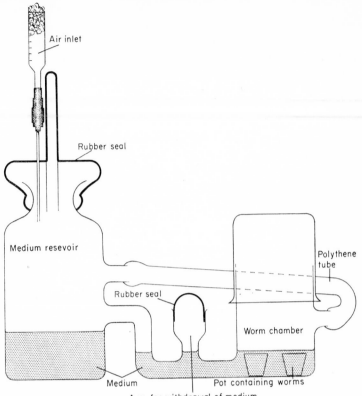

FIGURE 5.2 Culture apparatus for maintenance of pairs of adult schistosomes.
(From Smyth, 1966; after Robinson, 1960.)

1:1 with Tyrode's solution. He considered that this success was achieved because the worms were in close proximity in the worm chamber so that if the pairs happened to part, re-copulation was not difficult.

Schistosoma mansoni Adult
(Senft & Senft, 1962)

MEDIUM

NCTC 109 (p. 351).

TECHNIQUE

Individual worm pairs are hooked out of the mesenteric veins of the liver from an infected white mouse (using sterile procedures) and transferred to sterile NCTC 109. They are washed in this several times before being transferred to the culture test-tubes (1 or 2 pairs/test-tube) containing 2 ml of culture medium. The tubes are tightly stoppered and incubated in an upright position at 37°c. The medium should be changed every 2–3 days.

The Senfts found that schistosomes laid eggs and appeared normal for 20 days after which they deteriorated.

II. FASCIOLIDAE

1. *FASCIOLA HEPATICA*

The first systematic attempt to cultivate the liver fluke of sheep was made by Stephenson (1947) who was interested in determining the conditions required by adults for survival *in vitro*. He obtained flukes from sheep and cattle at the local abattoir, removing them from the bile ducts 1–6 hr after the animal had died. These flukes were transported to his laboratory in cold bile where they were washed many times in saline. Subsequently the worms were maintained in a variety of media under a wide range of physico-chemical conditions and during each experiment the medium was changed every 16–24 hr. Stephenson assessed his media according to the numbers of worms surviving in them. Ringer's solution amongst others, was not found to be a satisfactory medium, the most satisfactory one consisting of 150 mM NaCl, 10 mM KCl, 1 mM CaCl$_2$, 6 mM sodium borate, 30 mM glucose. The optimum pH range was found to be 8·2–8·6 and the optimum temperature 36°c.

The worms survived for a maximum of 60 hr in the best medium at 36°c, pH 8·6; Stephenson included sodium borate in his medium because he considered it effective in controlling bacterial contamination which otherwise had a harmful effect on the worms. He found sugars, especially monosaccharides, to be beneficial to the worms and also showed, by ligaturing their bodies, that the sugars could be absorbed through the cuticle as well as through the gut.

Seven years later, Dawes (1954) attempted to maintain *F.hepatica in vitro*. He found Hédon-Fleig's solution (borate free) to be a satisfactory medium and maintained the worms in it for 72 hr without loss of movement or natural coloration. Sometimes the worms survived for as long as 5 or 6 days and exceptionally up to 12 days. He attributed part of his success to the fact that the worms were removed aseptically from intact livers which had been kept warm during transport from the abattoir. He considered that in Stephenson's experiments the shock of lowering the temperature before culture partly explained the lower rate of survival of his worms. Dawes also criticized Stephenson for his use of borax in the medium as Dawes had found it harmful to the worms *in vitro*.

In 1957 the results shown above were considerably improved upon by Rohrbacher who set out to repeat Stephenson's experiments. He took the precaution of removing the flukes aseptically from infected livers immediately after the sheep had died and transferring them to saline which was maintained at 37°c throughout the journey to his laboratory. The worms were then transferred to sterile basic saline (see Stephenson, 1947) plus antibiotics and kept in this at 37°c for a further 18–24 hr. Those flukes which were bacteria-free (contaminated flukes had a blanched appearance) were then cultured. Rohrbacher found that the flukes survived in a variety of saline media, including Tyrode's solution, for 21 days but that towards the end of this time they showed signs of deterioration; significantly, if glucose was withheld from the medium, only 72 hours' survival was obtained. He tried supplementing the medium with individual amino acids or mixtures of them and also such products as chicken plasma, horse serum or bovine embryo extract but none of these substances prolonged the worms' survival. However some slight improvement was obtained by adding cholesterol in that, although the total survival period was not altered, the worms remained more normal in appearance and more active for the first 10 days. The addition of autoclaved liver extract was even more beneficial to the worms, for under these conditions they retained their normal colour and motility for 14 days and survived for 21 days (see p. 174). This was improved upon still further by the addition of commercial liver extract together with the autoclaved extract and in this medium the worms remained normal in appearance for 21 days and survived up to 30 days. During these experiments Rohrbacher confirmed Stephenson's previous observations that the worms preferred aerobic to anaerobic conditions, as shown by their more normal appearance under aerobic conditions, although their survival period was the same. He also confirmed that they tolerated a wide range of physico-chemical environments. Rohrbacher repeated the ligaturing experiments, confirming Stephenson's results and showing that glucose, fructose and glycerol were the only substances that would support the worms during the 6 days that he kept them ligatured. Lactose, ribose, maltose and sucrose had no effect.

The criteria of success in the above experiments were similar in each case, namely the motility, coloration and general appearance of the worms. This has been criticized by Clegg (see Dawes & Muller, 1957 and Smyth, 1962) who demonstrated that physiological abnormalities could be detected after only 3 hr *in vitro* in Hédon-Fleig's solution. He maintained *F.hepatica*, taken freshly from infected rabbits, for 18 days when they were contained within cellulose tubing, which provided them with an artificial surface for attachment.

It is apparent therefore from all these experiments that it is very important to obtain the flukes aseptically from freshly killed animals and to maintain them at 37°c in as good a medium as possible before attempting *in vitro* culture experiments.

Fasciola hepatica Adults
(Rohrbacher, 1957)

MEDIUM

Balanced Saline

	g/l.
NaCl	2·4
KCl	0·75
CaCl$_2$	0·55
MgCl$_2$.6H$_2$O	0·2
Na$_2$HPO$_4$.2H$_2$O	2·7
NaHCO$_3$	0·84
Sodium citrate	2·9
Glucose	3·6

1　Dissolve all above compounds except CaCl$_2$, MgCl$_2$.6H$_2$O, NaHCO$_3$ and glucose, in 600 ml double distilled water.
2　Dissolve CaCl$_2$ and MgCl$_2$.6H$_2$O in 200 ml double distilled water.
3　Add 1 to 2 stirring all the time. Sterilize by filtration.
4　Dissolve NaHCO$_3$ in 100 ml double distilled water and sterilize by positive pressure filtration.
5　Dissolve glucose in 100 ml double distilled water and autoclave.
6　Mix 3, 4 and 5 thoroughly, maintaining sterility.

Autoclaved Liver Extractct
Prepare by macerating bovine liver in a Waring blender with an equal volume of distilled water, autoclaving to precipitate the protein and filtering. The filtrate is then bottled and autoclaved. It is used in the proportion of 200 ml liver extract to 800 ml of saline.

Crude Liver Extract

Injection crude liver—MRT (manufactured by Marvin R. Thompson Inc.) is dispensed in quantities of 10 ml/l. of medium.

TECHNIQUE

The parasites are removed from infected bovine livers immediately after the slaughter of the animals. They are expressed from the bile ducts into sterile balanced saline without glucose and transported rapidly to the laboratory (50 flukes/200 ml saline) at a temperature of 37°c.

On arrival at the laboratory, the flukes are transferred to fresh sterile saline containing 250 mg streptomycin and 100,000 units penicillin G/100 ml saline. After 18 hr in this solution, at 37°c, any contaminated flukes (i.e. discoloured) should be discarded and the remainder cultivated in the full culture medium. Each fluke can be cultured in 50 ml of medium in a rubber-stoppered 4 oz oil sample bottle. The medium should be changed at least once a week.

Rohrbacher found that adult flukes survived under the above conditions for 3–4 weeks.

2. *FASCIOLOIDES MAGNA*

In contrast to *F.hepatica*, of which the adult flukes only have been cultivated, the larval stages of *Fascioloides magna* have received attention. It is relevant to mention here that among the earliest attempts at culturing larval Fasciolidae were those of Barlow (1925) who reported that the miracidium of *Fasciolopsis buski* underwent metamorphic changes followed by sporocyst growth and development in snail lymph.

More recently Friedl (1961a, b) has carried out some experiments on the survival *in vitro* of rediae of *Fascioloides magna* dissected from the snail *Lymnaea stagnalis jugularis*. He first tested a variety of physiological saline solutions containing individual amino acids and also media containing denatured proteins and protein degradation products. In his earlier studies (1961a) he found that the rediae survived better when hydroxyproline, proline and serine were included individually in Ringer C solution (the most satisfactory saline tested). Subsequently (1961b) he extended this work under improved technical and axenic conditions and confirmed his previous record of better survival in the presence of L-hydroxyproline (10 days) or DL-serine (8 days) than in Ringer C solution alone (p. 176) but surprisingly the inclusion of sugars, sodium acetate or denatured proteins did not prolong survival.

Fascioloides magna
(Friedl, 1961a, b)

MEDIUM

1   *Ringer C Stock Solution*

$$
\begin{array}{ll}
\text{NaCl} & \text{6·5 g} \\
\text{KCl} & \text{0·14 g} \\
\text{CaCl}_2.2\text{H}_2\text{O} & \text{0·16 g} \\
\text{NaHCO}_3 & \text{0·1 g} \\
\text{NaH}_2\text{PO}_4 & \text{0·012 g} \\
\text{Distilled water to} & \text{600 ml}
\end{array}
$$

Ringer C stock solution is sterilized by autoclaving.

The precipitate formed in the presence of bicarbonate is allowed to settle out and the supernatant diluted with sterile distilled water (3:2) immediately prior to use.

2   *Stock Amino Acid Solutions*

L-hydroxyproline or DL-serine are prepared as 100 mM aqueous solutions and sterilized by filtration.

3   An appropriate amount of the amino acid stock solution (to yield 2, 4 or 6 mM final concentration) is then added to 600 ml of the supernatant of Ringer C solution and the volume made up to 1 l. with sterile distilled water.

TECHNIQUE

Laboratory infected *Lymnaea stagnalis jugularis* (Friedl, 1960) are dissected under Ringer C solution (containing 0·025 g/ml bovine serum albumin, 100 i.u./ml penicillin G, potassium salt and 100 μg/ml streptomycin sulphate). The liberated rediae are subsequently washed several times in the above solution (under aseptic conditions) before culture in rubber-stoppered test-tubes (100×10 mm) containing 0·5 ml of test medium. Two rediae are added to each tube and kept at room temperature (25–$29°$c) throughout the experiment.

Friedl found that rediae survived a maximum of 10 days in the L-hydroxyproline medium and 8 days in DL-serine medium.

III. STRIGEIDAE

1. *DIPLOSTOMUM PHOXINI*

Ferguson (1943a) working with species of *Diplostomum* occurring in the eyes of fishes, showed that their cercariae will infect a wide variety of animals, including frogs, turtles, birds and mammals. He developed a technique for obtaining large numbers of metacercariae for *in vitro* culture by injecting cercariae into the orbit of the eye or by placing them on the cornea. The cercariae then penetrated the lens and developed into metacercariae which were infective to chicks, where they developed into normal egg-producing adults within one week.

The cercariae obtained by this method were grown on cultures of lens tissue taken from fishes, rats, rabbits or cattle together with either Tyrode's solution or frog Ringer. Development occurred to the metacercarial stage, even when the lens tissues became opaque or disintegrated. However the combination of lens tissue and saline was critical, since if trout, rabbit or bovine lens tissues were grown in Tyrode's solution unsuccessful cultures of cercariae resulted whereas if frog Ringer's solution replaced the Tyrode's solution the cultures were successful.

Unfortunately these cultured metacercariae were uninfective in spite of the fact that they were normal in appearance and had developed at the normal rate. Ferguson fed laughing gulls (*Larus atricilla*) with these metacercariae embedded in the bodies of small rainbow trout (*Salmo irideus*) and also injected them into the duodenum of 2 day old unfed chicks but the larvae failed to develop into adult flukes.

Later Bell & Hopkins (1956) worked with *Diplostomum phoxini*, the adult of which inhabits the duodenum of the duck, the metacercariae being found in the brain of minnows. The maturation of the adult in the definitive host normally requires 3–4 days and Bell & Hopkins set out to achieve this development *in vitro*.

Initially they tried to determine whether the metacercariae required an exogenous source of energy for development by keeping the larvae in various balanced salt solutions and adding supplements. Metacercariae died within 18 hr when kept in Locke's, Tyrode's or Hanks's balanced salines but when 1% glucose was added they lived for 144 hr and tolerated a range in pH of 6·3–7·4.

Subsequently Bell & Hopkins (1956) used Tyrode's solution containing 1% glucose as their basal medium and to this were added various supplements. Their criterion of success was not only the appearance and development rate previously used by Ferguson, but also the mitotic index technique (p. 159). When the basal medium was supplemented with serum, the mitotic activity of the metacercariae was stimulated, whereas 4% chick embryo extract had no effect. Still better results were obtained when the basal medium was supplemented with duck serum and 10% unfertilized duck-egg yolk. The cultures were maintained at 39°C in roller tubes under aerobic conditions (p. 179). Mitotic activity and development were good under these conditions and within 48 hr adult flukes were obtained which contained a few active sperm. However even though they remained alive for up to 5 days, no further development occurred and Bell & Hopkins presumed that this was due to the absence of solid food in the rather viscous liquid medium.

This work was continued by Bell & Smyth (1958) who confirmed the stimulatory effect of the complex egg yolk medium. They induced further development of the flukes by simulating intestinal movement in the cultures by discontinuously shaking them. This resulted in an increased mitotic rate which approximated that found *in vivo* and the flukes produced both sperm and eggs but the latter were abnormal in appearance. The best medium they found was one containing egg albumen in addition to the yolk (p. 180).

These results were analysed in more detail by Bell & Smyth (see Smyth, 1959) who showed that within 1 hr of immersion in the egg yolk and albumen medium the fluke's gut had become filled with solid material. The worms evidently possessed enzymes which were capable of metabolizing such a highly complex medium for during this time their mitotic index rose from 50 to 100 (c.f. 150 to 200 *in vivo*).

Hopkins and his students (Wyllie *et al.*, 1960; Williams *et al.*, 1961) then undertook to investigate the nutritional and growth promoting factors of the yolk medium. Wyllie *et al.* (1960) found that the worms developed almost as well in a medium consisting of Tyrode's solution, horse serum, yeast extract and amino acids as they did in the yolk medium with albumen (p. 180). In the new medium 5% of the worms produced eggs within 6 days at 40°C compared with 43% in the yolk medium. If the amino acids were omitted only 1% of the worms produced eggs and if the yeast extract was omitted none of the worms produced eggs. The effect of the amino acids was dependent upon the presence of horse serum, and even in the best cultures great variability was obtained.

Further experiments were carried out by Williams *et al.* (1961) to determine the active component of yeast extract and to discover to what extent a chemically defined medium could replace it. They used as their basal medium Tyrode's solution containing 0·6% glucose, 25% horse serum and 12% fresh hen-egg albumen. Their results showed that the yeast extract contained 2 active fractions. One of these was dialysable and could be replaced effectively with an amino acid mixture. The second was a basically charged non-dialysable fraction which was resistant to acid or alkaline hydrolysis. Its activity appeared to be associated with a substance of small molecular size which was possibly bound to a larger molecule since if dialysis was preceded by mild acid hydrolysis, the activity of this fraction was lost. Because vitamin B_6 is a substance of this nature, Williams and his colleagues tried to replace this fraction with it. Vitamin B_6 however was only active at concentrations far above those found in yeast so they concluded that some other substance, together with this vitamin and amino acids was required to replace yeast extract in the medium.

Diplostomum phoxini Larvae
(Bell & Hopkins, 1956)

MEDIUM

Two millilitres of duck serum to which has been added 10% of unfertilized duck-egg yolk (obtained by inserting a wide bore pipette into the centre of the yolk).

TECHNIQUE

The metacercariae are removed aseptically from the brain of minnows. The minnow is held in a clamp facing the operator and the head sterilized with 90% alcoholic iodine. When it is dry the skin is scraped off the roof of the cranium and the skull resterilized. The roof of the cranium is removed by a median cut to expose the brain which is then removed into sterile Hanks's saline (p. 350). The larvae emerge on teasing the brain with blunt needles and can be picked up in a pipette to be washed again in Hanks's saline before culture.

The larvae are cultured in roller tubes, containing the above medium, incubated at 39°c and rotated at 15 rev/hr. The gas phase in each culture tube is air.

Bell & Hopkins found that within 48 hr the flukes showed the presence of a few active sperm. No further development took place although the flukes were still alive 5 days later when the cultures were last examined.

13

Diplostomum phoxini
(Bell & Smyth, 1958)

This paper should be referred to for a full account of the development of this species both *in vivo* and *in vitro*.

MEDIUM

Yolk. This is removed by aseptically inserting a wide bore pipette into the centre of the yolk of a hen's egg.

Albumen. The liquid fraction of hen-egg albumen is most distinct in fresh eggs from which 5–10 ml can be sucked off with a fine pasteur pipette.

TECHNIQUE

Metacercariae of *Diplostomum phoxini* can be obtained from the brain of minnows according to the method of Bell & Hopkins (p. 179). These larvae are cultivated in tubes containing the hen-yolk albumen medium. The tubes are incubated at 40°c and shaken at irregular intervals. The gas phase in each tube is air. Bell & Smyth found that the larvae matured in this medium to the extent of producing active sperm, but abnormal eggs, at the same rate as obtained *in vivo*.

Diplostomum phoxini
(Wyllie *et al.*, 1960)

MEDIUM

Balanced Saline. Hanks's saline (p. 350) without bicarbonate and glucose *or* Tyrode's solution (p. 350) modified by omitting bicarbonate and increasing phosphates (0·18 g/l. $NaH_2 PO_4.2H_2O$; 0·30 g/l. Na_2HPO_4). To avoid precipitation the latter is prepared at normal strength, not as a concentrated stock solution, and sterilized by filtration.

Glucose. This is made as a 6·5% solution in water (approximately isotonic to balanced salt solution) and the appropriate volume added to the medium to give 0·5% or 1·0% final concentration.

Albumen. The liquid fraction of hen-egg albumen is used. This is most distinct in fresh eggs, from which 5–10 ml can be aspirated with a fine Pasteur pipette.

Yeast. Concentrated (12 times) yeast extract is prepared by dissolving 600 mg of dehydrated water-soluble portion of autolysed fresh yeast

(Difco) in 10 ml water and sterilizing at 110°c for 10 min. One millilitre is added to each culture of 12 ml to achieve a final concentration of 5 mg/ml.

Horse Serum. The serum used was supplied by Burroughs Wellcome and stored for up to 2 months at 4°c.

Amino Acid Concentrate (as in Parker's medium 703, Healy *et al.*, 1965)

	mg/l.		mg/l.
L-Arginine	70·0	DL-Isoleucine	40·0
L-Histidine	20·0	DL-Valine	50·0
L-Lysine	70·0	DL-Glutamic acid	150·0
L-Tyrosine	40·0	DL-Aspartic acid	60·0
DL-Tryptophan	20·0	DL-Alanine	50·0
DL-Phenylalanine	50·0	L-Proline	40·0
L-Cystine	20·0	L-Hydroxyproline	10·0
DL-Methionine	30·0	Glycine	50·0
DL-Serine	50·0	Cysteine hydrochloride	260·0
DL-Threonine	60·0	L-Glutamine	100·0
DL-Leucine	120·0		

1 The above amino acids, with the exception of L-glutamine, cysteine hydrochloride, L-tyrosine and L-cystine are added to about 400–450 ml of water stirring continuously and heated to about 80°c. After the solution has cooled to room temperature the L-glutamine and cysteine hydrochloride are then added. The ingredients of Earle's balanced salt solution (p. 350) are then added and finally the solution is made up to 500 ml with distilled water.

2 L-tyrosine (200 mg) and L-cystine (100 mg) are dissolved with moderate heating in 100 ml of 0.075 N HCl.

3 All of solution 1 and 20 ml of solution 2 are then combined, the final volume made up to 1 litre and the whole sterilized by filtration.

Combined medium

Two millilitres of albumen are added to 10 ml of balanced saline containing 1% glucose. To this is added 1·5 ml of amino acid concentrate. One millilitre of yeast extract is then added and horse serum added to a final concentration of 25–30%. If necessary the pH of the medium is adjusted to an initial value of 6·5 with 0·2 N HCl.

Metacercariae from the brains of the minnow are removed aseptically, washed in balanced saline solution and transferred into culture (see Bell & Hopkins 1956 or p. 179). Cultivation is carried out in 1 oz (30 ml) screw-top vials, held in a water bath at $39 \cdot 5 \pm 1°$c and shaken intermittently at 150 rev/min for 10 sec in every min. The volume of medium used can vary from 12–15 ml, forming a layer approximately 3 cm deep. Cultures usually have 50–100 metacercariae per vial.

Wyllie *et al.* showed that the combined medium supported the production of large masses of sperm and moderate amounts of vitellaria in these metacercariae during the 7 days observation period. The yolk reservoir was often distended with vitelline cells but abnormal eggs were formed in only 5% of the flukes. Culture results were best within the pH range of 6·0–7·0.

2. *POSTHODIPLOSTOMUM MINIMUM*

The metacercariae of this fluke occur encysted within a hyaline membrane in the viscera of pumpkinseed sun-fish (*Lepomis gibbosus*) and they can be readily removed by pepsin treatment. The natural definitive host of this parasite is the heron and Ferguson (1940) showed that the metacercariae would also mature in chicks within 36 hr. He found *P.minimum* particularly useful for cultivation experiments because after the metacercariae had been removed from the fish tissues and washed several times in sterile Ringer's solution to sterilize them, they could be stored in Tyrode's solution at 4°c for periods of up to 1 month before *in vitro* culture.

Ferguson maintained the flukes in a variety of saline solutions in static cultures under aerobic conditions. Tyrode's solution proved to be the most effective maintenance medium and supported the metacercariae for 2–3 days. He next tried the effect of various supplements on the growth of *P. minimum* and found that neither the addition of horse or rabbit serum, extracts of chicken liver, kidney, duodenum, muscle, ovary, pituitary gland, 10 day old chick embryo extract nor the injection of metacercariae into the chorioallantoic membrane of 10 day old chicks supported metacercariae for more than 2 days, during which no development occurred. Even when the viscosity of the medium was increased with agar, egg white or coagulated blood no better results were obtained.

However, when defibrinated blood from 3 days old unfed chicks was added to Tyrode's solution, the metacercariae survived for up to 2 weeks but again without further development. The addition of either 2%

bovine ovarian extract, yeast extract or ground heat-killed yeast resulted in marked development after 10 days' incubation and a few of the meta-cercariae grew into adult worms containing eggs and sperm. Subsequently Ferguson found that dilution of the Tyrode's solution with water (5:3) was an advantage and even better results were obtained by using serum from chicks up to 6 months old plus unheated yeast extract at pH 6·5 (see below). This medium induced the maturation of large numbers of adult worms within 4–10 days. However the worms produced were abnormal with infertile eggs (Table 5.1). Ferguson also found that serum from the black crowned night heron (an abnormal host of *P.minimum*) was toxic.

TABLE 5.1. Comparison between worms matured in Herons, Chicks and *in vitro*

	Heron	Chick	*In vitro*
Time of egg production	35–40 hr	2–7 days	4–10 days
Gametogenesis	Normal	Abnormal	Abnormal
Sperm	Active	Inactive	Inactive
Eggs	Normal shape fertile	Normal shape fertile	Abnormal shape infertile

Posthodiplostomum minimum
(Ferguson, 1940)

MEDIUM

1 *Tyrode's solution* (p. 350) diluted with distilled water, 5:3.
2 *Serum* from chickens up to 6 months old (starved for 24 hr previously).
3 *Yeast extract*—prepared by placing living baker's yeast cells, free from bacteria, on the surface of a medium composed of 1% glucose in 2% nutrient agar contained in Blake bottles. After about 4 days of growth at room temperature, 10 ml of sterile tap water are added to each bottle and the yeast cells washed from the surface of the medium. This suspension is transferred to test tubes whereupon the yeast cells gradually sink to the bottom. Enough sterile melted petroleum jelly is added to each tube to form a film ½ in. thick over the yeast suspension. The tubes are then incubated at 37°c for 1 month after which time the yeast cells are killed by heating at 75–80°c for 1 hr. The supernatant fluid comprises the yeast extract.

The above ingredients are combined in the proportions of 2 ml of Tyrode's solution to 3 drops of chicken serum to 3 drops of yeast extract.

TECHNIQUE

Metacercariae are obtained from infected pumpkinseed sun-fish (*Lepomis gibbosus*) by removing the infected organs carefully (usually liver or kidney) into test tubes containing filtered pepsin solution (Berkefeld N). The tubes are incubated at 37°c for 1 hr during which time the metacercarial cysts become freed from the tissues and later the larvae themselves are liberated. The cysts and larvae are washed several times in sterile Ringer's solution (p. 350) to remove tissue debris before final treatment with pepsin solution (20 min at 37°c). The metacercariae are then rewashed several times in sterile Ringer's solution before being surface sterilized by rapid gravity separation from Ringer's solution several times. Metacercariae are allowed to fall through a column of sterile Ringer's solution; they deposit faster than bacteria and are thus separated from them. These metacercariae can then be stored up to 1 month in Tyrode's solution at 4°c or used directly for culture experiments.

The metacercariae are cultured in 2 ml of medium in test-tubes (13 × 100 mm) plugged with cotton wool, covered with Parafilm (Lindsay & Williams Ltd.) and incubated at 39°c.

Ferguson found that metacercariae developed into adults within a few days. Spermatozoa and ova were produced but were abnormal and non-viable.

IV. PLAGIORCHIDAE

1. *HAPLOMETRA CYLINDRACEA*

This trematode inhabits poikilothermic hosts and probably has less rigid metabolic demands since it can survive in physiological saline at room temperature for several days, even under non-sterile conditions. Dawes & Muller (1957) have carried out several experiments to compare Ringer's and Hédon-Fleig's solutions as suitable culture media for this frog lung-fluke. *Haplometra cylindracea* were removed from the lungs of infected frogs and maintained in the balanced salt solutions at a pH of 8·2–8·4 at 20°c. The worms survived for several days under non-sterile conditions but the maximum survival period was obtained in Hédon-Fleig's solution which kept the flukes active for a maximum period of 105 days (48–105 days). The addition of 0·5% glucose had no effect on longevity although in the absence of glucose their endogenous glycogen reserves dropped from 1·5% to 0·8% of the wet weight. The addition of beef extract or tryptose was slightly beneficial in that the maximum survival period was increased to 110 days but the worms were abnormal. This was apparent within the first 5 days of culture for in all the specimens examined the rate of mitosis had dropped from 24 divisions/1,000 spermatocytes *in vivo* to 14 divisions/1,000 spermatocytes *in vitro* (see Bell & Smyth, 1958 for a description of their mitotic index technique).

Haplometra cylindracea
(Dawes & Muller, 1957)

MEDIUM

1   *Hédon-Fleig solution* (modified by the substitution of NaH_2PO_4 for Na_2HPO_4 with consequent alteration of the pH range from 8·4–8·8 to 8·2–8·4):

	g/l.	Molarity
NaCl	7·0	0·120
KCl	0·3	0·004
$CaCl_2$	0·1	0·0009
$MgSO_4.7H_2O$	0·3	0·0011
$NaH_2PO_4.2H_2O$	0·5	0·0032
$NaHCO_3$	1·5	0·018

2   *Frog Ringer solution* (p. 350).
Either of the above solutions, sterilized by filtration, may be used with the addition of 0·5% glucose.
3   Hédon-Fleig solution enriched with 'Bacto' beef extract (0·3%), NaCl (0·5%), 'Bacto' tryptose (1·0%) and glucose (0·5%).

TECHNIQUE

The flukes are removed aseptically from the lungs of frogs and cultured in Macartney bottles each containing 20 ml of medium and 1 fluke. The bottles are incubated at 20°c and the medium changed weekly.

Dawes & Muller showed that similar survival periods could be obtained with Hédon-Fleig's or Ringer's solution with or without glucose (64–71 days mean survival periods) but the best medium was the supplemented one shown above (3). The mean survival period in this was 88 (57–110) days. However, after 5 days of culture, abnormalities could be detected in the testes and in spermatogenesis.

2. *HAEMATOLECHUS MEDIOPLEXUS*

A few experiments have been carried out on another frog lung-fluke, *Haematolechus*. Some slight success has been obtained by Churchill & Crowther (1961) who managed to maintain 1 adult on Difco nutrient agar with an overlay of Ringer's solution for 40 days. During this time fresh Ringer was added on the 4th, 18th and 33rd days but no mention was made of the histological picture of the worm.

Burton (1962) demonstrated the uptake of glucose by *H.medioplexus in vitro*. Maintenance of the worms for 50 hr in saline containing 1–2% glucose yielded constant glycogen levels whereas glycogen was partially lost from the oral sucker, pharynx and subcuticular parenchyma in the absence of glucose during the same period. He also incubated the worms in saline containing radioglucose and demonstrated radioactivity in the same areas as had become depleted of glycogen in the absence of glucose. Radioactivity was also demonstrated in newly developed sperm. Thus the worms required an exogenous supply of glucose for the maintenance of glycogen reserves and for spermatogenesis.

V. TROGLOTREMATODAE

1. *PARAGONIMUS*

The earliest attempts to cultivate these flukes were made by Yokogawa *et al.* (1955, 1958). They removed metacercariae of *Paragonimus westermani* from *Eriocheir japonicus* and incubated 107 of them in sterile Tyrode's solution (pH 8·0–8·4) at 38°c for 8–10 hr. The excysted metacercariae thus obtained remained alive for 2–3 weeks in Tyrode's solution alone or they could be cultured in a medium consisting of equal parts of cat serum and Tyrode's solution plus antibiotics (penicillin, 100 i.u./ml; strepto-mycin, 100 µg/ml) at pH 7·0–7·4 (p. 187). Small quantities of cat erythro-cytes and chick embryo extract were added after 3 weeks and thereafter at irregular intervals and the blood cells were seen to be ingested by the larvae. They survived for 202 days under these conditions and during this time showed a 12-fold increase in size and marked signs of organo-genesis, particularly of the ovary, uterus and testis.

The use of human, dog, cow, rabbit or goat sera, or chick embryo extract as media were no improvement on the above medium and neither was there any difference noted between serum from infected or uninfected cats.

Subsequently Beaver *et al.* (1964) have described a technique for maintaining the eggs of *Paragonimus kellicotti* in Harada-Mori cultures. These consisted of a thin film of infected faeces spread on a strip of filter paper dipping into a shallow reservoir of water in an upright test tube. The cultures were stoppered and maintained at 22–26°c and within 17–20 days all the eggs had developed miracidia. These remained viable for up to 3 months and would infect snails either by allowing the latter to feed directly on the infective unhatched eggs or by first hatching the eggs by exposure to water and a sudden drop in temperature (in a refrigerator).

Paragonimus westermani Metacercariae
(Yokogawa *et al.*, 1955)

MEDIUM

Serum. Dog, cat, horse, ox or rabbit.
Tyrode's solution (p. 350). pH adjusted to 7·4.
Antibiotics. Penicillin, 100 units/ml; streptomycin, 100 μg/ml.
Erythrocyte suspension. One millilitre of cat blood is collected into sodium citrate and the cells washed 3 times in physiological saline (0·9%) by centrifugation. The cells are finally suspended in 1 ml of Tyrode's solution.

To make up the final medium, the serum is diluted with an equal volume of Tyrode's solution and the antibiotics added. To 1 ml of this solution add 1 drop (1/40 ml) of the erythrocyte suspension and 0·1 ml chick embryo extract (p. 345).

TECHNIQUE

Metacercarial cysts can be isolated from the crab (*Eriocheir japonicus*) intermediate host and washed thoroughly with Tyrode's solution containing the above antibiotics. The metacercariae are incubated overnight (10–12 hr) in small test-tubes (100 × 8 mm) at 39–40°c (20 metacercariae in 3 ml Tyrode's solution); 80% will be active and excysted by this time.

The larvae should be transferred to rubber-stoppered Carrel flasks (4 cm diameter) containing 3 ml of culture medium and incubated at 37°c (2 larvae/flask). The medium is changed after 3 weeks and subsequently every 3–4 days by transferring the larvae (using a wide bore pipette to avoid injury) to fresh medium in a clean flask.

NOTE: for the first 3 weeks the larvae are cultured in Tyrode/serum medium alone, thereafter in this medium plus blood cells and chick embryo extract.

Yokogawa and his colleagues grew these worms from a length of 0·6 mm and a width of 0·26 mm to 2·5–3·0 mm length and 1·5–2·0 mm width. The male reproductive system started to develop and the worms survived for a maximum of 202 days.

VI. OTHER TREMATODA

The conditions favouring the excystment of metacercariae are referred to in a paper by McDaniel (1966) who has studied the excystment of Cryptocotyle lingua metacercariae in detail.

1. CLONORCHIS SINENSIS

Attempts have been made by Hoeppli and his colleagues (Hoeppli & Chu, 1937; Chu, 1938; Hoeppli et al., 1938) to culture both the adults and metacercariae of Clonorchis sinensis in a variety of media. The adults were found to survive at 37°c for 5 months in either horse serum diluted 1:1 with Tyrode's solution or undiluted rabbit plasma, provided the medium was changed weekly. Metacercariae survived for a maximum of 2 weeks in a variety of media. During this time the larvae continued excreting waste products through the excretory bladder but no indications of growth were obtained.

Clonorchis sinensis
(Hoeppli & Chu, 1937)

MEDIUM

Serum. Horse, rabbit, cat or human serum can be used.
Balanced saline. Tyrode's solution (p. 350).
Plasma. Undiluted heparinated rabbit plasma.

Either serum diluted with an equal volume of Tyrode's solution or undiluted rabbit plasma can be used to culture Clonorchis sinensis.

TECHNIQUE

Adult and immature C. sinensis are obtained, with due sterile precautions, from experimentally infected cats and rabbits. The worms are cultured in 3 ml of medium (1–3 worms/flask) in rubber-stoppered, modified Carrel flasks (0·4 cm high). This volume of medium almost completely fills the flasks, which are incubated at 37°c. The optimum pH lies between 7 and 8 and the medium should be changed weekly.

Hoeppli & Chu maintained both immature and adult worms for 5 months in the above media but no growth was obtained. Worm fragments were maintained for 1 month when haemoglobin was added to the medium and muscular contraction continued throughout this period. The addition of small quantities of glycogen, cystine, lecithin, haemoglobin or bile to the medium had no effect on the growth or survival of whole worms.

2. CYCLOCOELUM MICROSTOMUM

The only attempt to cultivate *Cyclocoelum microstomum* has been made by Ingersoll (1956) who tested 19 different culture media on the redia stage. The most successful medium tried ('Medium B') consisted of 10 ml of 0·9% sodium chloride; 2 ml 2% agar; 4 ml 2% glucose; 7·5 ml fresh rabbit-blood serum; 6·5 ml Carriker's saline and 8 ml chick embryo extract. This supported normal activity in the larvae for 12 days with a maximum survival time of 14 days, provided several rediae were cultured together (cultures containing only a few rediae did not survive as well) but no growth occurred during this time.

3. GYNAECOTYLA ADUNCA

The metacercariae of *Gynaecotyla adunca* have been grown into adults *in vitro* by Hunter & Chait (1952). The larvae were induced to excyst and then cultured in 1% sea water (pH 7·4–7·8) at 40°c. Spermatozoa appeared in the cirrus 1–3 hr after excystment and normal eggs were shed within 80 hr. The maximum survival time obtained *in vitro* was 8 days.

4. MONOGENEA

Llewellyn (1957) has outlined a culture technique for maintaining monogenean trematode adults and larvae, obtained from fishes, prior to morphological examination. The parasites he studied were *Diplectanum aequans*, *Entobdella soleae*, *Acanthocotyle lobianchi*, *Polystoma integerrimum*, *Rajonchocotyle emarginata*, *Plectanocotyle gurnardi*, *Anthocotyle merluccii*, *Gastrocotyle trachuri*, *Microcotyle labracis*, *Diclidophora merlangi* and *D.luscae*. The adult trematodes were transferred as soon as possible to dishes of fresh sea water and rinsed free of mucus in several changes of Berkefeld-filtered sea water. They were then maintained in filtered sea water in Petri dishes kept in the dark at various temperatures. No attempts were made to keep the cultures sterile.

The worms survived under these conditions and continued to produce eggs for 3–6 days at 13°c but they survived longer (2–3 weeks) at 3–7°c although they did not produce eggs at all at this lower temperature. When egg capsules were maintained in a similar manner little or no development took place below 8°c. At 13°c embryonic development of *P.gurnardi* was found to be completed in 21–30 days whereas the embryos of *A.merlucci*, *G.trachuri* and *D.merlangi* failed to complete development at this temperature. At 18°c *P. gurnardi* hatched after 13–16 days incubation and *A.merlucci* after 21 days. At 20°c the periods, in days, of embryonic development were as follows: *Dip.aequans*, 5; *P.gurnardi*, 8–11; *A.merlucci*, 10; *E.soleae*, *M.labracis* and *G.trachuri*, 14–16; *R.emarginata*, 25; and *D.merlangi*, 27.

5. *PHILOPHTHALMUS*

Fried (1962a, b) studied the survival of metacercariae of the ocular trematode *Philophthalmus* recovered from infected snails. A variety of saline media were tried and the survival times varied from 2 hr in sea water to 3 days in sea water plus glucose. The best results were obtained in serum-Tyrode's solution in which 1 fluke survived 9 days when the medium was changed every 3 days. If yolk was added the flukes ingested it and the genital primordium increased in size. Immature adults survived in medium 199 for 5 days.

TABLE 5.2. Cultivation of Trematoda

Species	Stage	Maximum survival (days)	Author	Date
Clonorchis sinensis	L	14	Chu	1938
	A	5 months	Hoeppli & Chu	1937
	—	—	Hoeppli *et al.*	1938
Cyclocoelum microstomum	L	14	Ingersoll	1956
Diplostomum	L	—	Ferguson	1943a
	L	—	Ferguson	1943b
Diplostomum phoxini	L	5	Bell & Hopkins	1956
	L	>5	Bell & Smyth	1958
	—	—	Williams *et al.*	1961
	—	—	Williams	1963
	L	6	Wyllie *et al.*	1960
Fasciola hepatica	A	12	Dawes	1954
	A	60 hours	Stephenson	1947
	A	30	Rohrbacher	1957
Fascioloides magna	L	8	Friedl	1961a
	L	8	Friedl	1961b

TABLE 5.2—*contd.*

Species	Stage	Maximum survival (days)	Author	Date
Fasciolopsis buski	L	—	Barlow	1925
Gynaecotyla adunca	L	8	Hunter & Chait	1952
Haematolechus	A	40	Churchill & Crowther	1961
Haematolechus medioplexus	A	50 hours	Burton	1962
Haplometra cylindracea	A	105	Dawes & Muller	1957
Monogenea	A & L	A 21; L 30	Llewellyn	1957
Paragonimus kellicotti	E	3 months	Beaver *et al.*	1964
Paragonimus westermani	L	98	Yokogawa *et al.*	1955
	L	203	Yokogawa *et al.*	1958
Philophthalamus	L	9	Fried	1962a
	L	9	Fried	1962b
Posthodiplostomum minimum	A	10	Ferguson	1940
Rhabdias bufonis	A	51	Churchill & Crowther	1961
Schistosomes	A	—	Senft	1958
Schistosoma japonicum	A	—	Chu	1938
	E	6 months	Ito	1955
	A	64	Ito & Komiya	1955
	A	12	Ito *et al.*	1955
	A	70	Lee & Chu	1935
	A	16	Mao & Lyu	1957
Schistosoma mansoni	L	28	Cheever & Weller	1958
	L	21	Chernin	1963
	L	21	Chernin	1964
	L	42	Clegg	1959
	L	—	Clegg	1961
	L & A	24–42	Clegg	1965
	L	—	Jensen & Stirewalt	1963
	L	—	Jensen *et al.*	1965
	L	76	Mao & Lyu	1957
	E	—	Newsome	1957
	—	—	Newsome & Robinson	1954
	—	—	Otero	1963
	A		Robinson	1956
	A	28–56	Robinson	1957
	A		Robinson	1958
	A		Robinson	1960
	A	18	Ross & Bueding	1950
	A	21	Senft	1963
	A	—	Senft	1965
	A	20–45	Senft & Senft	1962
	A	35	Senft & Weller	1956
	L	51 hours	Targett & Robinson	1964

A = Adults; L = Larvae; E = Eggs.

REFERENCES

BARLOW C.H. (1925). The life cycle of the human intestinal fluke *Fasciolopsis buski* (Lankester). *Am. J. Hyg. Monogr. Ser.* No. 4: 1–98.

BEAVER P.C., MALEK E.A. & LITTLE M.D. (1964). Development of *Spirometra* and *Paragonimus* eggs in Harada-Mori cultures. *J. Parasit.* **50**: 664–666.

BELL E.J. & HOPKINS C.A. (1956). The development of *Diplostomum phoxini* (Strigeidae Trematoda). *Ann. trop. Med. Parasit.* **50**: 275–282.

BELL E.J. & SMYTH J.D. (1958). Cytological and histochemical data for evaluating development of trematodes and pseudophyllidean cestodes *in vivo* and *in vitro* *Parasitology* **48**: 131–148.

BURTON P.R. (1962). *In vitro* uptake of radioglucose by a frog lung fluke and correlation with the histochemical identification of glycogen. *J. Parasit.* **48**: 874–882.

CHEEVER A.W. & WELLER T.H. (1958). Observations on the growth and nutritional requirements of *Schistosoma mansoni in vitro Am. J. Hyg.* **68**: 322–339.

CHERNIN E. (1963). Observations on hearts explanted *in vitro* from the snail *Australorbis glabratus. J. Parasit.* **49**: 353–364.

CHERNIN E. (1964). Maintenance *in vitro* of larval *Schistosoma mansoni* in tissues from the snail *Australorbis glabratus. J. Parasit.* **50**: 531–545.

CHU H.J. (1938). Certain behavior reactions of *Schistosoma japonicum* and *Clonorchis sinensis in vitro. Chin. med. J.* (Suppl. 2): 411–417.

CHURCHILL H.M. & CROWTHER H. (1961). Survival of *Haematolechus spp.* and *Rhabdias bufonis* in artificial media. *J. Parasit.* **47**: 962.

CLEGG J.A. (1959). Development of sperm by *Schistosoma mansoni* cultured *in vitro. Bull. Res. Coun. Israel* **8E**: 1–6.

CLEGG J.A. (1961). A continuous-flow apparatus for *in vitro* culture of *Schistosoma mansoni.* Correspondence *Bull. Res. Coun. Israel* **9E**: 168–170.

CLEGG J.A. (1965). *In vitro* cultivation of *Schistosoma mansoni. Expl Parasit.* **16**: 133–147.

DAWES B. (1954). Maintenance *in vitro* of *Fasciola hepatica. Nature, Lond.* **174**: 664.

DAWES B. & MULLER R. (1957). Maintenance *in vitro* of *Haplometra cylindracea. Nature, Lond.* **180**: 1217.

FERGUSON M.S. (1940). Excystment and sterilization of metacercariae of the avian strigeid trematode *Posthodiplostomum minimum* and their development into adult worms in sterile cultures. *J. Parasit.* **26**: 359–372.

FERGUSON M.S. (1943a). Development of eye-flukes of fishes in lenses of frogs, turtles, birds and mammals. *J. Parasit.* **29**: 136–142.

FERGUSON M.S. (1943b). *In vitro* cultivation of trematode metacercariae free from microorganisms. *J. Parasit.* **29**: 319–323.

FRIED B. (1962a). *In vitro* studies on *Philophthalamus sp.* an ocular trematode. *J. Parasit.* **48**: 510.

FRIED B. (1962b). Growth of *Philophthalamus sp.* (Trematoda) on the chorioalantois of the chick. *J. Parasit.* **48**: 545–550.

FRIEDL F.E. (1960). Induced hatching of operculate eggs. *J. Parasit.* **46**: 454.

FRIEDL F.E. (1961a). Studies on larval *Fascioloides magna.* I. Observations on the survival of rediae *in vitro. J. Parasit.* **47**: 71–75.

FRIEDL F.E. (1961b). Studies on larval *Fascioloides magna.* II. *In vitro* survival of axenic rediae in amino acids and sugars. *J. Parasit.* **47**: 244–247.

HEALY G.M., FISHER D.C. & PARKER R.C. (1954). Nutrition of animal cells in tissue culture. IX. Synthetic medium No. 703. *Canad. J. Biochem.* **32**: 327–337.

HOEPPLI R. & CHU H.J. (1937). Studies on *Clonorchis sinensis in vitro*. In *Festschrift Bernhard Nocht*: 199–203. Hamburg: Inst. Schiffs Tropen-kran kleiten.

HOEPPLI R.J.C., FENG L.C. & CHU H.J. (1938). Attempts to culture helminths of vertebrates in artificial media. *Chin. med. J.* Suppl. No. 2: 343–374.

HUNTER W.S. & CHAIT D.C. (1952). Notes on excystment and culture *in vitro* of the microphallid trematode *Gynaecotyla adunca* (Linton, 1905). *J. Parasit.* **38**: 87.

INGERSOLL E.M. (1956). *In vitro* survival of rediae of *Cyclocoelum microstomum*. *Expl Parasit.* **5**: 231–237.

ITO J. (1955). Studies on hatchability of *Schistosoma japonicum* eggs in several external conditions. *Jap. J. med. Sci. Biol.* **8**:175–184.

ITO J. & KOMIYA Y. (1955). Studies on the survival of *Schistosoma japonicum in vitro*. 2. Survival in a chemically defined medium. *Jap. J. Parasit.* **4**: 258–261.

ITO J., YASURAOKA K. & KOMIYA Y. (1955). Studies on the survival of *Schistosoma japonicum in vitro*. 1. Survival in blood or serum media. *Jap. J. Parasit.* **4**: 12–18.

JENSEN D.V. & STIREWALT M.A. (1963). Development of cercariae of *Schistosoma mansoni* under dialysis membranes in Rose multipurpose chambers. *J. Parasit.* **49** (5. Sect. 2, Suppl.): 61.

JENSEN D.V., STIREWALT M.A. & WALTERS M. (1965). Growth of *Schistosoma mansoni* cercariae under dialysis membranes in Rose multipurpose chambers. *Expl Parasit.* **17**: 15–23.

LEE C.U. & CHU H.J. (1935). Simple technique for studying schistosome worms *in vitro*. *Proc. Soc. exp. Biol. Med.* **32**: 1397–1400.

LLEWELLYN J. (1957). The larvae of some monogenetic trematode parasites of Plymouth fishes. *J. mar. biol. Ass. U.K.* **36**: 243–259.

MAO S.P. & LYU K.L. (1957). [Studies on the cultivation of *Schistosoma japonicum in vitro*.] *Medskaya Parasit.* **26**: 166–172. [In Russian: English summary pp. 171–172].

McDANIEL J.S. (1966). Excystment of *Cryptotyla lingua* metacercariae. *Biol. Bull. mar. biol. lab., Woods Hole* **130**: 369–377.

NEWSOME J. (1957). Storage of live schistosome eggs. *Trans. R. Soc. trop. Med. Hyg.* **51**: 299–300.

NEWSOME J. & ROBINSON D.L.H. (1954). Investigations of methods of maintaining *Schistosoma mansoni in vitro*. *Ann. trop. Med. Parasit.* **48**: 194–200.

OTERO J.G. (1963). The toxicity of *Schistosoma mansoni in vitro*. *Diss. Abstr.* **24**: 1764.

ROBINSON D.L.H. (1956). A routine method for the maintenance of *Schistosoma mansoni in vitro*. *J. Helminth.* **29**: 193–202.

ROBINSON D.L.H. (1957). *Schistosoma mansoni* schistosomulae *in vitro*. *Trans. R. Soc. trop. Med. Hyg.* **51**: 300.

ROBINSON D.L.H. (1958). Demonstration of egg laying by *Schistosoma mansoni in vitro*. *Trans. R. Soc. trop. Med. Hyg.* **52**: 24.

ROBINSON D.L.H. (1960). Egg laying by *Schistosoma mansoni in vitro*. *Ann. trop. Med. Parasit.* **54**: 112–117.

ROSS O.A. & BUEDING E. (1950). Survival of *Schistosoma mansoni in vitro*. *Proc. Soc. exp. Biol. Med.* **73**: 179–182.

ROHRBACHER G.H. (1957). Observations on the survival *in vitro* of bacteria-free adult common liver flukes, *Fasciola hepatica*. *J. Parasit.* **43**: 9–18.

SENFT A.W. (1958). A perfusion apparatus for maintenance and observation of schistosomes *in vitro*. *J. Parasit.* **44**: 652–658.

SENFT A.W. (1963). Observations on the amino acid metabolism of *Schistosoma mansoni* in a chemically defined medium. *Ann. N.Y. Acad. Sci.* **113**: 272–288.

SENFT A.W. (1965). Recent developments in the understanding of amino acid and protein metabolism of *Schistosoma mansoni in vitro. Ann. trop. Med. Parasit.* **59**: 164.

SENFT A.W. & SENFT D.G. (1962). A chemically defined medium for the maintenance of *Schistosoma mansoni. J. Parasit.* **48**: 551–554.

SENFT A.W. & WELLER T.H. (1956). Growth and regeneration of *Schistosoma mansoni in vitro. Proc. Soc. exp. Biol. Med.* **93**: 16–19.

SMYTH J.D. (1959). Maturation of larval pseudophyllidean cestodes and strigeid trematodes under axenic conditions; the significance of nutritional levels in platyhelminth development. *Ann. N.Y. Acad. Sci.* **77**: 102–105.

SMYTH J.D. (1962). *Introduction to animal parasitology*. London: English Universities Press.

SMYTH J.D. (1966). *The physiology of trematodes*. Edinburgh: Oliver and Boyd Ltd.

STEPHENSON W. (1947). Physiological and histochemical observations on the adult liver fluke *Fasciola hepatica* L. I. Survival *in vitro. Parasitology* **38**: 116–144.

TARGETT G.A.T. & ROBINSON D.L.H. (1964). Observations on the *in vitro* survival of miracidia of *Schistosoma mansoni. Ann. trop. Med. Parasit.* **58**: 453–456.

WILLIAMS M.O. (1963). Studies on the nutritional requirements of *Diplostomum phoxini in vitro. Summary of Theses of University of Glasgow*, 1961–1962: 105–106.

WILLIAMS M.O., HOPKINS C.A. & WYLLIE M.R. (1961). The *in vitro* cultivation of strigeid trematodes. III. Yeast as a medium constituent. *Expl Parasit.* **11**: 121–127.

WYLLIE M.R., WILLIAMS M.O. & HOPKINS C.A. (1960). The *in vitro* cultivation of strigeid trematodes. II. Replacement of a yolk medium. *Expl Parasit.* **10**: 51–57.

YOKOGAWA M., OSHIMA T. & KIHATA M. (1955). Studies to maintain excysted metacercariae of *Paragonimus westermani in vitro. J. Parasit.* **41** (6 Sect. 2, Suppl.): 28.

YOKAGAWA M., OSHIMA T. & KIHATA M. (1958). Studies to maintain excysted metacercariae of *Paragonimus westermani in vitro*. II. Development of the excysted metacercariae maintained *in vitro* at 37°c for 203 days. *Jap. J. Parasit.* **7**: 51–55.

YOLLES T.K., MOORE D.V., DE GIUSTI D.L., RIPSOM C.A. & MELENEY H.E. (1947). A technique for the perfusion of laboratory animals for the recovery of schistosomes. *J. Parasit.* **33**: 419–426.

CHAPTER 6

CESTODA

Reference to the excellent review of the 'Biochemistry and Physiology of Tapeworms' by Read & Simmons (1963) is recommended before attempting to culture tapeworms, especially those that have not been previously cultivated *in vitro*. In addition to this the reviews by Smyth (1947b), Baer (1952) and Wardle & McLeod (1952) are recommended for reference to work prior to 1952.

The earliest known reference to the maintenance of cestodes *in vitro* is that of Frisch (1734) who kept the plerocercoids of *Schistocephalus solidus* alive for more than 2 days in river water. Since then numerous workers have attempted to keep cestodes outside the body of the host; in 1793 Abildgaard kept *S.solidus* plerocercoids alive for more than 8 days in fresh tap water and isolated proglottids of *Dipylidium caninum*; *Taenia pisiformis* and *Hymenolepis fringillarum* were kept alive for several days by Dujardin (1837) in a water saturated atmosphere. The most successful of the earlier workers was Lönnberg (1892) who kept *Triaenophorus tricuspidatus* alive for 3–4 weeks in a slightly acid dilute pepsin-peptone solution in sodium chloride, at 10°c in the dark with frequent medium changes (to keep down bacterial contamination).

Thus it was possible to maintain tapeworms *in vitro* for varying periods in simple media but no growth was obtained until it was realized that the cultures must be maintained aseptically. The earliest of such experiments were carried out by Reid & Boles (1949) and by Joyeux & Baer (1938, 1942) who cultured the plerocercoids of *Ligula intestinalis* in a variety of media under aseptic conditions. When the cultures were raised to the temperature of the definitive host some of the larvae became sexually mature and underwent oviposition but were abnormal in that spermatogenesis had not taken place. However major advances in the cultivation of cestodes have been made within the last 20 years and it is to such work that attention is directed.

I. PSEUDOPHYLLIDEA

Smyth has done much to pioneer the *in vitro* cultivation of pseudophyllidean cestodes and has also reviewed the problems relating to such work (1947a, 1955, 1959).

1. *DIPHYLLOBOTHRIUM*

The majority of experiments on the cultivation of *Diphyllobothrium* have been made by Smyth (1947a, 1955, 1958, 1959). He selected *D.dendriticum*, a parasite of seagulls and other fish-eating birds because the adult is smaller (about 40 cm long) than other species (e.g. *D.latum*: 9–12 m long). Another advantage of using this species was that the intermediate stage or plerocercoid which develops in the viscera of fish, if fed to laboratory rats, matured to the adult in the intestine. Initially when the cultivation experiments were started, no satisfactory criteria for assessing development were available and survival alone was used as an indication of success. Later, cell multiplication was used to determine the value of media. In biological media such as serum, the plerocercoids survived up to 10 days but no growth was obtained. However, the value of embryo extract as a growth stimulant was soon recognized and formed the basis of media used in subsequent work. Several difficulties were encountered before a satisfactory technique for culturing this worm was achieved. The worms knotted themselves *in vitro* and degenerated in the region of knotting. Roller tube and cellophane tube cultures were tried but had no effect in overcoming this problem. Eventually, after unsuccessfully trying several methods of culture, Smyth conceived the idea of culturing fragments of the larvae, thus overcoming the physical difficulties associated with culturing such a large plerocercoid larva. Fragments, 1–2 mm long, were cut from the posterior end of the larva and incubated at 40°c in either static Carrell flasks or screw-cap vials which were shaken discontinuously (about 100 times/min). The basic medium that he used was 20% duck embryo extract and this was also supplemented with other nutrients such as serum, monosaccharides and protein hydrolysates. The medium could be renewed every 24, 48 or 72 hr with no significant difference between these cultures or between those that were at rest or were shaken.

In the most successful experiments (in 20% duck embryo extract alone, p. 197) fragments became segmented by the second day, developed uterine and testis anlagen by the third day and by the sixth day had differentiated into proglottids containing cirrus, cirrus sac, testes (containing abnormal sperm), uterus, and ovaries. Differentiated fragments showed little apparent increase in size with the result that each fragment formed a chain of about 20 'miniature' proglottids, about one-fifth to one-tenth the size of mature proglottids from the rat. By the seventh or eighth day autolysis had set in, even in the best cultures. This is the time when the vitellaria should develop and is a time of intense protein synthesis which makes considerable demands on the organism. Smyth considered that the development of these fragments into proglottids was not true cytoplasmic growth and he further postulated that the autolysis of developed proglottids was due to the embryonic tissue attempting to satisfy its excessive nutritional requirements at the expense of its own cells.

Takahashi *et al.* (1959) have attempted the cultivation of the plerocercoids of *D.mansoni*, a species infective to dogs. They tried a variety of saline solutions and temperatures; 0·9% NaCl and a temperature range of 10–20°c was found to be the most satisfactory. When canine serum was added to the saline the plerocercoids survived for 65 days and although they did not grow or develop further, they were still infective to dogs.

Diphyllobothrium dendriticum
(Smyth, 1958, 1959)

MEDIUM

Duck embryo extract. 4 g of embryonic tissue are homogenized in 10 ml Tyrode solution (p. 350). After standing for about 1 hr the supernatant is removed, after centrifugation, and the extract used as the culture medium (EE20).

TECHNIQUE

Fragments, 1–2 mm long, are cut from the posterior quarter of the plerocercoid (see Fig. 6.1) and cultured at 40°c in screw-cap vials (shaken discontinuously about 100 times/min).

Smyth found that the fragments became segmented by the second day, developed genital anlagen by the third day and by the sixth day had become differentiated into recognizable proglottids containing a cirrus, cirrus sac, coiled uterus and testes capsules. However, further cultivation resulted in autolysis on the seventh or eighth day.

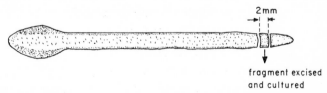

2mm

fragment excised
and cultured

FIGURE 6.1 Position of fragments excised from plerocercoids of *Diphyllobothrium dendriticum* for *in vitro* culture. (From Smyth, 1959.)

2. LIGULA INTESTINALIS

The earliest experiments carried out on the cultivation of *Ligula intestinalis* were those of Joyeux & Baer (1938, 1942) who attempted to culture plerocercoids at 38–42°c in a variety of media, including physiological saline. Maturation was obtained in horse serum and ascitic fluid and eggs were produced in great abundance but were abnormal.

More recently Smyth (1947c, 1949, 1959) turned his attention to the *in vitro* cultivation of this species. Initially (1947c) he obtained development of plerocercoid larvae in plugged tubes containing peptone broth and incubated at 40°c. Sexually mature adults resulted within 7 days (twice the time required *in vivo*) but fertilization and the production of eggs could not be induced by such treatment. Better results were obtained when Smyth (1949) tested a variety of culture media consisting of horse serum alone or media containing various proportions of meat extract and peptone broth in saline. Provided the culture medium was changed daily, horse serum alone induced maturation and oviposition occurred within 70–100 hr, a time comparable with that required *in vivo*. Some of the eggs (6%) were probably fertile since morphologically normal coracidia hatched from them but their infectivity to copepods was not tested. In addition to this Smyth obtained maturation of plerocercoid larvae with either the scolex or the posterior half removed, or of fragments (1–3 cm long) of these larvae. These also developed to the stage of oviposition *in vitro* in peptone broth when the medium was renewed daily.

Smyth attributed his success to the raising of the culture temperature to 40°c and to the efficient buffering powers of serum, since quantities of acid metabolites are produced by the worms *in vitro*. However, Smyth is of the opinion that 'These plerocercoids are unusual in that they contain carbohydrate and protein reserves (Hopkins, 1952) sufficient to satisfy the energy and synthesis requirements of maturation. The medium and culture procedures adopted, therefore, merely provide suitable environmental conditions under which *differentiation* but not *growth* . . . can take place; the medium contributes nothing to the metabolism of development.'

Ligula intestinalis **Plerocercoids**
(Smyth, 1947c, 1949)

MEDIUM

Peptone broth is prepared from ox-heart muscle following the standard bacteriological procedure; 1% peptone is added to replace the precipitated proteins.

Horse serum is used undiluted.

TECHNIQUE

Plerocercoids can be obtained from the roach, *Rutilus rutilus*. Infected fish show a slight but noticeable swelling of the abdomen and dissection reveals the larvae closely packed but free in the body cavity. Fish are killed by pithing with a long fine needle and the surface of the skin is carefully dried and sterilized with alcoholic iodine. The head of the fish is clamped so that the ventral side of the body is nearest the operator. The coelomic cavity is opened under aseptic conditions and the larvae transferred directly into the culture tubes with sterile forceps.

Larvae are cultured in plugged 15 × 3 cm rimless culture tubes containing 50 ml culture medium (1 larva per tube) and incubated in the dark at 40°c (the body temperature of the definitive host, the duck). Either whole larvae, larval fragments (1 cm long) or half larvae (anterior or posterior) may be cultivated. The medium must be changed daily.

Smyth obtained maturation of whole plerocercoid larvae or segments in peptone broth, but these took twice as long to mature as *in vivo* and a few produced abnormal eggs. When the peptone broth was replaced by horse serum, maturation occurred at a speed comparable with that *in vivo* (70–100 hr) and about 6% of the eggs produced were viable, provided the medium was changed daily.

3. *SCHISTOCEPHALUS SOLIDUS*

Armed with the experience gained during experiments on *Ligula intestinalis*, Smyth (1946–1954) developed methods for the cultivation of *Schistocephalus solidus*; these have been reviewed by Smyth (1959).

Initially (Smyth, 1946) the progenetic plerocercoids of *S.solidus* were cultivated at room temperature (16–19°c) in tubes containing peptone broth. They remained active and apparently normal for 300 days but did not undergo any further development at this temperature, indicating that the metabolic processes of plerocercoids could be extremely slow. Following this experiment, Smyth determined the conditions necessary to bring about maturation of the worm. Raising the incubation temperature to 40°C (the temperature of the definitive host) produced dramatic results. The larvae became sexually mature and apparently normal spermatogenesis, oögenesis, vitellogenesis and shell formation occurred within 4–6 days, after which time the worms died. However, fertilization did not occur and consequently the eggs were not viable. Thus a temperature change to that of the definitive host seemed necessary to stimulate maturation *in vitro*.

Replacement of the peptone broth with highly buffered media such as serum alone or calcium carbonate buffered Locke's solution (diluted 1 part in 4 with water) resulted in maturation of the larvae within 40 hr (a time comparable with that required *in vivo*) and production of 0–86% viable eggs (Smyth, 1950); maximum embryonation of eggs occurred from worms cultured in serum. Hopkins (1952) has demonstrated that plerocercoids of this species contain large glycogen reserves and that these were maintained *in vitro* only when glucose was present in the medium; subsequent experiments on the optimum cultivation temperature for these larvae (Smyth, 1952) were carried out in horse serum containing 1% glucose. Normal eggs were not produced at temperatures below 35°c, the optimum being 40°c.

No further development occurred until Smyth (1953, 1954) devised a new cultivation technique to overcome one of the difficulties encountered in this work, namely the inability of the worms to fertilize themselves *in vitro*. This was overcome by culturing them within a length of 6 mm seamless cellulose tubing suspended in a tube of horse serum and shaken at 40°c for 2 days (p. 202). The tubing provided the necessary compression of the larvae during maturation and being semi-permeable it permitted the escape, by diffusion, of metabolic waste products. Most worms matured under these conditions had receptacula filled with spermatozoa and produced eggs with up to 77% fertility. The most successful results were obtained when more than one larva was cultured within the same length of tubing.

Hopkins & McCaig (1963) have pointed out that Smyth's work indicates that the development of adult *Schistocephalus* in the definitive host is primarily a matter of differentiation of tissue and the utilization of endogenous reserves built up during the plerocercoid stage. They went on to determine the growth requirements of plerocercoids and earlier larval stages (Hopkins & Sinha, 1965; McCaig & Hopkins, 1965). A variety of media was tried and several criteria used to assess them. These included the appearance of the worm by eye and microscopy, increase in dry weight, water and glycogen contents, the ability to mature at 40°c and the ability to grow for a subsequent period, and all were compared with normal plerocercoids taken directly from fish.

Negligible weight loss occurred in plerocercoids cultured for 8 days in a control medium (Hanks's saline + 0·65% glucose); all more complex media were therefore compared to this one (McCaig & Hopkins, 1965; see p. 203). The addition of either serum or yeast extract prevented weight loss but supported only a low level of growth; however, when combined, a synergic effect was produced, similar to that found with *Diplostomum phoxini* (Wyllie *et al.*, 1960). In this medium of 0·65% glucose, 0·5% yeast extract and 0·25% horse serum in Hanks's saline at pH 7·1, 21°C and 95% air+5% carbon dioxide, the plerocercoids grew at a rate approaching that found *in vivo* (p. 203). Plerocercoids over 50 mg fresh weight at the end of cultivation were capable of producing eggs but were unable to grow (during a successive culture period of 8 days) as fast as plerocercoids of the same weight taken from fresh fish. Electron microscopy revealed a 'deposit' over the microvilli of cultured plerocercoids, thin at 8 days but dense after 21 days *in vitro* which may explain this inhibition in growth rate. McCaig & Hopkins (1965) also showed that small plerocercoids were metabolically much more active than old plerocercoids; the specific growth rate of a 4 mg dry weight worm being 8–10 times that of a 40 mg worm.

Hopkins & Sinha (1965) using a slightly modified culture medium (0·6% glucose, 0·5% yeast extract, 20% horse serum in Hanks's saline) showed that plerocercoids grow with little diminution of growth rate for 16 days; the rate of growth depending on the size of plerocercoid. When worms of between 10–100 mg fresh weight doubled in weight, their growth rate was halved, the maximum growth rate being obtained at 23°C (over the range 4–31°C). Cultivation at 31°C of worms weighing more than 60 mg resulted in immediate maturation without any growth even though growth occurred in the same medium at lower temperatures. Cultivation for 8 days resulted in 15% weight loss at 32°C, 25% at 35°C and 55% at 40°C. The greater weight loss at the higher temperatures was attributed to greater sperm and egg production. However, worms weighing less than 60 mg grew for an initial period at 32°C, the length of which decreased the closer the weight of the plerocercoid approached 60 mg; after this period growth ceased and the worms matured producing eggs and sperm. Thus Hopkins, McCaig & Sinha have been able to simulate the second intermediate host *in vitro* and induce maturation of these worms.

Schistocephalus solidus Plerocercoids
(Smyth, 1954)

MEDIUM

Horse serum, with or without 1% glucose.

TECHNIQUE

Plerocercoid larvae of *S.solidus* are common parasites of sticklebacks (*Gasterosteus aculeatus*). Infected fish may be kept in the laboratory in fresh running water and killed as required by pithing. The fish is held by its head only and a long fine needle is pushed firmly down the neural canal so that a secure hold can be obtained on the fish for further manipulation without touching the skin (slight pressure on the abdomen of heavily infected fish will prematurely force out the larvae thus risking bacterial contamination). The skin of the fish is carefully dried and sterilized with iodine solution before the needle is firmly clamped to hold the fish horizontal with the ventral surface uppermost. The body cavity is opened, anterior region only, under aseptic conditions and the larvae contained therein transferred to culture with a sterile platinum loop (larvae in the posterior abdomen may be contaminated by faecal droppings and therefore should not be used for culture).

The basis of the culture method is a seamless cellulose tubing (manufactured by the Visking Corporation,) ¼ in. (6 mm) in diameter, which serves admirably as an artificial gut, compressing the worms during cultivation and at the same time, being semipermeable, permitting the undesirable metabolic by-products to escape. It has the added advantage of being able to withstand autoclave sterilization.

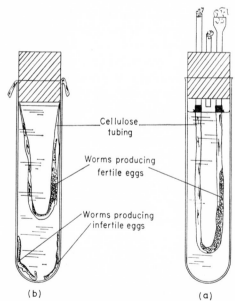

Cellulose tubing

Worms producing fertile eggs

Worms producing infertile eggs

(b)   (a)

FIGURE 6.2 Two varieties of culture tubes incorporating cellulose tubing as an artificial gut. (From Smyth, 1954.)
a. The type used for research work.
b. A simpler type suitable for student experiments.

The cellulose tubing is tied to short glass tubes which pass through a rubber bung, fitting tightly into a large 9×1 in. $(23 \times 2 \cdot 5$ cm) culture tube; one short tube is widened for use as an entrance tube for larvae. A third glass tube opens into the air space above the medium to prevent air pressure differences. The whole is sterilized. Using standard sterile procedure, the large tube is almost filled with horse serum and the inside of the cellulose tubing is moistened with about 1 ml of the same medium (Fig. 6.2a). A simpler modification of this tube (for students' use) is shown in Fig. 6.2b.

Plerocercoids of *Schistocephalus* are inserted into the entrance tube; assisted by gentle shaking or manipulation, larvae move downwards into the cellulose tubing, 1–4 larvae being used per tube. Culture tubes containing larvae are clipped vertically into shaking racks in a water bath at 40°C, and shaken continuously with a horizontal motion throughout the entire period of incubation (2 days). By this means, the medium in each culture tube is maintained in a state of active circulation, with the result that any toxic metabolites produced by the worms are rapidly removed from the immediate region of the cellulose tube and diffused into the medium.

After 48 hr incubation, worms are removed, fixed and sectioned; the cellulose tubing is washed out with water and the eggs collected. They are transferred to water in a watch glass and allowed to develop at 25°C following the usual procedure. When embryonation is complete and hatching commences, the percentage of eggs producing coracidia is estimated by counting 2 samples of 200 eggs, the counting error being estimated at about $\pm 2\%$.

Smyth found that worms, matured by this method, mostly showed receptacula filled with spermatozoa and produced eggs with up to 77% fertility. The most successful results were obtained when more than 1 larva was used per tube.

Schistocephalus solidus Plerocercoids
(McCaig & Hopkins, 1965)

MEDIUM

(i)   Hanks's balanced salt solution (p. 350).

(ii)   Glucose, made up as an isotonic $(6 \cdot 5\%)$ solution and added to give a final concentration of approx. $0 \cdot 65\%$.

(iii)   Horse serum supplied commercially by Burroughs Wellcome. (This is collected in potassium oxalate, recalcified and pasteurized for 2 h at 58°C.)

(iv) 'Difco' dehydrated yeast extract used in a final concentration of 0·5%.

(v) Penicillin 50 units/ml, streptomycin 100 units/ml, and phenol red (as a pH indicator) 2 mg/100 ml of medium.

The complete culture medium consists of 25% horse serum, 0·5% yeast extract, 0·65% glucose in Hanks's saline at pH 7·1.

TECHNIQUE

Schistocephalus plerocercoids are recovered from *Gasterosteus aculeatus*. The fish are killed by pithing, dipped in alcoholic iodine, allowed to dry, and the abdominal cavity opened by a ventral incision. Plerocercoids are removed with fine sterile forceps and placed in culture.

Cultivation is carried out in 125×20 mm roller tubes containing 5 ml of medium which is changed every 48 hr. Culture tubes are closed by placing a 7 cm diameter disc of sterile aluminium foil on top of the tube and twisting tight below the rim, followed by a slightly larger square piece of Parafilm (Lindsay & Williams Ltd.). This method of closure is speedy, aseptic, and permits carbon dioxide equilibration but only a negligible water loss. The roller drum fits inside a gas-tight container, the whole being rotated at 30 rev./hr. On setting up and after changing the medium, the container is flushed with a gas mixture (95% air, 5% carbon dioxide) for 15 min. The amount of gas used is arrived at empirically, the object being to add sufficient to stabilize the pH at $7·1 \pm 0·2$ units. In most cases cultures are run for 8 days at $21°c \pm 1·5°c$.

McCaig & Hopkins recorded dry weight increases of up to 500% for plerocercoids grown for 8 days in the above medium. The specific growth rate of large plerocercoids was only one-tenth of the rate observed with small plerocercoids.

4. *SPIROMETRA MANSONOIDES*

Mueller's work (1958, 1959a, b, c, d, e, 1961a, b, 1966) on the culture of *Spirometra mansonoides*, together with the maintenance of its laboratory hosts (copepods, mice and cats), provides one of the most complete examples of the culture of the larval stages of one particular parasite. His subsequent collaboration with Berntzen (Berntzen & Mueller, 1963, 1964; Berntzen, 1966) made possible the cultivation of the adult worms. Consequently these workers were able to cultivate two-thirds of the life-cycle of *S.mansonoides in vitro*, a most significant and noteworthy feat.

Initially Mueller (1959b, c, 1961a, 1966) described his techniques for recovering large numbers of eggs from infected cats (see also Beaver *et al.* 1964), for hatching large numbers of coracidia simultaneously and for using these to obtain large numbers of copepods (mostly *Cyclops* sp.) infected with procercoid larvae. He used these infected copepods to infect mice and later attempted the *in vitro* culture of advanced plerocercoid larvae recovered from them (1958, 1959a, d, e, 1961b). The larvae were decapitated before culture and the resulting scoleces survived, without further development, up to 12 months *in vitro* in *mixture* 199 (medium 199 plus 10% calf serum). However when chick embryo extract was added to these 9–10 months old cultures the results were dramatic: 'The tip of the head grew out to a needle nosed affair in 24 hr. Then the worms died as though the effort had exhausted the starved tissues.' When freshly decapitated scoleces from large plerocercoids were placed in *mixture* 199 containing chick embryo extract, no such effect occurred and no growth was demonstrated. Mueller remarked that this was reminiscent of cultures of procercoid origin which seemed to slow down markedly after they had attained a length of 5–7 mm (see below). He suggested that the development of this mass of tissue appears to initiate a new phase of the biological clock mechanism which may require a new stimulus not available in the medium.

Mueller later obtained growth of plerocercoids *in vitro* when young larvae were used; these developed in *mixture* 199 with chick embryo extract when incubated in roller cultures at 37°c, provided the medium was changed daily. The larvae grew rapidly at first, almost doubling in size within 24–36 hr but after a length of 5–8 mm had been attained, their metabolism slowed down considerably with consequent depression of growth rate (see above). However the larvae developed from 0·15 to 7 mm within 60 days *in vitro*; they were infective to cats at the end of this period and normal, viable eggs were produced. Similar results were obtained using proceroid larvae recovered from laboratory infected copepods. These larvae grew to a length of 20 mm within 60 days and all were infective to cats. Second generation procercoids, resulting from this infection by cultured material, were also grown *in vitro* and once again were infective to cats. Thus Mueller was able to replace the second intermediate host by *in vitro* culture.

Berntzen & Mueller (1963, 1964) successfully grew adult *S.mansonoides in vitro*. Initially Mueller grew the procercoid to the infective plerocercoid stage in his laboratory and then sent these cultures to Berntzen who applied his continuous flow technique to them using a similar apparatus to the one he had used previously for the culture of *Trichinella spiralis* (Berntzen,

1965). The process involved cultivation in a medium (115) containing an evaginating solution for the first 72 hr followed by cultivation in the medium alone until the cultures were terminated (p. 208). The optimum gas phase was 90% nitrogen and 10% carbon dioxide. Upon introduction into the culture chamber the plerocercoid scolex evaginated and growth of the neck tissue continued until by 14 days 36% of the worms had segments containing primordia. After 18 days *in vitro* these worms contained 194–301 morphologically normal proglottids (the posterior segments containing double primordia) and measured 48–64 mm in length. During the next 2 days the growth rate slowed down and the cultures were terminated in order to economize in the cost of media. Thus Berntzen successfully supplied the culture conditions required to replace the definitive host in the life-cycle of this parasite.

Spirometra mansonoides Procercoids and Plerocercoids
(Mueller, 1959, a–e, 1966)

MEDIUM

Medium 199 (p. 355 or purchase from Glaxo Ltd. or Microbiological Associates, Inc.). Store at 4°C.

Calf Serum (purchased from Oxo Ltd. or Microbiological Associates, Inc.) Store at −20°C.

Hanks's Balanced Saline (p. 350). Store at 4°C.

Chick Embryo Extract (CEE) is prepared from 11-day-old chick embryos harvested in the usual manner (p. 345) and rinsed in Hanks's saline. The embryos are homogenized in a cooled Waring Blender with an equal volume of cooled Hanks's saline (containing the required amount of antibiotic to give 1,000 units of penicillin and 1,200 μg streptomycin per ml) for 2–3 min. The supernatant is removed after centrifugation in the cold (15 min, 2,000 rev/min) and cleared by filtration through glasswool. Store at −20°C.

Mixture 199 is made by mixing 30 ml of medium 199 (p. 355) concentrate × 10), 30 ml calf serum and 240 ml demineralized water. Store at 4°C.

TECHNIQUE

1 *Procercoids Recovered from Infected Copepods*
Mueller has devised efficient but complicated techniques for the harvesting and hatching of *Spirometra* eggs (1959b, 1966) and for obtaining large

numbers of procercoid larvae from mass cultures of copepods (1959c, 1966). These techniques are outlined below but the original papers give detailed accounts of the methods.

(a) Mueller (1959b, 1966) describes a method for maintaining a colony of cats infected with *S.mansonoides*. (i) The cats are fed a diet of pure horse-meat for 1 week (see Mueller, 1966) when faeces are to be processed for eggs. (ii) The eggs are almost completely freed from foreign matter by a rapid sieving and decanting process. They can be stored in tap water (containing a few drops of alcoholic iodine solution) at 4°c indefinitely. (iii) The eggs are ripened in tap water (to which iodine solution has been added) by incubation for approximately 10 days at 25–27°c. Uniform development of the eggs is obtained by continuously aerating and mechanically agitating the cultures. (iv) Hatching of the eggs is induced by exposure of cultures to direct sunlight (change of water or change of temperature may also be used) yielding dense concentrations of coracidia.

(b) Mueller (1959c, 1966) describes a method for maintaining continuous cultures of copepods (various species of *Cyclops*) infected with *S.mansonoides* and for harvesting mature procercoid larvae from them. (i) Copepods are cultured on screened hay infusion, aerated continuously and incubated at 23°c. Periodically (at least once a week) activated charcoal is added to reduce fouling of the medium to a minimum. (ii) Late nauplii and early copepodid larvae are more susceptible to infection with coracidia than early nauplii or adults. (iii) Copepods are infected by concentrating large numbers in a beaker with a massive hatch of coracidia; crowding promotes infection by increasing the number of copepods colliding with coracidia. (iv) Procercoids (from copepods infected 14–15 days previously) may be used *either* for feeding mice (10 g) on infected copepods any time after the tenth day of infection (see below) *or* by collecting them axenically in a miniature Baermann apparatus (p. 361). Mature procercoids can force their way out of intact copepods under the influence of heat.

A harvest of procercoids (0·1–0·3 mm long), several thousand or more, is drawn off into a sterile screw-cap tube containing 6 ml *mixture* 199 and allowed to settle. The supernatant is replaced with *mixture* 199–chick embryo extract (1 part chick embryo extract to 4 parts *mixture* 199) and the tubes (a thousand or more larvae per tube) incubated in a roller culture at 37°c. The medium should be replaced daily but sometimes very active cultures require more frequent changes of medium. In addition to the routine medium change, weekly washing of cultures must be carried out to remove precipitated proteins. The worms are washed in saline several times before being transferred to new tubes containing fresh medium.

Mueller has been able to keep cultures for as long as 90 days with very frequent changes of medium. The worms grew rapidly at first and some attained a length of 1 mm within 1 week. The best growth rate he obtained was 10 mm in 28 days. As the worms grew in size, so the numbers per culture tube had to be reduced. Cultured plerocercoids from 3–10 mm long (of procercoid origin) were on various occasions fed to 15 worm-free cats. All of them became infected. The ova so produced were infective to copepods and the second generation procercoids were cultured to infective plerocercoids *in vitro*.

2   *Plerocercoids (Sparganules) Recovered from Infected Mice* (Mueller 1959d) When a culture of infected copepods (see above) is fed to 10–15 g mice, the procercoids penetrate the intestinal wall in from 5–10 days and break out into the abdominal cavity. These immature plerocercoids (sparganules) range from 0·5–1·0 mm in length and may be collected as follows: the infected mouse (5–7 days after infection) is lightly etherized and exsanguinated by decapitation. The animal is then skinned, rinsed under warm tap water to wash off any excess blood and placed in a dish of physiological saline. The abdominal wall is cut and removed leaving the intestinal loops to float freely and the dish is warmed gently by an overhanging lamp: 15 min later the carcass is removed after gentle washing with a pipette and large numbers of minute white worms can be found on the bottom of the dish. These can be picked up with a fine pipette and removed to a tube of saline or *mixture* 199 for washing. Larger plerocercoids should be decapitated and the ragged larval scoleces, measuring 3–5 mm in length, are cultured in *mixture* 199. The screw-cap culture tubes (16 ml capacity) containing several larvae and 6–7 ml of culture medium, are placed in a roller culture apparatus (12 rev/hr) and incubated at 37°c.

Mueller found that although the worms survived up to 9–12 months, and that at the end of this time could be regenerated by intraperitoneal injection into mice, growth of the worms *in vitro* could not be demonstrated. Some elongation of the body occurred but apparently only by exhaustion of tissue reserves, for the worms became thin and transparent.

Spirometra mansonoides Adult
(Berntzen & Mueller, 1964)

MEDIUM

1   *Medium* 115

Berntzen & Mueller obtained their best results in a medium designated 115, composed of several stock solutions as follows:

Stock Solution A (amounts in mg): $NaH_2PO_4.H_2O$, 114; $NaHCO_3$, 35; KCl, 224; $CaCl_2$ (separate), 50; NaCl, 600; $MgSO_4.7H_2O$, 100; and distilled H_2O, 20 ml.

Stock Solution B (amounts in mg): L-arginine hydrochloride, 42; L-aspartic acid, 26·6; L-asparagine, 26·4; L-alanine, 17·8; L-cystine (dissolve in N HCl), 48·0; L-glutamic acid, 29·4; L-glutamine, 29·2; glycine, 15·0; L-histidine, 31·0; L-isoleucine, 26·2; L-leucine, 26·2; L-lysine-hydrochloride, 36·4; L-methionine, 29·8; L-proline, 23·0; L-phenyl alanine, 33·0; L-serine, 21·0; L-tyrosine (dissolve in N HCl), 36·2; L-tryptophan, 40·8; L-threonine, 23·8; L-valine, 23·4; distilled H_2O, 20 ml.

Stock Solution C (amounts in mg): glucose, 500; β glycerophosphate, 150; d-ribose, 50; glycogen, 50; distilled H_2O, 20 ml.

Stock Solution D (amounts in mg): adenosine triphosphate (disodium), 40·0; adenylic acid, 36·5; guanylic acid, 42·5; cytidylic acid, 32·3; uridylic acid, 32·4; thymidylic acid, 10·26; α- and β-globulin, Cohn Fraction IV (10 mg/ml), 100; distilled H_2O, 20 ml.

Stock Solution E (amounts in mg): sodium acetate, 50·0; sodium pyruvate, 100·0; malic acid, 70·0; α-ketoglutaric acid, 45·0; DL-β-hydroxybutyric acid, 10·0; γ amino-n-butyryl choline chloride, 10·0; fumaric acid, 7·5; (neutralize organic acids with KOH); distilled H_2O, 20 ml.

Stock Solution F: vitamins—thiamine hydrochloride, riboflavin, calcium pantothenate, pyridoxine, *p*-amino benzoic acid, niacin, folic acid, and *i*-inositol, 2·5 mg each; biotin, 1·25 mg; choline chloride, 25·0 mg; vitamin B_{12}, 60·0 units; distilled H_2O, 25 ml. Folic acid and biotin are dissolved in an alkaline solution (KOH in water). Riboflavin is dissolved by heating to 50°c.

Stock Solution G: reducing solution—glutathione (reduced), 1 g; cysteine-hydrochloride, 1 g; Earle's salt solution (p. 350) 100 ml. After dissolving the compounds, the pH of the solution is brought up to 9·0 by the addition of NaOH.

Stock Solution H: a-gamma calf serum (Hyland Laboratories) i.e. serum from newly born unsuckled calves. Such serum contains no γ-globulins.

The working medium is prepared in the following manner: stock solutions A, B, C, D and E are mixed together in the order and in the full amounts indicated. To the resulting solution add 5 ml of vitamin concentrate (stock solution F).

The combined solutions, A, B, C, D, E and F represent the stock medium which is diluted 1:1 with Earle's salt solution (with 0·5% glucose). To complete the working medium, sufficient serum (component H) must be added to equal 20% by volume. Sufficient reducing solution (stock solution G) is added to the medium to give an oxidation-reduction potential of -170 to -190 mv at a pH of 7.2 to 7.4. The pH is corrected by the addition of $NaHCO_3$ or 0.1 N HCl. The amount of solution G needed is approximately 2 ml per 30 ml working medium.

After preparation, the working medium must be sterilized by filtration and stored at $5°c$ until used. Only the amount of working medium needed at one time is prepared from the stock solutions.

2 *Evaginating fluid:* sodium taurocholate, 2 g; trypsin (1:250), 1 g; glutathione (reduced), 400 mg; in 100 ml Earle's salt solution (p. 350) used in a ratio of 3:8 with medium 115 for the first 72 hr of culture.

TECHNIQUE

Either mouse-reared plerocercoids or those reared *in vitro* for 30–60 days (p. 208 or Mueller 1959c) can be used. Only the anterior 10 mm of mouse-reared plerocercoids are introduced into culture, the 'tail' being cut off and discarded; cultured plerocercoids measure from 5–20 mm in length when introduced into the culture apparatus figured below (Fig. 6.3). This apparatus is similar to the one used by Berntzen for the culture of *Trichinella spiralis* (1965) but is modified for *S.mansonoides* culture as follows: a peristaltic-type pump is introduced into the flow line from the reservoir for precise control of medium flow over extended periods of time and a micro gas machine to supply the desired gas mixture and flow rate to the culture chamber (thus eliminating the use of pre-mixed gases).

The continuous-flow apparatus should be used with a gas phase of 90% nitrogen and 10% carbon dioxide and should flow at the rate of 50 ml/24 hr. Medium 115 plus evaginating solution (8:3 by volume) is used for the first 72 hr followed by Medium 115 alone. The apparatus is incubated at $38°c$.

Berntzen & Mueller found that on introduction to the culture chamber the plerocercoid scolex evaginated, attached itself to the surface of the chamber and began rhythmic contractions of its body. After 48 hr the scolex began to change form becoming heavier and more spade shaped. Tissue directly posterior to the scolex elongated and the characteristic folding of larval tissue disappeared. Between 72 and 120 hr the scolex differentiated with the formation of the neck. All larval tissue posterior to this either disintegrated or sloughed off. Growth of the neck tissue continued until segmentation was observed, sometime between 8 and 10 days. Growth and segmentation continued until a chain of proglottids had formed and by 14 days all the proglottids contained pri-

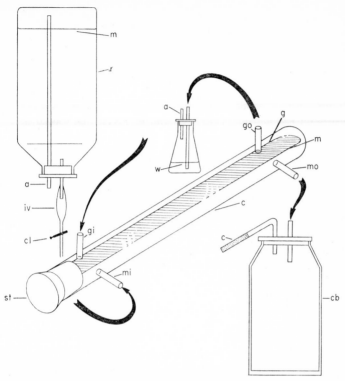

FIGURE 6.3 Continuous flow apparatus. (From Berntzen, 1965). a, Air tube
with cotton wool filters; c, culture chamber (2·5 cm inside diameter, 18 cm
length); cb, medium collecting bottle (500 ml Abbot bottle); cl, flow rate
clamp; g, indicates level of gas phase within the culture chamber; gi, gas inlet
tube (3 mm inside diameter); go, gas outlet tube (3 mm inside diameter); iv,
intravenous drip set; m, indicates medium level; mi, medium inlet tube (3 mm
inside diameter); mo, medium outlet tube (3 mm inside diameter); r, medium
reservoir (1 litre Baxter bottle); st, silicone rubber stopper; w, gas phase exhaust
bottle containing water with merthiolate (rate of gas flow can be determined
by the number of bubbles emitted per unit time). Medium flows by gravity
from the reservoir through the culture chamber and out into the collecting
bottle. The gas is metered from cylinders through a microvalve and cotton
filter into the culture chamber. The flow-rate of the medium is controlled by a
screw-type clamp on the medium inlet line.

mordia, the posterior ones having double primordia. Thirty-six per cent
of cultured worms differentiated and grew, producing a chain of proglottids 48–64 mm long after 18 days *in vitro* when the experiments were
terminated.

15

II. CYCLOPHYLLIDEA

1. *ECHINOCOCCUS*

Although it is generally stated that 2 species of *Echinococcus* (*E.multi-locularis* and *E.granulosus*) exist it should be noted that speciation of this genus is still a matter of dispute.

One of the earliest recorded attempts to culture *Echinococcus* was that of Dévé (1926) who maintained cysts of *E.granulosus* from the lung and liver of sheep for 2 weeks in hydatid cyst fluid containing horse serum at 37°c. This result was improved upon a year later by Coutelen (1927a, b) who maintained hydatid cysts (*E.granulosus*) from sheep's liver for 1 month in hydatid fluid (or peptone broth) containing either horse or ox serum or an alcoholic extract of sheep's liver at pH 7·4 and 37–39°c.

No further attempts to culture *Echinococcus* appear to have been made during the following 20 years.

(i) *Eggs*
Meymarian (1961) carried out some experiments on the hatching and activation of the eggs of *E.granulosus in vitro*. He found that the most effective method was to expose the eggs to whole sheep bile for 30 min at 37°c in test tubes. Later, Webster & Cameron (1963) carried out some preliminary experiments on the culture of *E.multilocularis* onchospheres. They removed eggs from a ripe proglottid and washed them in 6 changes of antibiotic solution. The eggs were then hatched according to the method of Meymarian (1961) and the free onchospheres were transferred to pieces of sponge held in deep-well slides containing a chemically defined medium M150 (p. 217) plus biotin (10 μg/l.) and glycogen (1 g/l.). Thin walled vesicles developed in a few cultures within 13 days but the majority of the cultures became contaminated, even after repeated washings in anti-biotic solution.

(ii) *Larval Stages*
For those who are not familiar with this species of tapeworm it should be mentioned that the larval protoscoleces possess a double potential of development, depending upon the environment to which they are exposed. Thus should the protoscoleces leak out or be injected into a new tissue site (within the same or in a new host) they will develop into

a hydatid cyst, as in secondary hydatidosis. On the other hand if they are ingested by a dog they are capable of strobilization and develop into the adult. This maturation process is a relatively long one (40 days) and this factor, together with the double potential of the protoscoleces, present special problems for *in vitro* culture.

The first report of significant success in the *in vitro* cultivation of *Echinococcus* was that of Rausch & Jentoft (1957), who cultured *E.multilocularis*. Undifferentiated germinal membrane, cut from the cyst wall, was placed in a medium consisting of 40% ascitic fluid in Hanks's saline plus antibiotics supplemented with other nutrients such as vole embryo extract. The temperature of cultivation was 35°c and the medium was changed every 3–4 days. Some cultures were carried out in the presence of HeLa cells. The best cultures proliferated and produced vesicles (cysts) by the twenty-ninth day; in some cultures the subgerminal membrane was present so that by about 55 days up to 20 protoscoleces, which were infective to voles, were present in some of these vesicles. The maximum period of culture was 134 days but unfortunately no details were given of the method.

Lukashenko (1964) carried out some similar experiments with minced tissues, separate cysts and protoscoleces of *E.multilocularis*. His best results were obtained in medium 199 supplemented with bovine serum, cotton rat embryo extract (*Sigmodon hispidus*) and lactalbumin hydrolysate. Within 36 days *in vitro*, vesicles could be seen with the naked eye, a laminated membrane appeared after 54 days and protoscoleces appeared inside the cysts at 99 days.

Growth of *E.granulosus* cysts was reported by Sergeeva & Evranova (1962) who followed the development of cysts for 30 days *in vitro*. They tested 9 media and found that tissue culture of kidney tissue from a new-born rabbit or fibroblasts from chick embryos and a liquid medium containing 45% bovine amniotic fluid, 45% Hanks's saline and 10% calf serum produced the best results. During culture they successfully transferred cyst tissue to fresh media. The following year Schwabe *et al.* (1963) reported on their attempts to maintain *E.granulosus* scoleces *in vitro* in order to test the effect of drugs on them. It is perhaps worth noting that the scoleces survived for at least 8 days in Krebs-Ringer diluted 1 part in 4 with distilled water.

Several workers (Gurri, 1963; Pauluzzi *et al.*, 1965) have demonstrated that when *E.multilocularis* protoscoleces are cultured in medium 199 supplemented with 20% bovine serum or other natural media, they normally differentiate into the cystic stage and secrete a laminated membrane. During the same period extensive studies on the culture of the hydatid organism were carried out by Smyth (1962, 1964), Yamashita *et al.* (1962) and by Webster & Cameron (1963). Yamashita *et al.* worked exclusively on *E.multilocularis* in Japan and Smyth exclusively on *E.granulosus* in Australia, but the results of these 2 groups of workers were almost identical.

Smyth obtained the *E.granulosus* protscoleces from the lungs or liver of sheep or cattle; pepsin was used to free the protoscoleces from the germinal membranes. He used a variety of natural media (hydatid fluid, bovine serum, bovine amniotic fluid), embryo extracts (chick and bovine) and synthetic media (medium 199) and combinations of these as culture media. Yamashita *et al.* on the other hand freed the protoscoleces from the germinal membrane of the brood capsules with trypsin, before culturing them in a basic medium of 0·5% lactalbumin hydrolysate in Hanks's saline reinforced with bovine serum, bovine bile and liver extract. Both groups of workers found that protoscoleces became vesicular under the culture conditions provided and after a time secreted a laminated membrane. They showed that vesiculation could take place either by the protoscolex itself becoming vesicular and secreting a laminated membrane or by the formation of a posterior vacuole. Smyth reported the formation of 'cells or clusters of cells within the cysts' and Yamashita *et al.* described the formation of germinal cells, similar to the early stage of a brood capsule, in some of the cysts.

Quite clearly both groups of experiments induced the development of the vesicular larval stage but in neither case were protoscoleces actually formed nor was there any indication of strobilization, although Smyth reported worm-like movements of some of the protoscoleces in his experiments.

Somewhat more encouraging results were obtained by Webster & Cameron (1963) mainly with *E.multilocularis* but also with *E.granulosus*. They tested an extensive range of 46 media and found Morgan's medium M150 to be the most useful. Small intact cysts produced new vesicles in this medium, even when unsupplemented, and proliferated by the fourth day *in vitro*. Numerous vesicles usually developed but only once did new protoscoleces develop, when the medium was supplemented with glucose, glycogen, Bacto yeast (Difco), vitamins and co-enzymes. However when protoscoleces were used, Webster & Cameron found that by changing the culture conditions they could induce either the formation of new vesicles or the formation of segments. Vesiculation occurred in most media in much the same way as in the cultures of Yamashita *et al.* and Smyth. However in certain complex media, made up mainly of synthetic materials but containing some natural ingredients, larvae became segmented forming

3 segments and attaining a length of 0·55 mm within 3 weeks before ultimately degenerating at the end of 7 weeks. Somewhat comparable results were obtained with *E.granulosus*. Webster & Cameron deduced that vesiculation of protoscoleces was an indication of abnormal culture conditions (e.g. the inclusion of 5% serum in any of the media resulted in vesiculation) and that slight acidity of culture (pH 6·8) induced strobilization. Thus the first major step in the development of *Echinococcus in vitro* was achieved, the inducement at will of development in the adult *or* larval direction.

Smyth and his colleagues (Smyth *et al.*, 1966; Smyth, 1967) have now had some success in analysing the factors controlling the differentiation of the hydatid organism and have obtained development of the protoscolex *in vitro* either to a hydatid cyst or to a 3 segment strobilate adult (Fig. 6.4 and p. 222) once again, depending upon the culture conditions they used. One of the chief problems to be overcome was that of obtaining satisfactory evagination of the protoscoleces. Although some evagination occurred without treatment, the process was greatly accelerated by treatment with pepsin (de Rycke & van Grembergen, 1965) followed by pancreatin and trypsin in the presence of bile (Smyth *et al.*, 1966). This induced rapid evagination of more than 90% of the protoscoleces. Having overcome the problem of evagination in this way, they attempted to culture the parasite in both mono- and di-phasic media with both liquid and solid phases. They found that if the evaginated larvae were cultured in liquid media they developed to the cystic stage, whereas if cultured in a diphasic medium with a nutritive substrate (e.g. coagulated bovine serum) with which the worm can establish intimate contact, development to the strobilate stage resulted (Fig. 6.4). It is interesting to note that the gas phase in either type of culture contained quite a high proportion of oxygen (8·8% oxygen and 5% carbon dioxide in nitrogen). Smyth and his colleagues consider that the solid substrate acts both as a supporting surface and a direct source of nutriment since they regard the scolex of *Echinococcus* as essentially placental in nature. This view is supported by the facts that intimate contact is maintained with the intestinal villi by the scoleces of the worms *in vivo* and that electron microscopy has revealed that microtriches (cuticular projections probably concerned with the process of absorption) are present only in the anterior region of the worm.

The strobilate worms produced in these diphasic cultures have not matured or produced eggs *in vitro*. Some success has been achieved in this direction (Smyth & Howkins, 1966) by culturing strobilate immature worms taken from the dog. Such worms have been successfully surface sterilized with antibiotics before culture in a liquid or, more successfully, in a diphasic medium (p. 222) resulting in maturation of 28–38 day-old worms within 6–14 days *in vitro*. Ova produced *in vitro* appeared to be normal but, because of the risks involved, were not tested for infectivity to sheep.

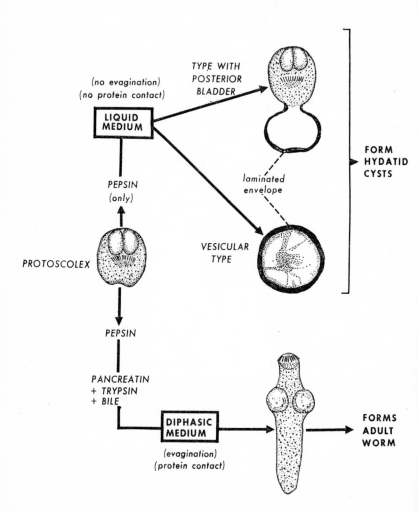

FIGURE 6.4 Pattern of differentiation of the protoscoleces of *Echinococcus granulosus* in liquid (monophasic) and diphasic media: strobilization only occurs in diphasic medium. Unevaginated protoscoleces form miniature hydatid cysts. (From Smyth *et al.*, 1966.)

Echinoccus

(Webster & Cameron, 1963)

MEDIA

1 M150 (p. 356) excluding penicillin, supplemented as follows (quantities/ l. final medium).

2 H-10

M150 supplemented with 0·1 ml biotin (10 mg biotin + 1 ml N-HCl in 100 ml distilled water) and 1 g glycogen.

3 H-17

M150 supplemented with 0·1 ml biotin solution (see above), 10 ml vitamin C solution (cysteine hydrochloride, 260 mg; glutathione, 100 mg; ascorbic acid, 50 mg; distilled water to 100 ml. Dilute 1/100 for working solution), 1·0 ml vitamin B_{12} (1 mg crystalline vitamin B_{12} in 10 ml distilled water), 2·0 ml coenzyme solution [TPN, 2 mg; coenzyme A, 2 mg; cozymase (coenzyme 1), 2 mg; distilled water 10 ml], 0·1 ml sodium taurocholate (500 mg/100 ml distilled water), 10 ml glucosamine (500 mg/50 ml distilled water), 150 mg ADP, 1 g glucose, 1 g glycogen and 2 g bacto-yeast (Difco).

4 H-24

M150 supplemented with 5 ml biotin solution (see above), 10 ml vitamin C solution (see above), 2 ml vitamin B_{12} solution (see above), 2 ml coenzyme solution (see above), 10 ml sodium taurocholate solution (see above), 10 ml glucosamine (see above), 2 ml cholic acid (125 mg/10 ml 95% ethanol), 100 mg ADP, 1 g glucose, 1·5 g glycogen, 250 mg bacto-yeast (Difco), 2 g bacto-peptone (Difco), 1 g lactalbumin hydrolysate, 50 ml bovine serum.

TECHNIQUE

Echinococcus multilocularis var. *sibiricensis* is readily maintained in the laboratory in cotton rats (*Sigmodon hispidus*), gerbils (*Gerbillus gerbillus*), and white mice (B6AF-1 strain). Both primary and secondary infections are easily established in cotton rats and mice, whereas gerbils are refractory to primary infections but excellent secondary hosts. Primary infections are made on lightly anaesthetized animals by feeding 0·1 ml of a suspension of onchospheres in water. The cysts develop rapidly in cotton rats and contain mature scoleces within 8 weeks. Secondary infections are established by injecting intraperitoneally, 0·2 ml of a penicillin solution containing scoleces. Twelve consecutive serial passages may be carried through cotton rats, but the parasite alters physiologically and consequently only material of primary or first transfer origin should be used for culture work.

E.multilocularis cysts are aseptically removed from the animal; all of the extraneous tissue is cut away and the cysts are washed in several changes of Hanks's salt solution (p. 350). If small intact cysts are to be used, they are removed at this point and placed in culture vessels. The remainder of the cystic material is minced with scissors in small chopping dishes, placed in a fine mesh sieve, and washed again with Hanks's solution. The filtrate consists almost entirely of scoleces; these are washed once with Hanks's solution and finally with medium, and then transferred with a Pasteur pipette to the culture vessels. The residue remaining in the sieve, composed of cyst wall, brood capsules and scoleces, is used in making minced tissue cultures.

E.granulosus cysts are washed with Wescodyne (obtained from West Chemical Products Ltd.); the fluid and scoleces are then removed with a sterile syringe. This material is transferred to centrifuge tubes and, once the scoleces have settled, the fluid is poured off. After several washings with Hanks's solution, the scoleces are ready to put into culture vessels.

Intact *E.multilocularis* cysts, approximately 0·3 cm in diameter, are cultured in 15 mm test tubes with 4–5 ml of medium. Best results are obtained when the cysts are held in position on the wall of the tube with an adhesive such as M 161 (M 150 without bicarbonate) or held under a loosely fitting layer of perforated cellophane, but new vesicles will develop when the cysts float free in the medium. The tubes are kept stationary in an upright position; any type of agitation causes the delicate new vesicles to break away from the original cyst.

Good vesicular development may be obtained when minced *E.multi-locularis* tissue is cultured in T-15 flasks under a layer of perforated cellophane. The flasks are filled with 4 ml of medium (see below) and kept in a horizontal position, either stationary or on a rocking machine (one turn through a 20° arc/min). Routinely, scoleces are suspended in 4 ml of medium in T-15 flasks. Alternatively, small pieces of glass tube may be lined with filter paper which has been folded at one end to form a sac-like structure; this prevents the scoleces from passing straight through the tube. The tubes are inserted in T-15 flasks and the medium added. All cultures are kept at 37°c. The medium is changed every 24–48 hr.

Webster & Cameron found that they could obtain either proliferation of cyst material or strobilization of scoleces depending upon the culture conditions as follows:

(i) *Whole cysts or minced cyst tissue*

Medium H-17 supported cysts for a maximum of 5 weeks *in vitro*. The optimum pH was 7·4. Five per cent of fertile or sterile cysts (0·3–0·5 cm) or undifferentiated cyst material produced vesicles *in vitro* within 4–5 days. Vesicle formation usually continued for 14 days after which the new cysts degenerated. The maximum size attained by new cysts was 0·15 mm. Often new vesicles became separated from the parent cyst and these in turn continued development and produced new cysts.

(ii) *Scoleces*

Webster & Cameron found that scoleces would start to vesiculate in the presence of unfavourable conditions (e.g. in media H-10, H-17, M 150 or on the addition of serum). The presence of antibiotics in the medium also had an adverse effect and resulted in abnormal development *in vitro*.

In medium H-24 at a pH of 6·8 scoleces remained motile for 7 weeks, increased in size (0·55 mm maximum size), developed a powerful scolex and produced 2–3 segments. If the pH of the medium was raised to neutrality vesiculation resulted. They also found that 'crowding' the worms was beneficial and used 0·1–0·2 ml 'hydatid sand' per flask. Several supplements to medium H-24 were tried and readers are advised to consult the original paper for the results.

Echinococcus granulosus Larval Stages
(Smyth, 1962)

MEDIUM

Beef embryo extract is prepared in the same manner as chick embryo extract (p. 345). Homogenized tissue is extracted with an equal weight of Hanks's saline (p. 350).

Medium 199 (p. 355)

Hydatid fluid is removed aseptically from hydatid cysts during the preparation of material for culture (see below).

Antibiotics—all media contain penicillin G and streptomycin, each 10,000 units/ml.

TECHNIQUE

Hydatids were obtained by Smyth from the lungs and livers of sheep or cattle slaughtered at the local abattoir. To obtain the cyst material or protoscoleces the surface of the liver is painted with alcoholic iodine solution (200 ml saturated alcoholic iodine solution diluted with 50 ml absolute alcohol) and about half the hydatid fluid present removed with a syringe.

Preparation of protoscoleces

The cyst is cut open and its contents, including the germinal membrane are transferred to 100 ml 0·02% crystalline pepsin solution in Hanks's saline at pH 2·0 and incubated at 38°c for 10 min whilst rocking gently. The supernatant is removed and the larvae are rinsed twice with medium 199 (containing 100 units/ml each of penicillin G and streptomycin sulphate). Again the supernatant is removed after allowing the larvae to settle. They are then transferred to culture.

Roller cultures (2 rotations/min) in screw cap tubes (10 or 20 ml McCartney bottles) containing 10–20 ml of medium are incubated at 38°c. The pH of the medium is adjusted to 7·4 initially with carbon dioxide but during culture the gas phase is air. Medium is renewed every 48 hr.

Smyth maintained protoscoleces for more than 100 days in a variety of media shown in Table 6.1 below. The best medium for stimulation of mitotic activity consisted of 10% beef embryo extract +50% hydatid fluid +40% bovine serum. The protoscoleces developed into cysts either by 'becoming vesicular, gradually growing in size and finally becoming enclosed in a laminated envelope, or by forming a "posterior bladder" which became relatively enormous and ultimately absorbed the scolex region, the whole forming a cyst within an "envelope".' No segmentation of protoscoleces was observed.

Echinococcus granulosus Protoscoleces to Adults
(Smyth *et al.*, 1966 and personal communication)

MEDIA

Enzyme solutions: Pepsin, 0·025% in Hanks's saline (p. 350) at a pH of 2·0; pancreatin (USP V) 0·3%; crystalline trypsin, 0·1%; dog bile, 5% (or 2% sodium taurocholate) all in Hanks's saline.

Diphasic medium This consists of bovine serum (15 ml contained in 4 oz Pyrex medical flats) which is coagulated by heat (100°c for 10 min) and the surface of which is roughened. The whole is covered by a liquid phase of medium 199 (p. 355) or Parker 858 (Healey *et al.*, 1955) plus 20% hydatid fluid or 10% inactivated bovine serum.

TABLE 6.1. Composition of media used for *in vitro* cultivation of
Echinococcus granulosus (Smyth, 1962).
(Volumes in ml)

Code no.	Bovine amniotic fluid	Hydatid fluid	Bovine serum	Beef embryo extract (BEE)	Medium 199	Medium L*
L	2	—	—	—	8	—
LS	—	—	2	—	8	—
N	—	—	—	2	—	2
Q	—	—	—	1	—	3
S	—	—	—	2	—	18
Sc	—	—	—	2	—	18
AB	—	—	10	—	—	—
AC	10	—	—	—	—	—
AD	—	10	—	—	—	—
AK	9	—	—	1	—	—
AP	—	9	—	1	—	—
AQ	—	5	4	1	—	—
AR	—	4	4	2	—	—
AS	—	6	4	—	—	—
LT	—	—	4	—	6	—

* See this table.

TECHNIQUE

Protoscoleces are obtained under sterile conditions as follows (Smyth, 1967):

1 Use hydatid cysts as fresh as possible.

2 Sterilize surface of cysts by painting with alcoholic iodine (1% iodine in absolute ethanol); allow to dry.

3 Using a hypodermic syringe (No. 18 needle) puncture the cyst wall and draw off the contained hydatid fluid.

4 Open cyst with sterile instruments using normal aseptic precautions.

5 Remove brood capsules and collect them into a sterile vessel containing hydatid fluid.

6 Treat brood capsules with 100 ml sterile pepsin for 15 min at 38°c.

7 Rinse twice with 50 ml of sterile Hanks's saline.

8 Treat with sterile trypsin—pancreatin—bile solution, at pH 7·6 for 30 min at 38°c.

9 Rinse twice with 50 ml of sterile medium 199.

10 Dispense protoscoleces into culture vessels containing gassed diphasic medium, the gas phase consisting of 5% carbon dioxide + 10% oxygen in nitrogen; the medium is gassed to pH 7·4.

11 Incubate at 38°C. Medium is renewed every 3 days.

Smyth and his colleagues obtained initial segmentation after 21 days culture and 3 segments developed within 50–60 days. Although spermatogenesis and oögenesis occur *in vitro*, shelled eggs do not appear, as impregnation does not occur under these conditions of cultivation. This system thus has the advantage that the physiology of growth, development and maturation *in vitro* can be studied without the formation of embryonated eggs which, of course, form a dangerous health hazard with this species.

These workers also found that differentiation of the protoscoleces into the vesicular or cystic form was encouraged by any 'abnormal' culture conditions such as monophasic medium, low oxygen tension, high oxygen tension ($>20\%$), low (6·5) or high pH or high levels of bile salts.

Echinococcus granulosus Adults
(Smyth & Howkins, 1966)

MEDIA

Hanks's salt solution (p. 350) pH 7·4
Medium 199 (p. 355) containing crystalline penicillin (sodium salt), 1,000 units/ml and streptomycin sulphate, 1,000 units/ml.

Diphasic medium consists of medium 199 plus 10% inactivated bovine serum over a solid base of heat coagulated bovine serum (p. 220). Tetracycline hydrochloride, 50 units/ml (Pfizer Corp.) and nystatin, 100 units/ml are added for the first 7 days of culture to improve the efficiency of the initial surface-sterilizing process.

TECHNIQUE

Dogs are infected by feeding with 1 ml of concentrated brood capsules collected from fresh hydatid cysts of sheep or cattle origin. The Australian strain used by Smyth & Howkins takes 40 days to reach maturity and worms were cultured 28–38 days after infection.

1   The fresh intestine of the dog is removed as rapidly as possible after autopsy (usually within 3 min) and cut into 10 cm lengths, each of which is incised longitudinally.

2   These pieces of intestine are placed immediately into dishes containing Hanks's salt solution (pH 7·4) at 39°c, and allowed to stand for 5–15 min at this temperature.

3   The dishes are examined for worms and all worms found are pooled and rinsed 5 times in medium 199 containing penicillin and streptomycin.

4 After rinsing, the worms are transferred to a culture vessel comprising a screw top 4 oz (150 ml capacity) 'medical flat' bottle containing 20 ml diphasic medium or a screw top Leighton tube (5 ml) and incubated at 39°c. All media are gassed with 8% oxygen plus 5% carbon dioxide in nitrogen. Media are renewed every 2 days or earlier if the pH falls below 7·0 and regassed at the same time. The addition of tetracycline hydrochloride and nystatin for the first 7 days of culture greatly improves the efficiency of the surface sterilizing procedure.

Smyth & Howkins obtained maturation of a 28 day old worm after 14 days *in vitro* and a 35 day old worm after 6 days. Normal ova were produced by these worms *in vitro*.

3. HYMENOLEPIS

Historically, the earliest attempts to maintain adult *Hymenolepis* were those of Dujardin (1837) who kept *H.fringillarum* alive for several days in a moisture saturated atmosphere and Green and Wardle (1941) who kept *H.nana* var. *fraterna* alive for 20 days in dilute Baker's (see Carrell & Lindberg, 1938) tissue culture medium A (10 drops to 5 ml Tyrode's solution) in Petri dishes. The worms were first sterilized by allowing them to fall 10 times through sterile Tyrode's solution.

Subsequent workers however, have directed their attention towards growing the adult worm from the larval stages, or from worm fragments, thus avoiding the difficulty of sterilizing the adult worm before culture. Schiller et al. (1959) were the first workers to obtain growth of *H.diminuta in vitro*. They cultured adult fragments consisting only of the scolex and neck; these were first washed several times in sterile Ringer's and Gey's solutions, containing antibiotics. The fragments were then incubated at 38°c in roller culture tubes containing a variety of media. They obtained growth in a medium consisting of either 50% horse serum and 50% Gey's solution with glucose or 50% horse serum ultra-filtrate and 50% Gey's solution supplemented with vitamins, glucose, amino acids, purines, pyrimidines and salts but optimal growth was obtained when the medium was supplemented with an extract of the worm itself. This resulted in a 30-fold increase in size of the worms by the eleventh day *in vitro* and the formation of 130 segments with some differentiation of reproductive organs. Three out of 5 worms from 11-day cultures were infective to rats resulting in the formation of normal adult *H.diminuta*.

Taylor and her colleagues (Taylor et al., 1960; Taylor, 1961) reported an extensive series of experiments on the cultivation of the early stages of *H.diminuta* and *H.nana*. Precysticercoid and cysticercoid stages were dissected from the beetle intermediate host (*Tribolium confusum*) and sterilized (by washing several times in Ringer's solution containing antibiotics) before culture; the cysticercoid stages were artificially excysted before culture by the technique of Rothman (1959). The media consisted of either a balanced saline solution supplemented with various extracts such as chick embryo, *Tribolium* larvae, rat or mouse intestine, whole tapeworms and metabolites from bacteria isolated from the intestine of rats or mice or medium 199 supplemented with horse or calf serum and additional amino acids. Both static and roller cultures were used over a temperature range of 25–38°C; the gas phase in the tubes was air.

The cysticercoid larvae of *H.diminuta* remained infective to rats after 6 days in a simple culture medium of Ringer's solution, proteose-peptone and glucose at 25°C; when rat serum was added to the culture the larvae remained infective at 30°C but not at 25°C. Similarly *H.nana* cysticercoids remained infective for 5 days at 25°C in a simple salt solution containing glucose. No growth was obtained with these cultures although some signs of development occurred with the early beetle stages of *H.diminuta* at 30°C. Excysted cysticercoid larvae of *H.diminuta* and *H.nana* survived *in vitro* at 38°C in a mixture of medium 199 and horse serum for 7 and 9 days respectively; when calf serum replaced the horse serum they retained their infectivity for 4 and 8 days respectively. However when *H.nana* cultures were supplemented with extract of mouse intestine, juvenile worms, having increased 2-fold in length, were produced.

Berntzen (1960, 1961, 1966) has established a continuous flow cultivation technique which he has successfully used for the cultivation of *H.diminuta* from the excysted cysticercoid to the adult worm containing developing onchospheres, a most dramatic breakthrough in the *in vitro* culture of tapeworms. The adult worms obtained after 15 days in his specially designed apparatus, showed normal scoleces and strobilization with the mature segments containing well developed gonads which could not be differentiated from those of worms which were grown in the normal rat host. The complex culture medium (p. 227) consisted of essential materials which Berntzen considered must be added in the correct sequence. Methyl testosterone was added because of previous reports by other workers that gonadectomized hosts did not support optimal growth of the tapeworm *in vivo*. When methyl testosterone was not included *in vitro*, differentiation of the young proglottid was inhibited. Similarly cultivation of larvae in flasks, tubes or Petri dishes, even though in the same medium and temperature, did not result in any growth or differentiation; Berntzen considered that the continuous movement of the medium with the resultant removal of metabolic waste products was essential for successful culture; also lining the culture tube with filter paper gave the worms a site for attachment of the scolex.

The work of Voge & Berntzen (1961) on the hatching of *H.diminuta* eggs is of interest because relatively few studies have been reported on the successful hatching of tapeworm eggs. They obtained maximum hatching in an extract of adult or larval beetles (*Dermestes vulpinus*) within 15–30 min, provided the shell had been broken mechanically (this was done by shaking with glass beads).

The following year Berntzen (1962) successfully applied his continuous flow technique to the culture of *H.nana* cysticercoids. He used a different and more fully defined medium consisting of balanced saline, amino acids, carbohydrates, Krebs'-cycle intermediates, vitamins and agamma calf serum. Improvements to the culture apparatus allowed more precise control of the gas phase (95% nitrogen and 5% carbon dioxide) and re-use of medium if desired. The cysticercoids took 1–2 days longer than *in vivo* to develop into adults containing viable eggs which were infective to the beetle intermediate host (see Fig. 6.5, below). The optimum temperature was 39°c and antibiotics were not used at any stage during culture as these, contrary to the findings of Taylor (1961), were considered to be harmful to the larvae. Berntzen found that the initial 3–5 days of culture were critical for both species; survival beyond this period resulted in egg-bearing adults without further loss of organisms. The major ingredients of Berntzen's medium (p. 234) were tested and claimed to be essential for successful cultivation (see also Hopkins, 1967 and below). Berntzen's technique has subsequently proved useful for *Spirometra mansonoides* (Berntzen & Mueller, 1964) and for the nematode *Trichinella spiralis* (Berntzen, 1965: see also review by Berntzen, 1966); attempts by other workers to use either his medium or his flow technique for *Echinococcus* (Smyth, 1962; Webster & Cameron, 1963), *Taenia* (Taylor, 1963a, b; Voge, 1963) or even *H.nana* (Hopkins, 1967) have proved unsuccessful.

Hopkins (1967), in a recent review of the *in vitro* cultivation of *H.nana*, criticized Berntzen's work in that he considers that Berntzen has produced little evidence as to which constituents of his medium are essential. Hopkins prefers to culture *H.nana* in roller cultures, for he finds these easier to handle than Berntzen's complex apparatus; one of Hopkins's students (Sinha referred to by Hopkins, 1967), has grown cysticercoid larvae to mature egg-producing adults in roller culture with a medium consisting of yeast extract, liver extract and serum, within 12 days (p. 236). The gas phase of these cultures consisted of 95% nitrogen and 5% carbon dioxide but the worms produced were smaller than those developed *in vivo*. Hopkins concludes in his review that oxygen may well

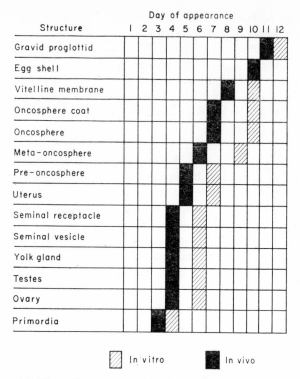

FIGURE 6.5 Time of appearance of various organs and structures in the terminal proglottids of *H.nana* grown *in vivo* and *in vitro*. Day 1 is 24 hr after infection of mice with cysticercoids or 24 hr after inoculation of young worms *in vitro*. For convenience the pre-onchosphere is the primary ball of cells; meta-onchosphere is the stage of onchosphere development where some differentiation has occurred but hooks have not yet formed; onchosphere is the term used when hooks have been formed. (From Berntzen, 1962.)

be necessary in the cultures, as evidenced by the presence of mitochondria in the adult worm (cf. Schiller, 1965; Smyth *et al.*, 1966 who used oxygen in their cultures of *H.diminuta* and *Echinococcus* respectively). He is also of the opinion that antibiotics (penicillin and streptomycin) are not harmful to the worms *in vitro*, thus agreeing with Taylor's previous findings (1961).

  Schiller (1965) has also devised a simplified method for the *in vitro* culture of *Hymenolepis*. He has successfully grown *H.diminuta* cysticercoids to the adult stage using a diphasic medium of a blood agar base (NNN) overlaid with Hanks's balanced saline (p. 233). The cysticercoid larvae were first excysted in undiluted ox bile, and then sterilized by washing in sterile saline containing antibiotics. The larvae were incubated at 37°c in flasks gassed with 97% nitrogen, 3% carbon dioxide and shaken continuously. The worms matured after 24 days *in vitro* producing viable hexacanths which were fully infective to beetles. The cysticercoids recovered from the beetles were also cultured to second generation adults *in vitro*. The only difference between cultured and rat grown worms was one of size, those grown *in vitro* being much smaller. However, Schiller found that if he cultured juvenile worms from the rat 6 days after infection, they grew to a size comparable with that attained *in vivo*.

Thus 3 different techniques have been successfully used to grow the adults of *Hymenolepis*; cultivation of the beetle stages must now be achieved to complete the life-cycle of this parasite *in vitro*.

Note added in proof

De Rycke & Berntzen (1967) have reported that they have grown *H.microstoma in vitro* from the cysticeroid stage to the young tapeworm bearing a terminal proglottid containing testes, seminal vesicle, seminal receptacle, cirrus and ovary. This development was achieved with a modification of medium 115 (Berntzen and Mueller, 1964) supplemented with 0·5% glucose, 30% serum and 1% hamster bile at a pH of 7·5. Cultures were contained in screw-cap culture tubes with a gaseous phase of air at 38°c. The worms increased in length from 0·16 mm to 4·75 mm.

Hymenolepis diminuta
(Berntzen, 1961)

MEDIUM

Base medium: Heparinated human blood is allowed to stand in a refrigerator and the blood cells allowed to settle. Plasma is removed and mixed 1:1 with Tyrode's solution (p. 350; pH 7·4–7·8) at room temperature under sterile conditions. The mixture is allowed to stand until a gel is formed. This is broken up and filtered through a Whatman No. 1 filter. The resultant filtrate is used as the base medium.

Chick embryo extract is prepared by homogenizing 18–20 day old embryos with 50 ml Tyrode's solution per embryo. Homogenization is followed by centrifugation for 10 min at 2,500 rev/min in sterile capped tubes.

16

Preparation of Medium

	Amount used
DL cysteine hydrochloride*	10 ml of 0·10 M
DL thyroxine*	25 ml of 0·025 M
Thiamine chloride*	50 ml of 0·05 M
Nicotinic acid*	50 ml of 0·05 M
Methyl testosterone*	100 ml of 0·025 M
Riboflavin*	25 ml of 0·10 M
Bacto-Yeast Extract* (Difco, B-127)	100 ml of 0·5% solution
Chick embryo extract	100 ml of extract

* Each of these substances is mixed in sterile pyrogen-free water, filtered through a Berkefeld filter and refrigerated until use.

To prepare the stock medium, the organic materials and extracts are added in the amounts and order designated above per 1,000 ml base medium. The base medium plus the organic substances and extracts represent the stock solution which is diluted 1:1 with Tyrode's solution just before use.

TECHNIQUE

H.diminuta cysticercoids are dissected from *Tribolium confusum* beetles in Ringer's solution (p. 350) and fed to male white mice. Concentrates of eggs are obtained from mouse faeces by the zinc sulphate flotation method. Starved *T.confusum* beetles are allowed to feed on the eggs for 24 hr and then maintained at 30°C on enriched flour. Cysticercoids for culture are dissected into Ringer's solution 8 days after feeding. They are sterilized and excysted as follows: cysticercoids, freed from all beetle tissue and as much debris as possible, are pipetted into clean 10 ml centrifuge tubes filled with sterile Tyrode's solution and centrifuged for 2 min at low speed (50–60 rev/min). The supernatant is aspirated by means of the apparatus shown in Fig. 6.6, 4 so that only 0·5 ml of fluid remains at the bottom of the tube. The washing procedure must be repeated 4 or 5 times. After the last wash the cysticercoids are pipetted into the first excysting solution. Both excysting solutions (see below) should be sterilized by filtration and placed in small Petri dishes. Aseptic precautions should be observed throughout the entire procedure.

The cysticercoids are placed in a Stender dish (1·5 in. diameter) containing a freshly prepared 1% solution of pepsin in Ringer's solution (pH 1·5 using N HCl). They are then gently shaken while being incubated in a water bath at 37°C for 30 min. At the end of this time the larvae are washed in dilute Ringer's solution and similarly incubated in a trypsin and bile salt solution (10 min in 0·5% trypsin plus 0·6% sodium tauro-cholate solution in buffered Ringer's solution pH 6·7).

Culture Apparatus (designed initially for the cultivation of *Trichinella spiralis*)

The recirculating culture apparatus operates in the following manner: medium flows by gravity from the reservoir (a) through stopcock (b), reservoir outlet tube (c), connecting tubing (h) and inlet tube (f) to the culture chamber proper (e) where the growing worms are located. The bottom of the culture chamber is lined with a strip of Whatman No. 4 filter paper. The worms attach their scoleces to the paper and flatten their strobilae against its surface. The flow of medium then continues by gravity out of the culture chamber through the outlet tube (d), connecting tube (h) and inlet tube (i) until equilibrium is established with the level of the medium in the reservoir. Medium recirculation then continues by the introduction of gas under continuous positive pressure through the gas inlet tube (j) which forces the medium between the intersection of the gas tube (j) and the medium inlet tube of the reservoir (k) back into the reservoir (a). With the expulsion of the medium into the reservoir the increased positive gas pressure to tube (j) is released and escapes via the exhaust tube (q), giving a reduced pressure in the gas line. This addi-tion of medium to the reservoir (a) creates an unequal state in fluid levels and medium again flows out of the reservoir, as described above, to reach a state of equilibrium. Medium again fills the reservoir return tube between points of intersecting gas line (j) and reservoir inlet tube (k). Thus, the gas escape route from the gas inlet tube (j) is blocked by medium, and positive pressure increases until sufficient pressure is obtained to push the medium over into the reservoir. In this manner controlled continuous flow of medium is achieved. The medium recirculation rate is dependent upon: (1) the rate of gas flow, (2) the inside diameter of the reservoir inlet tube, and (3) the level of medium in the reservoir. Knowing these 3 factors it is possible to calculate the rate of medium recirculation per unit time. There are 2 limiting factors in the rate of medium recircula-tion which are inherent in the culture apparatus. First, the gas flow rate must be slow enough to permit the medium to refill the reservoir inlet tube. Second, the reservoir inlet tube must be sufficiently small in diameter to maintain the gas-medium interface during the turnover of medium into the reservoir. The dimensions of the culture units used in these experiments are given in the legend of Fig. 6.6, 2.

Each culture unit can be used individually. If, however, more than 1 culture unit is required for an experiment, and if the same gas phase is used for all, the units may be employed in a series which is set into opera-

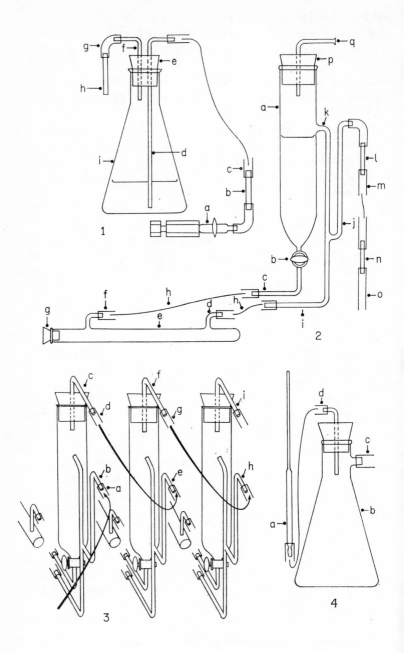

tion using one gas supply line to the first unit. All subsequent units are supplied by connecting the exhaust tube of the first culture unit to the gas delivery tube of the next unit and in this order for as many units as desired. An example of a culture assembly of 3 culture units is illustrated in Fig. 6.6, 3.

When completely assembled, the unit or units are placed in the autoclave and sterilized at 15 lb pressure for 20 min. The sterile culture unit is filled with medium in the following manner. The stopcock of the medium supply line is turned off and sufficient medium is poured into the reservoir

---

FIGURE 6.6 Recirculating apparatus for the cultivation of *Hymenolepis diminuta*. (From Berntzen, 1962.) 1. Gas balancing apparatus used to equilibrate the gas phase of the medium used in replenishing the culture: a, microvalve; b, cotton filter; c, $\frac{1}{8}$-in. surgical tubing; d, gas delivery tube to medium; e, rubber stopper; f, gas exhaust tube; g, $\frac{1}{8}$-in. surgical tubing; h, cotton filter; i, 500 ml Pyrex flask. 2. The complete assembly and dimensions of a single recirculating culture unit which operates on a maximum medium capacity of 100 ml: a, medium reservoir (3·5 cm inside diam. and 17·0 cm in length); b, stopcock (0·2 cm diam. bore); c, outlet tube from reservoir (0·4 cm inside diam. and 11·5 cm total length); d, medium outlet tube of culture chamber (0·4 cm inside diam. and 6·0 cm total length) bent at a right angle in the middle, located 3·5 cm from the sealed end of the culture chamber; e, culture chamber (1·2 cm inside diam. and 20 cm in length), one end of the culture chamber is sealed; f, medium inlet tube to culture chamber (0·4 cm inside diam. and 11·5 cm total length), bent at right angles in the centre, located 4·0 cm from open end of culture chamber; g, solid rubber stopper size No. 00; h, rubber (surgical) connecting tubing (0·5 cm inside diam. and 30 cm in length); i, medium return tube to gas exchange assembly and reservoir (0·4 cm inside diam. and 23 cm in length) bent at a right angle at k and at the opposite end 9·0 cm from the end; j, gas inlet tube (0·3 cm inside diam. and 11·0 cm total length) intersecting the tube i 8·5 cm from k; k, medium inlet tube to reservoir (0·4 cm inside diam.); l, cotton filter No. 2 on gas supply line; m, gas supply line; n, cotton filter No. 1 on gas line; o, gas line connecting tubing to microvalve (0·3 cm inside diam. and length determined by distance from gas source to culture unit); p, rubber stopper closing reservoir (solid rubber No. 8); and q, gas exhaust tube (0·3 cm inside diam. and 12·0 cm total length) bent at right angles in the centre, and filled with a cotton plug. Parts i, j, and k make up the gas exchange assembly and also act as the pump for medium recirculation. The whole unit is made of Pyrex brand glass unless otherwise noted. 3. Recirculating culture assembly of 3 culture units using 1 gas supply line: a, gas supply inlet to unit one; c, gas exhaust tube of culture unit one; d, rubber tube connecting exhaust of culture unit 1 to gas inlet of culture unit 2; e, gas inlet of unit 2; f, gas exhaust tube of unit 2; g, rubber tube connecting exhaust of unit 2 to gas inlet of unit 3; h, gas inlet of unit 3; i, gas exhaust of unit three with cotton filter. 4. Siphon apparatus for pipetting fluids under aseptic conditions: a, long Pasteur pipette (disposable); b, vacuum flask; c, rubber tube to vacuum source; and d, $\frac{1}{8}$-in. diameter surgical tubing.

to fill half the chamber. The stopcock on the medium supply line is then turned on and the rubber tube connected to the culture chamber is filled. When the medium has filled the tube the latter is compressed with the fingers at a point just above the culture chamber, and, with the other hand, pressure is applied to the rubber tubing in a squeezing motion to remove the air which has accumulated in the stopcock. After the air is removed at the stopcock, the culture tube is allowed to fill slowly. While the culture chamber is filling, it is slanted slightly so that the air may escape via the medium outlet tube of the culture chamber. The medium is then allowed to flow out through the outlet tube into the tube connected to the gas exchange assembly. After these steps have been completed the medium in the reservoir is adjusted to a level just below the reservoir inlet tube (k) (Fig. 6.6, 2) and the exhaust tube and stopper are put in place.

When the culture unit has been filled with medium it is connected to the gas supply tube and the gas is turned on to begin the medium exchange. This exchange of medium and gas is allowed to operate at least 30 min before introducing the worms, so as to allow equilibration. At this time the pH of the medium is determined and corrected if necessary.

Inoculation procedure. For inoculation of the culture tubes with excysted worms the following procedure is adopted: (a) the stopcock on the medium inlet is turned off; (b) a haemostat or clamp is placed on the medium outlet tube of the culture chamber; (c) the culture tube is tilted so that the inoculation stopper is upright; (d) the inoculation plug is removed, the organisms are pipetted into the culture chamber with a Pasteur pipette (usually 20 cysticercoid larvae) and an amount of fluid equal to that introduced with the organisms is then withdrawn; (e) the inoculation plug is replaced and the culture tube returned to its original position; (f) the medium outlet is freed of the clamp, the stopcock is turned on in the medium supply line, and the system is ready for operation. The whole apparatus is placed in an incubator and the gas pressure adjusted to the desired flow rate.

Gases used. The gas, 95% nitrogen and 5% carbon dioxide, is metered to the culture unit with a microvalve which is adapted at one end to fit the gas cylinder and at the other end to accept a $\frac{3}{8}$ in. inside diameter surgical rubber tube. This valve can be adjusted to release the gas one bubble at a time. It is by means of this valve that the recirculating rate and gas exchange are controlled. The gas which enters the culture unit is first filtered through 2 cotton filters (l and n, Fig. 6.6, 2) to eliminate another source of contamination of the culture.

Medium replacement. Medium is replenished in the following manner:

(a) the stopcock on the medium inlet is turned off; (b) the exhaust stopper is removed, and the reservoir is emptied of its contents by use of the suction device shown in Fig. 6.6, 4; (c) new medium is poured up to the original level, the exhaust stopper is replaced, and the stopcock opened.

Strict aseptic techniques are observed in all procedures. Contamination of the culture is fatal to the worms. Medium is replenished every 3–5 days depending on the number and age of the worms in culture.

Berntzen grew *H.diminuta* cysticercoids to gravid adults containing infective eggs within 15 days *in vitro*. The average length of worms recovered on day 15 was 20·8 cm. Usually a culture containing 20 larvae yielded about 2–6 adult worms.

Hymenolepis diminuta
(Schiller, 1965)

MEDIUM

A diphasic medium, consisting of a blood-agar base (Novy & MacNeal, 1903; Nicolle, 1908) overlaid with Hanks's balanced salt solution (p. 350) is employed. The medium is prepared as follows: 16 g Difco nutrient agar and 3·5 g NaCl are dissolved in 700 ml distilled water. Subsequent to autoclaving, this solution is mixed thoroughly with 300 ml sterile, defibrinated rabbit blood which has been inactivated by incubation in a water bath for 30 min at 56°c. The blood-agar mixture is then dispensed to sterile, cotton-stoppered 50 ml Erlenmeyer flasks in quantities of 10 ml per flask. After gelation of the blood-agar, 10 ml of Hanks's solution adjusted to pH 7·5 with $NaHCO_3$, and containing 100 units of penicillin and 100 μg streptomycin per ml, are added to each flask. The medium is then preincubated at 32°c for 24 hr to permit diffusion and to assure freedom from bacterial contamination. Before inoculation with tapeworm larvae, the fluid phase of the medium is readjusted to pH 7·5 with NaOH after saturation for 10 min with a gas mixture of 97% nitrogen and 3% carbon dioxide. The pH is determined with a glass electrode during continuous flow of the gas mixture through the solution.

TECHNIQUE

Hymenolepis diminuta cysticercoids dissected from experimentally infected flour beetles 16 days after infection may be excysted artificially by incubating them in undiluted ox bile for 30 min at 37°c. Before being inoculated into the culture medium the excysted larvae are washed 3 times in sterile normal saline containing 100 units of penicillin and 100 μg streptomycin per ml.

From 10 to 15 excysted tapeworm larvae are introduced into each of several flasks and the flasks placed in a metabolic shaking incubator. The cultures are incubated at 37°c, under a gas mixture of 97% nitrogen and 3% carbon dioxide, delivered at a flow rate of approximately 100 ml/min. The vessels are oscillated at about 30 cycles/min.

After 6 days of continuous incubation, the supernatant fluid from each flask is poured into a sterile Petri dish and the young worms are transferred aseptically to fresh media by means of a stainless-steel dissecting hook. The worms are again transferred on the eighth day. At this time powdered glucose is added to the medium, and subsequently throughout the period of incubation, in the amount of 1 mg/ml of fluid overlay. On the tenth day the worms are separated and transferred to individual flasks without further change in the glucose content of the medium. Thereafter, transfers are made every 24 hr. On the twentieth day the volume of Hanks's saline per flask is increased to 20 ml, with powdered glucose added again in the amount of 1 mg/ml. During subsequent cultivation the procedures for preparation of the medium remain unchanged.

By this means Schiller grew *H.diminuta* from the cysticercoid to the adult stage within 24 days *in vitro*. Viable eggs were produced (demonstrated by infectivity to beetles). One worm survived *in vitro* for 62 days and continued to produce eggs from the twenty-fourth day.

Hymenolepis nana
(Berntzen, 1962)

MEDIUM

Medium No. 102:

Amounts given in mg/amount of distilled water indicated for each solution.

Solution A: $NaH_2PO_4.2H_2O$, 114; $NaHCO_3$, 35; KCl, 224; $CaCl_2$ (keep separate), 50; $MgCl_2.6H_2O$, 220; $MgSO_4.7H_2O$, 250; H_2O, 20 ml.

Solution B: L-arginine hydrochloride, 70; L-aspartic acid, 50; L-asparagine, 50; L-alanine, 22·5; β-alanine, 20·0; L-cystine (dissolve in N HCl), 2·5; L-glutamic acid, 70·0; L-glutamine, 70·0; glycine, 85·0; L-histidine, 250·0; L-isoleucine, 5·0; L-leucine, 7·5; L-lysine hydrochloride, 62·5; L-methionine, 6·0; L-proline, 35·0; L-phenylalanine, 20·0; DL-serine, 110·0; L-tyrosine (dissolve in N HCl), 5·0; L-tryptophan,

10·0; L-threonine, 20·0; L-valine, 10·0; Phenol red (optional), 0·02; H_2O, 30·0 ml.

Solution C: Sucrose, 2,668; fructose, 40; glucose, 150; H_2O, 20 ml.

Solution D: Malic acid, 70; α-ketoglutaric acid, 45; succinic acid, 8·0; fumaric acid, 7·5; (neutralize organic acids with KOH); H_2O, 20 ml.

Solution E: Vitamins, separate stock solutions, amounts given in mg/25 ml distilled water: thiamine hydrochloride, 2·5; riboflavin, 2·5; calcium pantothenate, 2·5; pyridoxine hydrochloride, 2·5; *p*-aminobenzoic acid, 2·5; folic acid, 2·5; niacin, 2·5; *i*-inositol, 2·5; biotin, 1·25; choline chloride, 25·0.

Solution F: Agamma calf serum, 20 ml (i.e. serum from newly born calves before suckling—contains very little γ-globulin).

Preparation of medium 102. For preparation of the working medium, the following steps are required: (1) Solutions A, B, C and D are prepared separately and then mixed. (2) The vitamins are added as follows: (a) 2 ml of each vitamin stock solution are mixed together; (b) 0·2 ml of the vitamin mixture is added to each 100 ml of medium (fractions A, B, C and D). (3) The medium composed of fractions A, B, C and D with the added vitamins is sterilized by filtration. (4) The medium is completed by the addition of 20% agamma calf serum (F). The medium is ready for use after the pH is adjusted to 7·0–7·4 by the addition of sterile KOH. The amount of each solution given, when added together, is sufficient medium for 1 culture unit.

The chemicals L-cystine and L-tyrosine are dissolved in 0·1 N HCl. The vitamins folic acid and biotin are dissolved in an alkaline solution (KOH in water). Riboflavin is dissolved by heating to 50°c. The stock vitamins are stored at −20°c. Medium 102 is unstable if kept for long periods at warm temperatures. For this reason the solutions are stored in the refrigerator and filtering is done at 5°c. Berntzen considered that antibiotics were inhibitory to the worms and that they should not be added to the medium and bacterial contamination must be avoided: this is contrary to the findings of other workers (Taylor, 1961; Schiller, 1965; Hopkins, 1967). Medium which is to be used for replacement of old medium must have the gas content adjusted to that in the pumping system.

TECHNIQUE

This is essentially the same as for *Hymenolepis diminuta* (p. 227) with the following exceptions.

Cysticercoids are treated with 1% solution of pepsin in Ringer's solution (p. 350), pH 1·5 at 37°c for 15 min followed by 30 min incubation at 37°C, pH 6·7 in 0·5% trypsin+0·3% sodium taurocholate in buffered Ringer's solution. The worms are cultured in the same apparatus (Fig. 6.6, 2) using the same gas mixture (95% nitrogen and 5% carbon dioxide) and similar precautions have to be adopted for both species.

Berntzen grew *H.nana* cysticercoid larvae to adults containing infective eggs by this technique. The rate of growth *in vitro* (12 days to produce gravid females) compared favourably with that *in vivo* (11 days to produce gravid females).

Hymenolepis nana
(Sinha, reported by Hopkins, 1967)

MEDIUM

Hanks's saline (p. 350)
Liver extract is prepared by homogenizing rat liver with cold water (1 part by weight with 4 parts water)=Liver extract$_{20}$
Liver Extract Medium

Concentration of components	Volume (ml) stock solutions to prepare 100 ml of medium
30% Horse serum	30
0·3% Glucose	5
0·5% Yeast extract*	10
10% Rat liver extract$_{20}$	10
40% Hanks's saline	40
Antibiotics (Sodium penicillin G, 100 i.u./ml Streptomycin sulphate, 100 μg/ml) NaHCO$_3$ (1·4%)+NaOH (0·2 M)	≃ 5 to yield pH 7·5

* Supplied by Oxo Ltd.

TECHNIQUE

Cysticercoid larvae (approximately 400) are dissected from flour beetles and induced to excyst by the following technique: the larvae are placed in 1% pepsin in HCl (1:2,500) at pH 1·7–2·0 for 10–12 min. They are then washed 3 times in Hanks's saline before being placed in 0·5% trypsin (83:1) plus 0·3% sodium taurocholate for 7–10 min. They are again washed 3 times with Hanks's saline and approximately 20 excysted worms are transferred to each culture tube.

The worms are cultured in roller tubes (25 × 125 mm) in the liver extract medium. After adding the worms, the tubes are gassed for 30 sec with a mixture of 95% nitrogen and 5% carbon dioxide and closed by rubber bungs. The gas mixture, after equilibration, brings the pH down to 7·2–7·4 and the cultures are maintained at 37°c. The medium is changed every 3 days.

Sinha was able to grow 35% of the cysticercoid larvae to egg-bearing adults in 12 days, nearly the same time (11 days) as required *in vivo*.

3. *RAILLIETINA CESTICILLUS*

In 1954 Smith reported his attempts to cultivate the fowl cestode *Raillietina cesticillus in vitro*. Cystercercoid larvae were induced to evaginate either by mechanical pressure or by exposure to chicken bile. Evaginated scoleces survived for only 9 hr in Ringer's-glucose-corn starch medium. The phenomenon of evagination was most frequent at 7°c or 40°c, not room temperature; thus a temperature change appeared to be an important physical stimulant for evagination. This seemed also to depend upon the diffusion of liquids into the bladder which increased the internal pressure thus causing or aiding evagination.

When using adult worms, Smith found that they would not survive in semi-solid or solid Ringer's-glucose-corn starch cultures but that they would survive in a liquid culture medium. This consisted of Ringer's-glucose-corn starch medium containing additional vitamins and chicken serum in low concentrations. The cultures were constantly agitated at 40°c and maintained adult *R.cesticillus* in an active condition for 60 hr. High concentrations of vitamins and chicken serum were found to be toxic to the worms and the sterilization of the worms with streptomycin sulphate before culture increased their activity but decreased their survival times.

4. *TAENIA*

Apart from Dujardin (1837) who maintained isolated proglottids of *Taenia pisiformis* in a moisture saturated atmosphere for several days, Mendelsohn (1935) was the first worker to attempt the culture of *Taenia*. He maintained early blastocyst stobilocerci of *T.taeniaeformis* (*T.crassicollis*) *in vitro*. The larvae were removed from the liver of an infected rat and attached, together with a fragment of host tissue, to the wall of a test-tube with chicken plasma. The culture medium consisted of 7 parts balanced saline, 2 parts chick embryo extract and 3 parts filtered horse serum. The tubes were sealed and incubated in a roller culture apparatus at 37·5°C. The maximum survival period was 35 days during which time the scolex invaginated into the blastocyst but no suckers were formed.

Wilmoth (1938, 1940, 1945) investigated the possibility of culturing *T.taeniaeformis* with a view to studying their metabolism. He used both larvae (from cysts in the liver of infected rats) and adults (from infected cats). The larvae were used 5 months after feeding the rats on *Taenia* eggs and their survival noted in a variety of media. Wilmoth noted that survival was better in simple rather than complex media, under aerobic rather than anaerobic conditions. The larvae were able to withstand a wide range of pH (4·6–9·3) and temperature (14–37°C) and were cultured in static rubber-stoppered 250 ml Erlenmeyer flasks (36 larvae/flask) containing 150 ml of medium. Maximum survival (indicated by their activity *in vitro*) of 24 days was obtained in mammalian Ringer's solution with a trace of glucose when the medium was changed every 18 hr. The larvae survived 16 days in Tyrode's solution (containing double concentration of bicarbonate); cat serum was toxic. Wilmoth also tested a gravity-feed perfusion apparatus but the results were not as good as in the static cultures. When he cultured adult worms he obtained a maximum survival period of 3 days in tryptone digest agar (1%) containing a trace of sodium taurocholate and overlaid with Tyrode's solution.

Recently another species of tapeworm, *T.crassiceps*, (Freeman, 1962) has become available in the laboratory. This species is a particularly useful experimental tool because the larval stages bud prolifically (reminiscent of *Echinococcus*) and can be easily maintained in laboratory mice. The larval stages of this parasite were first cultured by Taylor (1963a, b) who used only chemically defined media in her experiments. Cysticerci survived for 12 days in Hanks's saline and considerably longer (33 days) in Eagle's medium. The larvae were treated with acid pepsin, trypsin and bile salt before being cultured in roller culture at 37°C with Eagle's medium, supplemented with sodium taurocholate (p. 239). Although no attempt was made to control the gas phase in the cultures, later experiments (Taylor *et al.* 1966) showed that *T.crassiceps* larvae would have used up all the available oxygen within 4 hr *in vitro*. The medium was changed every 2 days and thus anaerobic conditions prevailed for the greater part of the experiments. A length of 27 mm was attained by larvae cultured in the supplemented Eagle's medium and a few juveniles became segmented. During culture lactic acid was produced by the worms and, if glucose was withheld from the medium, their glycogen reserves were depleted (Taylor *et al.* 1966). Waymouth's medium, NCTC109 and medium 199 were also tried but were not as beneficial as Eagle's medium. Taylor adapted Berntzen's continuous flow apparatus (Taylor,

1961) for the culture of *T.crassiceps* larvae and found with this that neither Berntzen's medium for *Hymenolepis* culture nor the supplemented Eagle's medium supported the larvae for more than 20 days and during this time no growth occurred.

No attempt was made by Taylor to induce asexual reproduction *in vitro* but Robinson *et al.* (1963) briefly reported that larvae, maintained at 38°c in roller tube cultures with medium 199 under 5% carbon dioxide in air, underwent budding; strobilization of mature cysticerci was also obtained. Similarly Voge (1963) reported that a few cysticerci of *T.crassiceps* developed buds when maintained in screw-capped roller tubes at 37°c in a tissue culture medium consisting of Earle's balanced saline, lactalbumin hydrolysate, gelatin, yeast extract and calf serum buffered with sodium bicarbonate. The cysticerci survived from 1–4 months provided the gas phase contained at least 5% carbon dioxide. Voge also found that Berntzen's continuous flow culture used with Berntzen and Mueller's (1963) medium for *Spirometra mansonoides* was not successful for the culture of *T.crassiceps*.

Taenia crassiceps
(Taylor, 1963b)

MEDIUM

Composition of defined medium based on Eagle's medium (p. 355)

	mg/1,000 ml	Approx. equivalent (mM)
L–Arginine	17·4	0·1
L–Cystine	6·0	0·05
L–Histidine	3·2	0·02
L–Isoleucine	26·2	0·2
L–Leucine	13·1	0·1
L–Lysine	18·2	0·1
L–Methionine	7·5	0·05
L–Phenylalanine	8·3	0·05
L–Threonine	11·9	0·1
L–Tryptophan	2·0	0·01
L–Tyrosine	18·0	0·1
L–Valine	11·7	0·1
L–Glutamine	146·0	1·0

	mg/1,000 ml		mg/1,000 ml
Choline	1·0	KCl	400·0
Nicotinic acid	1·0	CaCl$_2$	140·0
Pantothenic acid	1·0	MgSO$_4$.7H$_2$O	100·0
Pyridoxal	1·0	MgCl$_2$.6H$_2$O	100·0
Riboflavine	0·1	Na$_2$HPO$_4$.2H$_2$O	60·0
Thiamine	1·0	KH$_2$PO$_4$	60·0
i-Inositol	1·0	NaHCO$_3$	350·0
Biotin	1·0	Phenol red	20·0
Folic acid	1·0	Penicillin	0·5
Glucose	1,000·0		
NaCl	8,000·0		

Additional supplements: glucose, 1,000 mg/l.; sodium taurocholate, 10 mg/l.

TECHNIQUE

Cysticerci of *T.crassiceps* multiply prolifically in the peritoneal cavity of the laboratory mouse by a process of budding, generally from the non-scolex pole of the larva. The parasites are maintained in the laboratory by injecting cysticerci into the peritoneal cavity of uninfected white mice (T.O. strain). Usually two cysticerci produce about 900–1,200 daughter cysts within 6 months. Some of the daughter cysts may be used for infecting other mice and the remainder used for *in vitro* cultivation. The latter, after aseptic removal from the peritoneal cavity of a freshly killed, infected mouse, are washed 5 times in a sterile, balanced salt solution before culture.

Treatment with enzymes before culture. This consists of pretreatment with 1% acid pepsin (from British Drug Houses Ltd.), acidified with HCl to a pH of 1·7, for 20 min at 37°c followed by exposure to a solution containing 0·2% trypsin and 0·1% sodium taurocholate (pH 7·4; both from Hopkin and Williams Ltd.) for 30 min at 37°c. All larvae after enzymic treatment have everted scoleces and are very active.

The larvae, in groups of about 200, are cultured axenically at 37°c in the above medium (25 ml/group) contained in rubber-stoppered 225 ml Soxhlet bottles. These culture vessels are constantly rotated (1 revolution in 8 min) in a roller culture apparatus and the medium is changed every 2 days. The optimum pH for culture is 7·4 indicated by 0·002% phenol red in the medium.

Taylor found that cysticerci grew into juvenile worms in Eagle's medium plus sodium taurocholate. The 'worms' grew to a length of 27 mm, developed lateral excretory canals, showed signs of strobilization and survived 25 days in an active condition, producing quantities of acid metabolites (e.g. lactic acid; Taylor *et al.*, 1966) *in vitro*.

III. OTHER CESTODES

1. *CREPIDOBOTHRIUM LONNBERGI*

This species was one of the earliest to have been grown *in vitro* (Stunkard, 1932). The adults were taken from *Nicturus* (mud-puppy) and washed in sterile Ringer's solution before being transferred to sterile isotonic glucose-saline (adapted from Craig's medium for intestinal protozoa) in Petri dishes held at room temperature. Various amounts of Hottinger broth (a veal digest) were added and pH 7·3 was found to be optimum. In one experiment the worms were transferred to new medium every 12 hr, and increased to 3–4 times their length and the terminal proglottids became segmented. These worms however were abnormal and sterile. The addition of saline extracts of intestinal mucosa, liver or pancreas (sterilized by filtration) from *Nicturus*, or the use of anaerobic conditions had no beneficial effect on the survival or growth of the worms.

2. *NYBELINA SURRENICOLA*

Wardle (1934) attempted to grow the larval stages of this parasite *in vitro*. These were obtained from the fish *Ophiodon elongatus*, 20% of which were found to be infected from the coastal waters of British Columbia. The larvae occur free in the coelomic cavity and infected fish harbour between 20 and 100 each. After removal from the fish all mucus was washed off the larvae by leaving them in sterile glucose-free Ringer-Locke solution at pH 7·5, for 1 hr. A variety of saline and nutrient media was tested but none induced growth of the larvae. Maximum periods of survival (17 days) were obtained in concentrated Locke's solution (2 times concentrate) containing 0·25% glucose. Wardle found daily changes of medium beneficial to the worms. When they were cultured on nutrient gels such as agar gel their appearance was more 'normal' but they survived for much shorter periods (7–9 days).

3. *MESOCESTOIDES*

This is apparently the first cestode for which presumably normal growth and differentiation of early organ systems of artificially hatched onchospheres has been achieved *in vitro*. Voge (1966, 1967) has reported on the hatching of onchospheres of *Mesocestoides in vitro* which subsequently developed to procercoid-like organisms and thence to stages resembling small tetrathyridia. The parasites increased in size (0·5 mm

TABLE 6.2. Cultivation of Cestoda.

Species	Stage	Survival (days)	Author	Date
Crepidobothrium loennbergi	A	32	Stunkard	1932
Diphyllobothrium dendriticum	—	—	Smyth	1947a
	—	—	Smyth	1955
	—	7	Smyth	1958
	—	—	Smyth	1959
Diphyllobothrium latum	—	—	Le Bas	1924
	—	—	Markov	1938
	—	—	Wardle	1932
	A	—	Wardle & Green	1941
Diphyllobothrium mansoni	L	65	Takahashi *et al.*	1959
Dipyllidium caninum	A	—	Dujardin	1837
Echinococcus	—	—	Smyth	1963
	L–A	49	Webster & Cameron	1963
Echinococcus granulosus	L	28	Coutelen	1927a, b
	L	14	Dévé	1926
	Eggs	—	Meymarian	1961
	—	—	Paluzzi *et al.*	1965
	L	8	Schwabe *et al.*	1963
	L	30	Sergewa & Evanova	1962
	L	—	Smyth	1962
	—	—	Smyth	1963
	—	—	Smyth	1967
	—	—	Smyth *et al.*	1966
	—	—	Smyth & Howkins	1966
Echinococcus multilocularis	L	—	Gurri	1963
	L	—	Lukashenko	1964
	L	134	Rausch & Jentoft	1957
	—	—	Yamashiti *et al.*	1962
Hymenolepis diminuta	—	—	Berntzen	1960
	L–A	15	Berntzen	1961
	A	—	Schiller *et al.*	1959
	L–A	24	Schiller	1965
	—	—	Taylor *et al.*	1960
	—	—	Taylor	1961
	Eggs	—	Voge & Berntzen	1961
Hymenolepis fraterna	A	20	Green & Wardle	1941
	A	20	Wardle & Green	1941
Hymenolepis fringillarum	A	—	Dujardin	1837
Hymenolepis nana	L–A	12	Berntzen	1962
	Eggs	—	Piringer & Piringer	1959
	—	—	Taylor *et al.*	1960
	—	—	Taylor	1961

TABLE 6.2—*contd.*

Species	Stage	Survival (days)	Author	Date
Ligula intestinalis	L	—	Joyeux & Baer	1938
	L	—	Joyeux & Baer	1942
	L–A	7	Smyth	1947c
	L–A	4	Smyth	1949
Mesocestoides	L	56	Voge	1966
	L	56	Voge	1967
	—	—	Voge & Coulombe	1966
	—	—	Tower	1900
Moniezia expansa	—	—	Wardle & Green	1941
Nybelina surrenicola	L	17	Wardle	1934
Raillietina cesticillus	—	—	Smith	1954
Schistocephalus solidus	L	8	Abildgaard	1793
	L	2	Frisch	1734
	L	16	Hopkins & Sinha	1965
	L	13	Smyth	1946
	—	—	Smyth	1947a
	L–A	1·5	Smyth	1950
	—	—	Smyth	1952
	L–A	2	Smyth	1953
	L–A	2	Smyth	1954
Spirometra mansonoides	L	—	Berntzen & Mueller	1963
	—	—	Berntzen & Mueller	1964
	L	12 mths	Mueller	1958
	—	—	Mueller	1959a
	L	60	Mueller	1959b, c, d
Taenia crassiceps	—	—	Robinson *et al.*	1963
	—	—	Taylor	1963a
	L	30	Taylor	1963b
	L	4 mths	Voge	1963
Taenia taeniaeformis	L	35	Mendelsohn	1935
	—	—	Wilmoth	1938
	—	—	Wilmoth	1940
	—	—	Wilmoth	1945
Taenia pisiformis	A	—	Dujardin	1837
Triaenophorus tricuspidatus	A	28	Lönnberg	1892
	A	63	Markov	1939
Miscellaneous	—	—	Ortner-Schönbach	1913
	—	—	Reid & Boles	1949
	L	—	Smyth	1947b
	—	—	Smyth	1955
	L	—	Smyth	1959
	—	—	Stunkard	1932
	—	—	Wardle & McLeod	1952

A = Adult; L = Larva

17

length maximum) within 8 weeks *in vitro* at 25–30°c. Voge & Coulombe (1966) have also obtained growth and multiplication of tetrathyridia removed directly from mice into a number of monophasic and diphasic media, with different gas phases and pH ranges. In diphasic media containing human blood [10% whole blood in Berntzen & Mueller's (1964) medium M115 (p. 208)] asexual multiplication *in vitro* occurred at a rate comparable to that *in vivo* (mouse).

REFERENCES

ABILDGAARD P.C. (1793). Allgemeine Betrachlungen über Eingeweidewürmer. Bemerkungen bei dem Bandwurme des Stachel-barsches oder der Egelschnecke und Beschreibung einiger neuen Bandewurmer mit Figuren. *Schr. naturf. bes. Kbh.* **1:** 1.

BAER J.G. (1952). *Ecology of animal parasites.* Urbana: University of Illinois Press.

BEAVER P.C., MALEK E.A. & LITTLE M.D. (1964). Development of *Spirometra* and *Paragonimus* in Harada-Mori cultures. *J. Parasit.* **50:** 664–666.

BERNTZEN A.K. (1960). An effective method for the *in vitro* culture of *Hymenolepis diminuta. J. Parasit.* **46** (5. Sect. 2, Suppl.): 47.

BERNTZEN A.K. (1961). The *in vitro* cultivation of tapeworms. I. Growth of *Hymenolepis diminuta* (Cestoda: Cyclophyllidea). *J. Parasit.* **47:** 351–355.

BERNTZEN A.K. (1962). *In vitro* cultivation of tapeworms. II. Growth and maintenance of *Hymenolepis nana* (Cestoda: Cyclophyllidea). *J. Parasit.* **48:** 785–797.

BERNTZEN A.K. (1965). Comparative growth and development of *Trichinella spiralis in vitro* and *in vivo* with a redescription of the life cycle. *Expl Parasit.* **16:** 74–106.

BERNTZEN A.K. (1966). *In vitro* cultivation of parasites. *Ann. N.Y. Acad. Sci.* **139:** 176–189.

BERNTZEN A.K. & MUELLER J.F. (1963). *In vitro* cultivation of *Spirometra* from procercoid to young adult. *J. Parasit.* **49** (5. Sect. 2, Suppl.): 60.

BERNTZEN A.K. & MUELLER J.F. (1964). *In vitro* cultivation of *Spirometra mansonoides* (Cestoda) from the procercoid to the early adult. *J. Parasit.* **50:** 705–711.

CARRELL A. & LINDBERG C.A. (1938). *The culture of organs.* New York: Paul B. Hoeber Inc.

COUTELEN F. (1927a). Essai de culture *in vitro* de scolex et d'hydatides echinococciques. *Annls Parasit. hum. comp.* **5:** 1–19.

COUTELEN F. (1927b). Sur l'evolution vesiculaire *in vitro* des scolex echinococciques. *Annls Parasit. hum. comp.* **5:** 239–242.

DÉVÉ F. (1926). Evolution vesiculaire du scolex echinococcique obtinue *in vitro.* La culture artificielle du kyste hydatie. *C.r. Séanc. Soc. Biol.* **94:** 440–441.

DUJARDIN F. (1837). Sur l'embryon des entozoaires et sur les mouvements de cet embryon dans l'oeuf. *Annls Sci. nat.* (2) **8:** 303–305.

FREEMAN R.S. (1962). Studies on the biology of *Taenia crassiceps* (Zeder, 1800) Rudolphi, 1810 (Cestoda). *Can. J. Zool.* **40:** 969–990.

FRISCH J. (1734). De taeniis in pisicculo aculeato qui in marchia Brandenburgica vocatur 'Stecherling'. *Misc. Berolina* **4:** 395–396.

GREEN N.K. & WARDLE R.A. (1941). The cultivation of tapeworms in artificial media. *Can. J. Res.* (D) **19:** 240–244.

GURRI J. (1963). Vitalidad y evolutividad de los escolices hidaticos *in vivo* et *in vitro*. *Ann. Fac. Med. Univ. Rep. Montev.* **48:** 372–381.

HEALEY G., FISHER D. & PARKER R.C. (1955). Nutrition of animal cells. X. Synthetic medium No. 858. *Proc. Soc. exp. Biol. N.Y.* **89:** 71.

HOPKINS C.A. (1952). Studies on cestode metabolism. II. The utilisation of glycogen by *Schistocephalus solidus in vitro*. *Expl Parasit.* **1:** 196–213.

HOPKINS C.A. (1967). The *in vitro* cultivation of cestodes with particular reference to *Hymenolepis nana*. *Symp. Br. Soc. Parasit.* No. 5: 27–47.

HOPKINS C.A. & McCAIG M.L.O. (1963). Studies on *Schistocephalus solidus*. I. The correlation of development in the plerocercoid with infectivity to the definitive host. *Expl Parasit.* **13:** 235–243.

HOPKINS C.A. & SINHA D.P. (1965). Growth of the fish tapeworm *Schistocephalus solidus in vitro*. *Parasitology* **55:** 19P.

JOYEUX C. & BAER J.G. (1938). L'évolution des plerocercoides de la *Ligule intestinale*. *C.r. Séanc. Soc. Biol.* **129:** 314.

JOYEUX C. & BAER J.G. (1942). Recherches sur l'évolution de la *Ligule intestinale*. *Bull. Mus. Hist. nat. Marseilles* **2:** 1–32.

LE BAS G.Z. (1924). Experimental studies on *Dibothriocephalus latus* in man. *J. Helminth.* **2:** 151–166.

LONNBERG E. (1892). Einige Experimente Cestoden kunstlich lebend zu erhalten. *Zentr. Bakl. ParasitKde* **11:** 89–92.

LUKASHENKO N.P. (1964). Study of the development of *Alvecoccus multilocularis* (Leukhart, 1863) *in vitro*. *Medit. Parasit. paray. bolezni.* **33:** 271–278.

MARKOV G.S. (1938). The survival of a broad tapeworm's plerocercoids (*Diphyllobothrium latum*) in artificial media. *Dokl. Akad. Nauk SSSR* N.S. **19:** 511–512.

MARKOV G.S. (1939). Nutrition of tapeworms in artificial media. *Dokl. Akad. Nauk SSSR* N.S. **25:** 93–96.

McCAIG M.L.O. & HOPKINS C.A. (1965). Studies on *Schistocephalus solidus*. 3. The *in vitro* cultivation of the plerocercoid. *Parasitology* **55:** 257–268.

MENDELSOHN W. (1935). A method for the cultivation, under sterile conditions, of the larvae of *Taenia crassicollis*. *J. Parasit.* **21:** 417.

MEYMARIAN E. (1961). Host-parasite relationships in echinococcosis. VI. Hatching and activation of *Echinococcus granulosus* ova *in vitro*. *Am. J. trop. Med. Hyg.* **10:** 710–726.

MUELLER J.F. (1958). *In vitro* cultivation of the sparganum of *Spirometra mansonoides* to the infective stage. *J. Parasit.* **44** (4. Sect. 2, Suppl.): 14–15.

MUELLER J.F. (1959a). Substitution of a cell-free culture system for the second intermediate host in the life-cycle of *Spirometra mansonoides*. *J. Parasit.* **45** (4. Sect. 2, Suppl.): 27.

MUELLER J.F. (1959b). The laboratory propagation of *Spirometra mansonoides* as an experimental tool. I. Collection, incubation and hatching of the eggs. *J. Parasit.* **45:** 353–361.

MUELLER J.F. (1959c). The laboratory propagation of *Spirometra mansonoides* as an experimental tool. II. Culture and infection of the copepod host and harvesting the procercoid. *Trans. Am. microsc. Soc.* **68:** 245–255.

MUELLER J.F. (1959d). The laboratory propagation of *Spirometra mansonoides* (Mueller, 1935) as an experimental tool. III. *In vitro* cultivation of the plerocercoid larva in a cell-free medium. *J. Parasit.* **45:** 561–573.

MUELLER J.F. (1959e). Physiologic studies on the larval and adult scolex of *Spirometra mansonoides*. *J. Parasit.* **45** (4. Sect. 2, Suppl.): 28.

MUELLER J.F. (1961a). The laboratory propagation of *Spirometra mansonoides* as an experimental tool. IV. Experimental inversion of the primary axis in the developing egg. *Expl Parasit.* **11**: 311–318.

MUELLER J.F. (1961b). The laboratory propagation of *Spirometra mansonoides* as an experimental tool. V. Behavior of the sparganum in and out of the mouse host, and the formation of immune precipitates. *J. Parasit.* **47**: 879–883.

MUELLER J.F. (1966). The laboratory propagation of *Spirometra mansonoides* (Mueller, 1935) as an experimental tool. VII. Improved techniques and additional notes on the biology of the cestode. *J. Parasit.* **52**: 437–443.

NICOLLE C. (1908). Culture du parasite du bouton d'orient. *C.r. hebd. Séanc. Acad. Sci.*, *Paris* **146**: 842–843.

NOVY F.G. & McNEAL W.J. (1903). The cultivation of *Trypanosoma brucei*. A preliminary note. *J. Am. med. Ass.* **41**: 1266–1268.

ORTNER-SCHÖNBACH P. (1913). Zur Morphologie des Glycogens bei Trematoden und Cestoden. *Arch. Zellforsch.* **11**: 411–449.

PAULUZZI S., SORICE F., CASTAGNARI L. & SERRA P. (1965). Contributo allo studio delle colture *in vitro* degli scolici di *Echinococcus granulosus*. *Annali Sclavo.* **7**: 191–218.

PIRRINGER W. & PIRRINGER E. (1959). Coprokulturen der eier von *Hymenolepis nana*. *Mikroskopie* **14**: 85–88.

RAUSCH R. & JENTOFT V.L. (1957). Studies on the helminth fauna of Alaska. XXXI. Observations on the propagation of the larval *Echinococcus multilocularis* Leuckart, 1863 *in vitro*. *J. Parasit.* **43**: 1–8.

READ C.P. & SIMMONS J.E. JR. (1963). Biochemistry and physiology of tapeworms. *Physiol. Rev.* **43**: 263–305.

REID W.M. & BOLES J.I. (1949). Antibiotics as bacteriostatic agents for the cultivation of cestodes *in vitro*. *J. Parasit.* **35** (6. Sect. 2, Suppl.): 37.

ROBINSON D.L.H., SILVERMAN P.H. & PEARCE A.R. (1963). The culture of *Taenia crassiceps in vitro*. *Trans. R. Soc. trop. Med. Hyg.* **57**: 238.

ROTHMAN A.H. (1959). Studies on the excystment of tapeworms. *Expl Parasit.* **8**: 336–364.

DE RYCKE P.H. & BERNTZEN A.K. (1967). Maintenance and growth of *Hymenolepis microstoma* (Cestoda: Cyclophyllidea) *in vitro*. *J. Parasit.* **53**: 352–354.

DE RYCKE P.H. & VAN BREMBERGEN G.Z. (1965). Etude sur l'évagination de scolex d'*Echinococcus granulosus*. *Z. Parasitkde* **25**: 518–525.

SCHILLER E.L. (1965). A simplified method for the cultivation of the rat tapeworm *Hymenolepis diminuta*. *J. Parasit.* **51**: 516–518.

SCHILLER E.L., READ C.P. & ROTHMAN A.H. (1959). Preliminary experiments on the growth of a cyclophyllidean cestode *in vitro*. *J. Parasit.* **45** (4. Sect. 2, Suppl.): 45.

SCHWABE C.W., HADIDIAN L. & KOUSSA M. (1963). Host-parasite relationships in echinococcosis. IX. *In vitro* survival of hydatid scoleces and the effects of drugs upon scolex respiration. *Am. J. trop. Med. Hyg.* **12**: 338–345.

SERGEEVA P.A. & EVANOVA V.G. (1962). Cultivation of the larval form of *Echinococcus granulosus* in nutrient media and in tissue cultures. (Preliminary note.) *Uchen. Zap. kazan. vet. Inst.* **89**: 145–150 (in Russian).

SMITH C.F. (1954). Attempts at *in vitro* cultivation of the fowl cestode *Raillietina cesticillus*. *J. Parasit.* **40** (5. Sect. 2, Suppl.): 41–42.

SMYTH J.D. (1946). Studies on tapeworm physiology. I. Cultivation of *Schistocephalus solidus in vitro. J. exp. Biol.* **23**: 47–70.

SMYTH J.D. (1947a). Studies on tapeworm physiology. III. Aseptic cultivation of larval diphyllobothridae *in vitro. J. exp. Biol.* **24**: 374–386.

SMYTH J.D. (1947b). The physiology of tapeworms. *Biol. Rev.* **22**: 214–238.

SMYTH J.D. (1947c). Studies on tapeworm physiology. II. Cultivation and development of *Ligula intestinalis in vitro. Parasitology* **38**: 173–181.

SMYTH J.D. (1949). Studies on tapeworm physiology. IV. Further observations on the development of *Ligula intestinalis in vitro. J. exp. Biol.* **26**: 1–14.

SMYTH J.D. (1950). Studies on tapeworm physiology. V. Further observations on the maturation of *Schistocephalus solidus* under sterile conditions *in vitro. J. Parasit.* **36**: 371–383.

SMYTH J.D. (1952). Studies on tapeworm physiology. VI. The effect of temperature on the maturation of *Schistocephalus solidus in vitro. J. exp. Biol.* **29**: 304–309.

SMYTH J.D. (1953). Fertilization of the cestode *Schistocephalus solidus in vitro. J. Parasit.* **39**: 573–574.

SMYTH J.D. (1954). Studies on tapeworm physiology. VII. Fertilization of *Schistocephalus solidus in vitro. Expl Parasit.* **3**: 64–71.

SMYTH J.D. (1955). Problems relating to the *in vitro* cultivation of pseudophyllidean cestodes from egg to adult. *Revta iber. Parasit.* Tomo extraordinario: 65–86.

SMYTH J.D. (1958). Cultivation and development of larval cestode fragments *in vitro. Nature, Lond.* **181**: 1119–1122.

SMYTH J.D. (1959). Maturation of larval pseudophyllidean cestodes and strigeid trematodes under axenic conditions; the significance of nutritional levels in platyhelminth development. *Ann. N.Y. Acad. Sci.* **77**: 102–125.

SMYTH J.D. (1962). Studies on tapeworm physiology. X. Axenic cultivation of the hydatid organism *Echinococcus granulosus*; establishment of a basic technique. *Parasitology* **52**: 441–457.

SMYTH J.D. (1963). Secretory activity by the scolex of *Echinococcus granulosus in vitro. Nature, Lond.* **199**: 402.

SMYTH J.D. (1964). The biology of the hydatid organism. In *Advances in parasitology* **2**: 169–219. B. Dawes (ed.). London and New York: Academic Press.

SMYTH J.D. (1967). Studies on tapeworm physiology. XI. *In vitro* cultivation of *Echinococcus granulosus* from the protoscolex to the strobilate stage. *Parasitology* **57**: 111–133.

SMYTH J.D. & HOWKINS A.B. (1966). An *in vitro* technique for the production of eggs of *Echinococcus granulosus* by maturation of partly developed strobila. *Parasitology* **56**: 763–766.

SMYTH J.D., HOWKINS A.B. & BARTON M. (1966). Factors controlling the differentiation of the hydatid organism *Echinococcus granulosus* into cystic or strobila stages *in vitro. Nature, Lond.* **211**: 1374.

STUNKARD H.W. (1932). Attempts to grow cestodes *in vitro. J. Parasit.* **19**: 163.

TAKAHASHI T., OKAMOTO K. & SONOE M. (1959). Studies on plerocercoids of *Diphyllobothrium mansoni in vitro. Jap. J. Parasit.* **8**: 677–686.

TAYLOR A.E.R. (1961). Axenic culture of the rodent tapeworms *Hymenolepis diminuta* and *H.nana. Expl Parasit.* **11**: 176–187.

TAYLOR A.E.R. (1963a). Maintenance of larval tapeworms (*Taenia crassiceps*) in a chemically defined medium. *Parasitology* **53**: 5P. (Abstract).

TAYLOR A.E.R. (1963b). Maintenance of larval *Taenia crassiceps* (Cestoda: Cyclo-phyllidea) in a chemically defined medium. *Expl Parasit.* **14:** 304–310.

TAYLOR A.E.R., BALL G.H. & VOGE M. (1960). Studies on the axenic culture of the rodent tapeworms *Hymenolepis diminuta* and *H.nana*. *J. Parasit.* **46** (5. Sect. 2, Suppl.): 11.

TAYLOR A.E.R., MCCABE M. & LONGMUIR I.S. (1966). Studies on the metabolism of larval tapeworms (Cyclophyllidea: *Taenia crassiceps*). II. Respiration, glycogen utilization and lactic acid production during culture in a chemically defined medium. *Expl Parasit.* **19:** 269–275.

TOWER W.L. (1900). The nervous system of the cestode *Moniezia expansa*. *Zool. Zentbl.* (Anat.) **13:** 359–384.

VOGE M. (1963). Maintenance *in vitro* of *Taenia crassiceps* cysticerci. *J. Parasit.* **49** (5. Sect. 2, Suppl.): 59.

VOGE M. (1966). Development *in vitro* of *Mesocestoides* (Cestoda) from oncosphere to young tetrathyridium. *J. Parasit.* **52** (5. Sect. 2, Suppl.): 45.

VOGE M. (1967). Development *in vitro* of *Mesocestoides* (Cestoda) from oncosphere to young tetrathyridium. *J. Parasit.* **53:** 78–82.

VOGE M. & BERNTZEN A.K. (1961). *In vitro* hatching of oncospheres of *Hymenolepis diminuta* (Cestoda—Cyclophyllidea). *J. Parasit.* **47:** 813–818.

VOGE M. & CLOUMBE L.S. (1966). Growth and asexual multiplication *in vitro* of *Mesocestoides tetrathyridia*. *Am. J. trop. Med. Hyg.* **15:** 902–907.

WARDLE R.A. (1932). Significant factors in the plerocercoid environment of *Diphyllo-bothrium latum*. *J. Helminth.* **11:** 25–44.

WARDLE R.A. (1934). The viability of tapeworms in artificial media. *Physiol. Zool.* **7:** 36–61.

WARDLE R.A. & GREEN N.K. (1941). The cultivation of tapeworms in artificial media. *Can. J. Res.* (D) **19:** 240–244.

WARDLE R.A. & MCLEOD J.A. (1952). *The zoology of tapeworms*. Minneapolis: University of Minnesota Press.

WEBSTER G.M. & CAMERON T.W.M. (1963). Some preliminary observations on the development of *Echinococcus in vitro*. *Can. J. Zool.* **41:** 185–195.

WILMOTH J.H. (1938). A note on the cultivation of *Taenia taeniaeformis* larvae *in vitro*. *J. Parasit.* **24** (6. Sect. 2, Suppl.): 35–36.

WILMOTH J.H. (1940). A further note on the cultivation of *Taenia taeniaeformis* larvae *in vitro*, with a preliminary report on the respiration of these parasites. *J. Parasit.* **26** (6. Sect. 2, Suppl.): 44.

WILMOTH J.H. (1945). Studies on the metabolism of *Taenia taeniaeformis*. *Physiol. Zool.* **18:** 60–80.

WYLLIE M.R., WILLIAMS M.O. & HOPKINS C.A. (1960). The *in vitro* cultivation of strigeid trematodes. II. Replacement of a yolk medium. *Expl Parasit.* **10:** 51–57.

YAMASHITI J., OHBAYASHI M., SAKAMOTO T. & ORIHARA M. (1962). Studies on Echinococcosis. XIII. Observations on the vesicular development of the scolex of *E. multilocularis in vitro*. *Jap. J. vet. Res.* **10** (3): 85–96.

CHAPTER 7

NEMATODA PARASITIC IN ANIMALS

Hoeppli *et al.* (1938) have reviewed the early literature on the cultivation of nematodes. Readers are also referred to Lee's recent book (1965) on the physiology of nematodes, particularly his chapter 'Hatching and Moulting'.

I. TRICHUROIDEA

1. *TRICHINELLA SPIRALIS*

McCoy (1936) undertook a series of experiments on the development of *Trichinella spiralis* in various abnormal environments. He attempted to grow larvae in sterile cultures of minced 10 day old chick embryo tissues suspended in Tyrode's solution, but although the larvae survived 4–5 days no further development occurred. He did however have some success when he injected the larvae into 12–14 day old chick embryos or rat embryos and obtained normal adult worms in a few cases.

The first successful growth of *T.spiralis in vitro* was obtained by Weller (1943). He used roller cultures (8–10 rev/hr) of chick embryo tissues maintained at 37°c. Minced 8–10 day old tissues were fixed to the walls of the tubes with a plasma clot. The larvae were inoculated into the overlay medium which consisted of 7 parts Simm's solution (Feller *et al.*, 1940), 2 parts chick embryo extract and 1 part chick serum; the gas phase was air and the medium was changed daily. Within 50 hr of culture a few of the larvae had incompletely moulted their second and third sheaths and these contained sexually differentiated worms. However by 65 hr, they had all begun to degenerate. Numerous modifications of the medium were tried which included the use of different types of mammalian embryonic tissues and extracts, yeast and liver extracts, various supplements of vitamins, bacto-tryptose, bacto-tryptone, bacto-peptone (Difco) and casein hydrolysates but no improvement of growth was obtained.

Levin (1940) briefly reported that he was able to maintain *T.spiralis* larvae in Tyrode's solution with glucose at 38°c for up to 11 days but no sexual development occurred. Kim (1961, 1962) using Weinstein & Jones' *Nippostrongylus* medium (1956a) was able to repeat Weller's results but in a shorter time. He used 50% chick embryo extract alone or supplemented with various amounts of ox serum ultra filtrate, rabbit, rat or chicken serum or amino acids. The larvae once again moulted incompletely producing up to 4 distinct sheaths containing sexually differentiated worms within 17 hr *in vitro*. This occurred in chick embryo extract or mouse embryo extract alone; the addition of the various supplements did not improve the results.

Kim found, as had previous workers, that the larvae did not lose their moulted sheaths *in vitro* and the resultant worms were smaller than normal. Similar results were also obtained by Meerovitch (1962, 1965a, b) who used roller cultures of larvae in media containing chick embryo extract and rabbit serum incubated at 37°C. The worms became sexually differentiated but again moulted incompletely, even when they were subjected to bile salts before culture. When vitamins were added to the above medium the first moult was obtained in 28 hr instead of 48 hr but the addition of amino acids and glucose had no effect on survival and development. The worms survived better under nitrogen or 5%–77% carbon dioxide than under air or 5% oxygen. Later Meerovitch (1965b) found that either low concentrations of an acetone extract of larvae and pupae of *Galleria mellonella* (believed to contain some ecdysone), or high concentration of carbon dioxide promoted complete exsheathment of some *T.spiralis* larvae *in vitro*.

The difficulties encountered by all previous workers were eventually overcome by Berntzen (1962, 1965, 1966) who obtained sexually mature normal adults with his continuous flow apparatus (p. 251). He originally (1962) used this apparatus with a medium designed for growing tapeworms *in vitro*; after excysting the encysted muscle larvae, they were grown to mature adults which produced embryos. During this time only 1 moult occurred *in vitro* in contrast to the several moults found by previous workers. Berntzen (1965) then undertook a comparative study of the *in vivo* and *in vitro* development of *T.spiralis*. Larvae were obtained from laboratory infected rats and were treated with pepsin solution followed by trypsin and pancreatin solution before culture. Berntzen used, amongst others, a new medium (102B) specially designed for *T.spiralis* cultivation, with a gas phase of 85% nitrogen, 5% carbon dioxide, 10% oxygen and maintained at 37°C. Growth and organogenesis of the worms occurred *in vitro* resulting in sexually mature adults within 120 hr. Eight to ten days after the initiation of the cultures, embryos and second stage juveniles were being produced. Berntzen considered that a reduced oxygen level, the presence of carbon dioxide and low levels of reducing agent provided the stimulus for normal sheath formation *in vitro* and that these conditions had to be constant throughout the culture period. Variation of any one of these factors during culture induced multiple sheathing resulting in non-gravid adults when de-sheathed, similar results to those observed by previous workers.

Berntzen was also able to achieve good development of gravid adults *in vitro* using a system whereby the larvae were grown in Erlenmeyer flasks through which the gas mixture was continuously bubbled (p. 255). However he considered that the continuous flow system was, on balance, the more successful of the two (see also reviews by Berntzen, 1966 and Denham, 1967).

Trichinella spiralis Larva to adult
(Berntzen, 1965)

MEDIUM (102B)

Solution A (amounts in mg): $NaH_2PO_4.H_2O$, 114; $NaHCO_3$, 35; KCl, 224; $CaCl_2$ (keep separate), 50; NaCl, 220; $MgSO_4.7H_2O$, 250; distilled H_2O, 20 ml.

Solution B (amounts in mg): L-arginine hydrochloride, 42; L-aspartic acid, 26·6; L-aspargine, 16·4; L-alanine, 17·8; L-cystine, 48·0; L-glutamic acid, 29·4; L-glutamine, 29·2; glycine, 15·0; L-histidine, 31·0; L-iso-leucine, 26·2; L-leucine, 26·2; L-lysine hydrochloride, 36·4; L-methionine, 29·8; L-proline, 23·0; hydroxyproline, 26·2; L-phenylalanine, 33·0; L-serine, 21·0; L-tyrosine, 36·2; L-tryptophan, 40·8; L-threonine, 23·8; L-valine, 23·4; phenol red (optional), 0·02; distilled water, 30·0 ml.

Solution C (amounts in mg): Glycogen, 50·0; glycerol-l-phosphate, 150; glucose, 500·0; sucrose, 1·5 g; distilled water, 20 ml.

Solution D (amounts in mg): Sodium pyruvate, 100; malic acid, 70·0; L-ketoglutaric acid, 45·0; succinic acid, 8·0; hydroxybutyric acid, 10·0; amino-n-butyric choline chloride, 10·0; fumaric acid, 7·5; distilled water, 20 ml (organic acids neutralized with KOH).

Solution E: Thiamine hydrochloride, riboflavine, calcium pantothenate, pyridoxine, *p*-amino-benzoic acid, niacin, folic acid, and *i*-inositol, 2·5 mg each; biotin, 1·25 mg; choline chloride, 25·0 mg, vitamin B_{12}, 60 units; water, 25 ml.

Solution F: 39 ml of chick embryo extract (CEE) is prepared in the follow-ing manner: 13–14 day old chick embryos are removed from their shell and rinsed in saline. To each embryo is added 50 ml distilled water and the mixture homogenized at high speed for 2 min. The homogenate is kept at 5°C for 24 hr, strained through cheesecloth to remove large pieces of tissue and centrifuged at 1500 rev/min for 20 min. The supernatant is filtered through a Buchner funnel specially prepared as follows. A piece of Whatman No. 4 filter paper is placed on top of the filter disc and sealed to it with water. Powdered asbestos is suspended in distilled water and poured over the filter paper and the vacuum turned on; this produces a thin asbestos filter pad. Next, coarse asbestos fibre is suspended in distilled water and layered over the first. The vacuum is then applied to remove water. The result is a two-layered filter pad. The pad is washed by passing distilled water through the funnel until the filtrate becomes clear. The appropriate amount of asbestos in each layer for any funnel size can be determined with practice. If the pad is too thin, a cloudy filtrate is obtained; if it is too thick the chick embryo extract will not pass through rapidly. The chick embryo extract filtrate is very clear and is sterilized by filtration.

Preparation of Medium 102B *Working Solution:* (1) Solutions A, B, C, D and E are prepared separately and then mixed. (2) The pH of the mixed solutions is raised to 7·0–7·2 by the addition of NaHCO$_3$. (3) This portion of the medium is then sterilized by filtration (p. 343). To the sterile mixed fractions the previously sterilized chick embryo extract is added and well agitated. The medium must be stored at 5°C until used and is stable for long periods of time; freezing will result in the formation of a precipitate.

Cysteine: 2 M cysteine hydrochloride is prepared in saline, sterilized by filtration and added to Medium 102B just before use yielding a final concentration of 0·01 M cysteine.

TECHNIQUE

1   *Maintenance of* T.spiralis *in the laboratory*

Rats are infected with 1,200–1,500 larvae per 300–350 g animal by stomach tube. Larvae for inoculating these rats are obtained by treating 40 g of ground infected rat muscle with 1 l. of a 1·0% pepsin (1:10,000 Difco) in 0·5% hydrochloric acid solution according to the method of Gursch (1948) for 16–18 hr at 37°C in 4 l. flasks on a horizontal shaker at moderate speed. The freed larvae are allowed to settle for 1–2 hr at room temperature; they are collected, pooled and washed free of debris by alternating suspension in 0·85% saline and centrifugation.

Pooled larvae are suspended in saline in a conical centrifuge tube and sufficient air is bubbled through the tube to keep the organisms well suspended. The number of worms in 3 small samples is counted and anaesthetized rats are given about 1,200 larvae by stomach tube.

2 Obtaining larvae for culture

Two grammes of well-ground infected rat muscle are treated with 100 ml 2% pepsin (1:10,000 Difco), in 1·0% hydrochloric acid for 4 hr at 37°c in 500 ml round-bottom flasks on a table shaker. The fluid is then passed through No. 24, 32 and 42 mesh sieves into a Baermann apparatus (p. 361). The larvae are allowed to settle for 1 hr; 400 ml of the bottom fluid is removed and centrifuged at 1,000 rev/min for 10 min. The pepsin solution is decanted and the worms re-suspended in 0·8% saline, re-centrifuged for 10 min, and again decanted.

The larvae are then put into a second solution prepared as follows: 1 million units crystalline trypsin (Tryptar, Armour Pharmaceutical Co.), 2 g pancreatine (porcine, California Corporation for Biochemical Research), and 2 g of sodium tauroglycocholate mixed in 500 ml Tyrode's solution (p. 350). This mixture is filtered through Whatman No. 4 filter paper and warmed to 37°c. After the worms have been added to the solution, it is again put on the shaker at 37°c for 2 hr. The suspension is then transferred to 50 ml conical centrifuge tubes and centrifuged at 1,000 rev/min for 5 min. The supernatant is siphoned off and the worms re-suspended in Tyrode's solution. This washing procedure must be repeated 3 times and the worms are then sterilized for culture.

3 Surface sterilization of larvae

Larvae which have been excysted and freed of host tissues and other debris are washed 10 times by repeatedly suspending them in sterile Tyrode's solution in a 50 ml conical centrifuge tube, centrifuging at 500–600 rev/min for 2 min, siphoning off the supernatant and re-suspending.

After the tenth wash, the worms are suspended in Tyrode's with 0·5 g streptomycin, 1 million units penicillin G (crystalline) and 5,000 units of nystatin per 100 ml. The larvae, which are kept in this solution for half an hour at 37°c and again washed 5 times with sterile Tyrode's without antibiotics, are used as an inoculum for the cultures. The usual aseptic techniques must be employed throughout.

4 Apparatus for sheath removal

If the worms are unable to free themselves from their cuticular sheath during culture, they may be passed through a special apparatus designed to enable the worms to rub against a special surface (Fig. 7.1). It consists essentially of a tube within a tube. The bottom of the inner tube is capped with a silk screen pad of several thicknesses. The worms migrate down through this pad into the second tube, which contains medium equilibrated with the gas mixture. The worms leave their sheaths during their course through the pad.

5 *Experimental procedure*

Worms, treated by the above techniques, are counted and introduced into either of 2 culture systems: (i) The continuous flow culture apparatus

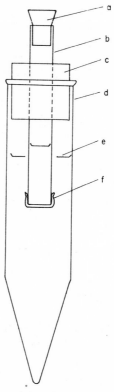

FIGURE 7.1. De-sheathing apparatus. (From Berntzen, 1965.) a, c, Rubber stoppers; b, inner tube which holds worms taken from culture; d, 50 ml conical centrifuge tube; e, level of gas—conditioned medium; f, silk screen pad of several thicknesses.

(see *Hymenolepis diminuta* culture, p. 229), approximately 1,000 worms/0·25–0·5 ml of inoculum. The apparatus is maintained at 37°c, the gas phase is 85% nitrogen, 5% carbon dioxide, 10% oxygen and the flow rate is adjusted to 100 ml/24 hr. The pH of medium 102B, containing cysteine hydrochloride (0·01 M), should be 7·4 and it should be renewed every 3–5 days. (ii) The bubble flask culture system. This consists of an Erlenmeyer flask one third full of medium through which a gas mixture (95% nitrogen, 5% carbon dioxide) is bubbled slowly. In this system the medium is replaced daily with fresh medium presaturated with the gas mixture.

Berntzen obtained development of adults with both of the above techniques, the continuous flow technique being the more successful. Growth and organogenesis of the worms occurred within 8 hr and differentiation with 1 moult within 48 hr *in vitro*. Adults free from their moulted cuticle appeared within 120 hr. In some cultures the worms did not free themselves of their moult and in this case they were put through the desheathing apparatus and on return to culture continued their development normally. Adults produced embryos and second stage juveniles within 8–10 days after the initiation of the cultures.

2. *CAPILLARIA HEPATICA*

Very little work has been done on the cultivation of *Capillaria hepatica*. Sato & Shimanti (1961) have described a method of obtaining eggs from infected rats. The infected liver was minced and incubated in an artificial gastric juice at 37°c for 24–72 hr. This treatment apparently did not affect the subsequent development of the eggs (removed in abundance from this mixture) when cultured on moist filter paper at 25–30°c. Within 15–20 days the eggs were fully developed.

II. RHABDIASOIDEA

1. *NEOAPLECTANA GLASERI*

Glaser, who with Fox (1930) originally discovered this parasite in 'dead fully grown Japanese beetle grubs', was the first worker to succeed in cultivating the whole life-cycle of a parasitic worm *in vitro* (Glaser, 1931). This notable achievement was carried out by culturing the worms in an aqueous suspension of growing yeast overlaid on standard meat infusion agar plates (containing 1% glucose) at pH 7·4. Within 2 days at room temperature the plates were swarming with larvae and one complete generation took 4–5 days to develop *in vitro*. Several cultures were carried in this way over a period of $5\frac{1}{2}$ months with transfers being made every

10–14 days. Unless the worms were passed through beetles at the end of this period (whereupon successful cultures could be set up for a further 5½ months) they died. For several years Glaser continued to participate in studies on the cultivation of this parasite (Glaser & Coria, 1935; McCoy & Glaser, 1936, 1938; Glaser, 1940a, b, c) and a new medium consisting of glucose and veal infusion in yeast agar was developed. However it was not until Glaser & Stoll (1940) developed a method for sterilizing the infective third stage larvae that Glaser (1940b) was able to bring the organism into bacteria-free culture. He used sterile raw rabbit-kidney tissue placed on glucose agar slants. Tissue from 10–12 day old chick embryos or 18–20 day old mouse embryos could be substituted for the kidney (Glaser, 1943) but without such luxuriant growth of the parasite. Liver tissue permitted an even more abundant growth than kidney tissue although it was more difficult to obtain in a sterile state.

Stoll obtained stock cultures of *N. glaseri* from Glaser's laboratory in 1944 and for several years studied the factors influencing their development *in vitro* with a view to defining the culture medium still further. He attempted to rear *N. glaseri* in a variety of media including nutrient broth, dilute serum and defined culture media (Stoll, 1948) and by 1951 had devised a convenient axenic culture system. This consisted of infusion broth supplemented with liver extract and he was able to obtain full-cycle development through more than one generation in test-tubes. Within 21 days 100–300 fold increase in numbers was obtained from an original inoculum of 25 larvae kept in tubes, containing 10 ml of medium, on a shaking machine in the dark at 22°c.

Such cultured parasites retained their infectivity to beetle grubs for at least 7 years (Stoll, 1953a, b, 1956). The culture medium was improved upon, firstly by using beef heart infusion broth and raw liver extract from rabbits in late pregnancy or early post partum (Stoll, 1954) and secondly by adding 1% peptone to the medium at pH 4·5–6·5 (Stoll, 1956, 1959). Finally Stoll (1961) showed that the raw liver extract from pregnant or post partum rabbits was more effective than other liver extracts when stored at 2–4°c for 15–90 days prior to use (p. 257).

Jackson (1961, 1962a), working in Stoll's laboratory, was the first to cultivate *N. glaseri* in a fully defined medium. He obtained development of one complete life-cycle, with low level reproduction, in a complex medium (p. 258). The optimal temperature for growth and reproduction was 21°c and a depth not exceeding 1·5 cm fluid in the tubes was necessary for good results in the defined medium as well as undefined media. Culture media 199 and NCTC 109 only maintained third stage larvae and did not induce development or growth.

Jackson & Siddiqui later (1965) showed that the *N.glaseri* requires folic acid for reproduction *in vitro* and Jackson (1965, 1966) went on to use *in vitro* culture techniques to differentiate between the 3 species of *Neoaplectana*: *N.glaseri*, *N.dutkii* and *N.carpocapsae* on the basis of the ability of these species to develop and reproduce in various culture media, including the fully defined medium.

Neoaplectana glaseri Life-cycle
(Stoll, 1961)

MEDIUM

Raw liver extract (RLE): Donor pregnant (4 weeks) or early post partum (1–7 days) rabbits are exsanguinated, their livers and gall bladders removed, promptly refrigerated and then frozen. This tissue may be stored at −20°c for 0·5–51 weeks before use.

The liver tissue is thawed overnight and homogenized in an electric blender (100 g liver to 400 ml triple distilled water). All processing should be carried out below 15°c. The brei, after bringing to pH 4 with N HCl, is centrifuged and the resultant clear fluid sterilized by filtration before being stored in 20 ml aliquots in the refrigerator.

Infusion broth: Fresh ox hearts with 1% peptone (pH 6·0) added are Arnoldized and used for culture in the ratio of 9 ml infusion broth to 1 ml raw liver extract contained in 22 × 180 mm culture tubes.

TECHNIQUE

The strain of *N.glaseri* is maintained in stock cultures of fresh sterile kidney tissue on glucose agar slants (Glaser, 1940a, b; Stoll, 1953a, 1954). Third stage larvae for the culture inoculum are removed from the walls of such cultures with a sterile bacterial loop and may be used either directly or stored at 4°c in lots of several thousand per 50 ml Erlenmeyer flask in sterile distilled water to a depth of 1 cm.

The larvae are counted and 25 larvae added to each culture tube in 0·5 ml suspension containing an addition of 25 mg glucose. The tubes are placed in racks in a shaker that has 2 cm traverse and operates at 100 strokes/min. This is kept at 22°c in the dark.

Stoll obtained better yields with this medium than hitherto and within 21 days of culture 3 generations of *N.glaseri* had developed.

Neoaplectana glaseri Life-cycle
(Jackson, 1962 a, b)

MEDIUM

Stock solutions

1   Calcium chloride

$CaCl_2$ ....0·26 g
H_2O ....100 ml

Autoclave and store at 5°c

2   Magnesium sulphate

$MgSO_4.7H_2O$ ....1 g
H_2O ....100 ml

Sterilize by filtration; store at 5°c

3   Metals

$ZnSO_4.7H_2O$ ....0·22 g
$FeSO_4.7H_2O$ ....0·10 g
$MnSO_4.7H_2O$ ....0·04 g
$CuSO_4$ ....0·005 g
$CoSO_4.7H_2O$ ....0·0044 g
H_3BO_3 ....0·0011 g
H_2O ....*to* 1 l.

Sterilize by filtration; store at 5°c

4   Vitamins, purines and pyrimidines

A. Adenine ....0·0068 g
Guanine ....0·0068 g
Xanthine ....0·0068 g
Uracil ....0·0068 g
Cytidylic acid ....0·0020 g

Dissolve in 2 ml of 6N HCl, dilute with H_2O to 80 ml; adjust pH to 6·7–6·8 with 2 ml of 6N NaOH, then slowly with very dilute NaOH. Make up to 200 ml with distilled water.

B. Riboflavin ....0·008 g
Thiamine ....0·008 g
Pyridoxine................0·008 g
Pyridoxamine ....0·008 g
Pyridoxal ....0·008 g
Ca pantothenate ....0·032 g
Para-aminobenzoic acid ....0·012 g
Nicotinamide ....0·020 g
Inositol ....0·012 g
Choline chloride ....0·012 g
Glucose ....20·000 g

Add B to H_2O (100 ml) then add 4 ml of a solution (0·02 g/100 ml) of commercial biotin, combine B with A and adjust final volume to 400 ml with H_2O. Sterilize by filtration; store in dark at 5°C.

5 Folic Acid. Grind 0·005 g with H_2O (50 ml + 6 drops 0·1 N NaOH), transfer with rinsing to volumetric flask, adjust with H_2O to 100 ml (pH should be 6·7). Sterilize by filtration; store frozen up to 3 months.

6 (L forms of amino acids wherever possible; if not D-L)

Glycine	0·20 g
Histidine	0·30 g
Tryptophan	0·40 g
Methionine	0·60 g
Arginine hydrochloride	0·60 g
Phenylalanine	0·80 g
Serine	0·80 g
Tyrosine	0·80 g
Proline	1·00 g
Threonine	1·00 g
Valine	1·00 g
Isoleucine	1·20 g
Alanine	1·40 g
Glutamic acid	3·80 g
Leucine	3·00 g
Aspartic acid	2·40 g
Lysine	2·50 g
Butyric acid	0·16 g
Citric acid	0·38 g
Fumaric acid	0·11 g
Lactic acid	0·18 g
Malic acid	0·13 g
Pyruvic acid	0·16 g
Succinic acid	0·11 g
Taurine	3·00 g
Urea	0·0002 g
NaCl	2·000 g
Na_2HPO_4	0·625 g
KH_2PO_4	0·250 g

Add to 400 ml distilled water and dissolve by boiling; adjust pH (with dilute NaOH) to 6·8; adjust total volume to 500 ml with distilled water. Sterilize by filtration or autoclaving; store at 5°C.

18

7 Final medium

Stock solutions	ml for 100 ml of final medium
1	10
2	10
3	10
4	10
5	3·2
6	50

Adjust pH to 6·8 with dilute NaOH or HCl and volume to 100 ml using double distilled water.

TECHNIQUE

Stock cultures of *N.glaseri* can be grown in large (22 × 100 mm) cotton-wool plugged tubes on 2% agar slants (containing glucose and 1% peptone-ox heart infusion as supplement) with a piece of fresh rabbit kidney placed at the bottom of the slant. The surface of the slant is wetted by water of condensation from the suspension of inoculated worms. Large, almost homogeneous populations of third stage larvae can be harvested from the inside walls of the tubes after 3–4 weeks. These are washed and stored in shallow distilled water at 5°C prior to inoculation into test cultures. Keeping the storage flasks at room temperature for 24–28 hr prior to inoculating into test cultures promotes ecdysis of the worms and allows elimination of some of their gut contents.

Test cultures consist of 22 × 180 mm cotton-wool plugged test-tubes containing 2 ml of the defined medium + 0·5 ml 5% glucose solution. Twenty-five larvae are inoculated into each test-tube; these are then shaken (on a shaking machine giving 100 strokes/min on a 1·5 cm traverse) at 21°C in the dark.

Jackson found that one generation developed in 6–7 days (not significantly different from the time required in undefined media) and that after the F_1 generation had developed into third-stage larvae further reproduction and development was minimal unless fresh medium was added.

2. *STRONGYLOIDES*

Chung (1936–37) carried out studies on the filariform larvae of *Strongyloides fuellerborni*, culturing them in different media as well as in tissue cultures. He kept larvae alive for at least 33 days under sterile conditions in floating tissue cultures of either rabbit testis suspended in Tyrode's solution, or rabbit liver, lung or kidney suspended in rabbit serum. The optimum pH was found to lie between 5·4 and 7·0 and under these conditions the larvae increased slightly in length.

Weinstein & Jones (1957b) briefly reported on their attempts to cultivate the rat parasite *S.ratti* and an unknown species of *Strongyloides* from the monkey. They obtained normal development of filariform larvae in a variety of media; males developed normal spicules but their testes remained immature. Similarly females grew incompletely, only a few showing egg formation and these being infertile. Weinstein & Jones's culture media consisted primarily of fresh chick embryo extract alone or supplemented with various growth factors. Development of the parasitic stages did not occur *in vitro*, even in media which had previously been used to grow *Nippostrongylus brasiliensis* to sexually mature adults (Weinstein & Jones, 1957a).

Silverman & Podger (1962) and Silverman *et al.* (1962) developed a technique for culturing *S.papillosus*, from the rabbit, *in vitro* with a view to studying its antigenic properties. Infective larvae were obtained from faecal cultures set up from infected rabbits. The larvae were cleaned and sterilized by sieving and washing in sterile physiological saline followed by treatment with antibiotic solutions. A mixture of streptomycin and penicillin (1000 units/ml) and nystatin (250 units/ml) was used. The larvae did not require exsheathment and were transferred directly to roller cultures of Tyrode's solution without glucose, supplemented with liver extract and incubated at 37°c. Unfortunately the cultures were terminated when 60% of the larvae had developed to the histotrophic ('L4') stage.

III. ASCAROIDEA

1. *ASCARIS*

Eggs

Apparently the eggs of *Ascaris* are dependent on a moist environment for their development, for Stewart (1934) was able to obtain segmentation of *Ascaris* eggs by spreading them over the inner surface of a sealed test-tube containing a small amount of water at the bottom. Pitts (1948) later showed that if *Ascaris* eggs were incubated in physiological saline at 37·5°c, 100% hatched within 4 weeks. However if the eggs were first dried before incubation in saline, hatching occurred in 2 days and better still if they were centrifuged, 99% hatched in 10 min. Pick (1948) studied the development of *A.megalocephala* eggs in 2% glucose or glycerine agar at 34°C and found it more rapid under these conditions than under natural conditions. If the eggs were first incubated in Ringer-serum at 28°C and then transferred to glucose-agar their development was even more rapid but no hatching occurred. Reducing the temperature to 20°C after the above treatment induced spontaneous hatching.

Rogers (1958) showed that the mechanism of hatching in *A.lumbricoides* eggs resulted from the liberation of chitinase and possibly other enzymes within the egg; the stimulus for this release being provided by external conditions which included a low oxidation-reduction potential and an abundant supply of free carbon dioxide. Under these conditions maximal hatching occurred in 2–3 hr. Fairbairn (1960, 1961) investigated the problem still further and devised an efficient hatching technique. The eggs were embryonated in 0·1 M sulphuric acid at 30°C for about 20 days when they were fully infective. The acid was neutralized with phosphate buffer and the eggs washed well. They were suspended in sodium hypo-chlorite and shaken for 4 hr at 35°C to remove the outer shell before being finally suspended in a hatching medium composed of equal parts of 0·25 ml sodium chloride containing 0·0025% Tween 80 and 0·1 M reducing agent and pre-gassed 0·1 M sodium bicarbonate. This suspension was then gassed for 15 min at 38°C with 95% nitrogen, 5% carbon dioxide and incubated for a further period of 2–3 hr.

Cleeland & Lawrence (1962) obtained essentially similar results by treating the eggs with sodium hydroxide and hypochlorite to remove the outer layers partially before incubating them at room temperature in 1% neutral formalin until they became infective, usually about 30 days. The eggs were then washed in saline and agitated whilst suspended in a balanced saline at 37°C until hatching occurred.

Larvae

Hoeppli *et al.* (1938) were among the first workers to attempt the culture of *Ascaris lumbricoides* var. *suum* larvae. They fed embryonated eggs to guinea pigs and obtained larvae from their livers 48 hr after infection. These larvae survived 2–3 days in dilute horse or dilute rabbit serum, or normal saline alone, or supplemented with guinea-pig liver extract, but no growth occurred during this time.

No further attempts appear to have been made to culture *Ascaris* larvae until Pitts & Ball published their series of brief reports (Pitts & Ball, 1953, 1955, 1958; Pitts, 1948, 1960, 1962, 1963). Initially, embryonated *A.lumbricoides* var. *suum* eggs were hatched by treatment with sodium hypochlorite and centrifugation (Pitts, 1948) and then cultured at 37°C (57–1,200 larvae/culture) in a medium composed of yeast nutrient broth,

25% pig serum and 10% raw liver extract. Maximum survival in this medium was 102 days with a maximum increase in length of 32·8%; survival was best when the medium was unchanged (Pitts, personal communication). Subsequently Fenwick's (1939) medium was substituted for the balanced saline and human serum for pig serum (Pitts & Ball, 1953) and the larvae were cultured in specially designed pyrex chambers (Pitts & Ball, 1958) which permitted observation of the larvae during culture without disturbing them (p. 265 and Fig. 7.2). At 37°C up to 34·8% of the larvae survived 40 days and 4·4% for 64 days but at 30°C 76·2% survived 41 days and 4% 102 days (Pitts & Ball, 1955). Continuous flow of the medium or renewal daily did not seem beneficial and no moulting was observed in the cultures; increase in size of up to 30% length and 25% diameter was observed in some of the larvae.

Pitts (1960) then attempted to culture, in addition to newly hatched larvae, older larvae (from mouse liver 8 days after infection) in hog serum and chick embryo extract in roller cultures. Larval length increased over 200% with a maximum of 282% and 93% increase in diameter in an 18 day old culture. He subsequently (1962, 1963) tried a new hatching technique (Fairbairn, 1961) and cultivation in Eagle's minimum essential medium supplemented with 10% fresh rabbit serum (p. 265 for media and hatching technique). The special chamber was again used at 35–36°C with weekly medium changes. The experiments were carried out on newly hatched *A.lumbricoides* and *A.lumbricoides* var. *suum*. The maximum size attained by the larvae (*A.lumbricoides* var. *suum*) was 965μ long and 59μ wide in 42 days, i.e. an increase of 304% in length and 500% in diameter. Some sheaths were shed in most cultures and in a few cases mass exsheathing occurred with up to 80% of the larvae exsheathing within the first 4 days. Pitts could find no apparent difference in the nutritional requirements between the human and pig strains of *Ascaris*.

More recently Cleeland & Lawrence (1962) attempted to culture newly hatched *A.lumbricoides* var. *suum* larvae with a view to studying some of the physico-chemical factors involved. They considered that the methods of hatching larvae *in vitro* previously reported by Pitts (1948), Haskins & Weinstein (1957) and Rogers (1958) were harmful to the larvae or else did not yield sufficient numbers for *in vitro* culture. Unfortunately they did not test Fairbairn's technique (1961) but evolved a new hatching technique (p. 268). Eggs were treated with sodium hydroxide and hypochlorite to remove partially the outer layers before maintaining them at 22–26°C in 1% neutral formalin until they became infective. The eggs then were hatched in balanced saline and cultured aerobically in Earle's balanced saline (3–4 days survival) or medium 199 (9–11 days survival).

Supplementing medium 199 with 20% bovine serum increased the survival time to 27 days during which time changes in internal structure of the larvae and a slight increase in size was obtained. When the larvae were kept anaerobically in deep culture in this medium they survived 50–60 days and active exsheathing and development of internal structures was observed, in one instance after 40 days a living larva measuring $609 \times 29 \, \mu$ was found. Growth ceased when the incubation temperature was lowered to below 26°c.

Cleeland (1963) continued these studies by investigating the effects of different atmospheres and various supplements to the above medium. Using medium 199 supplemented with 20% bovine or calf serum, he found that an atmosphere of pure oxygen killed the larvae in 10–20 days. Atmospheres of either pure nitrogen or 95% nitrogen, 5% carbon dioxide inhibited growth and the survival rate was reduced, whereas when larvae were cultured in an atmosphere of air they survived up to 90 days and growth comparable to that *in vivo* was obtained. Cleeland also demonstrated that when the amino acids and vitamins found in Eagle's medium were added to Earle's balanced saline containing glucose and serum, growth of larvae was obtained comparable to that occurring in the more complex medium 199. Crandall & Arean (1964) devised an interesting technique for culturing *Ascaris* which consisted of implanting Millipore chambers, containing second stage *Ascaris* larvae, intraperitoneally into mice where growth continued as normally.

Adults

Ascaris has long been a subject of study because of its large size and relative abundance and its biochemistry and physiology have been well reviewed by Fairbairn (1957). Early workers managed to maintain pig *Ascaris* in Tyrode's solution (changed daily) for 22 days (Adam, 1932) or physiological saline for 26 days (Hall, 1917). Fairbairn & Ressal (1950) however were the first workers to try to sterilize *Ascaris lumbricoides* before culture. They eliminated all bacteria from the external and intestinal surfaces of *Ascaris* by the application of complex mixtures of bacteriostats and bactericides including azachloramide, neutral acriflavine, sulphathiazole, streptomycin and penicillin and found that the viability of the worm was unimpaired by this treatment.

Several workers have carried out metabolic studies on *Ascaris* and their work should be consulted for clues to the nutritional requirements of this worm. Hobson (1948) and Hobson *et al.* (1952a, b) have investigated a number of conditions which were effective in maintaining the adult worms in a viable condition and such physiological studies were pursued further by Ichii *et al.* (1958, 1959) who were interested in the enzyme and glycogen content of *Ascaris* during *in vitro* culture; Ellison *et al.* (1960) who devised a nutrient medium for *Ascaris* culture (p. 270) prior to chemical analysis of the worm; Weinstein (1961) who studied the effect of vitamin B_{12} on *Ascaris* coelomocytes during culture of the worm and Salmenkova (1962) and Benediktov (1962) who were interested in the proteins and amino acids of *Ascaris*. Harpur (1962a, b) has devised an interesting technique for assessing the 'health' of *Ascaris in vitro* by measuring the anaerobic production of carbon dioxide by minced *Ascaris* muscle at intervals during culture; the amount decreased markedly during his 3 day experiments and he used these results as an index for investigating the effects of various factors on the worm. He devised an intermittent-flow culture apparatus described in detail in his original paper on the physiology of this worm.

The studies of workers, particularly Cleeland (1963), with ascarids indicate that oxygen is toxic for them and that 5% carbon dioxide is required as a stimulus for 'normal' metabolic activity.

A novel approach to the cultivation of *A.lumbricoides* var. *suum* was reported by Doran (1961) who cultured germinal cord tissue from adult females. This was apparently the first successful attempt to cultivate parasitic tissues *in vitro*. All microorganisms were eliminated from the female worms and uterine, germinal cord (rachis), intestinal and cuticular tissues were removed and cut into small pieces (explants). These were washed thoroughly in warm Ringer's solution, placed in Leighton culture tubes and allowed to dry slightly at 37°c enabling them to adhere to the glass surface before being covered with 2 ml of culture medium (pH 6·8–6·9) which was changed every 3–5 days. Explants of the rachis survived in calf serum supplemented Eagle's medium or medium 199. Within 6 days cells began growing out over the surface of the glass and after 3–4 weeks the cells had proliferated and migrated from the original explant. Most of the cells however were narrow and much longer than in living *Ascaris* and there was no evidence of cell division in the cultures.

Ascaris lumbricoides and
A.lumbricoides var. *suum* **Larvae**
(Pitts & Ball, 1958; Pitts, 1962, 1963)

MEDIUM

Eagle's minimum essential medium (p. 355) containing 10% rabbit serum.

TECHNIQUE

A.lumbricoides eggs were obtained from adult females taken from an infected human or, more commonly, (*A.lumbricoides* var. *suum*) were collected from swine at the time of slaughter in a local slaughterhouse.

1   *Egg culture*

The eggs are expressed from about the first 1·5 in. of the uterus and cultured in 20 ml 1% formalin solution in 250 ml Erlenmeyer flasks at 30°C for 30 days and then held at 18–20°C until required. The cultures are aerated daily by shaking and should be used when at least 75% of the embryos are active.

2   *Hatching*

Preparatory to hatching, the eggs are treated overnight with a solution of 2% 'Clorox' (Clorox Chemical Co.) and 2% NaOH at 39–40°C. Eggs are then suspended in the hatching medium (see below) in a culture tube and gassed for 15 min by bubbling with 95% nitrogen, 5% carbon dioxide at 39–40°C. The suspension is then incubated for a further 3 hr at this temperature. The resulting mixture of hatched larvae and unhatched eggs is washed 3 times by centrifugation in Tyrode's solution containing 300 units penicillin and 300 μg streptomycin/ml and then held overnight in this Tyrode's solution in a filter paper Baermann apparatus (p. 361) at the above temperature. Most larvae migrate through the filter paper into an ampoule below, while unhatched eggs remain on the filter paper.

3   *Hatching medium* (Fairbairn, 1961)

Equal volumes of 0·25 M sodium chloride (containing 0·0025% Tween 80), 0·1 M sodium bisulphite and 0·1 M pregassed (95% nitrogen, 5% carbon dioxide) sodium bicarbonate. The reducing agent (sodium bisulphite) must be added *before* the sodium bicarbonate. Gassing the hatching medium raises the pH from 6 to 7·0 or 7·1.

4   *Larval culture*

Larvae from the ampoule (see above) are concentrated and then inoculated into a special Pyrex culture chamber (Fig. 7.2I and Pitts & Ball, 1958) containing 7-8 ml of culture medium (approximately 15,000 larvae/culture). The cultures are incubated at 35–36°C and the medium is either changed every 7 days or else used with the continuous flow system (Fig. 7.2II).

Pitts found that a maximum size of 965 μ length and 59 μ diameter (300% increase in length and 500% increase in diameter over the size of

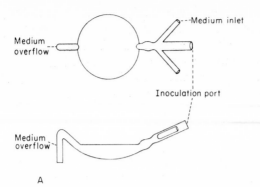

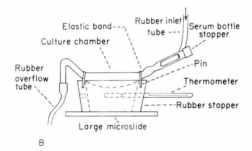

1   B

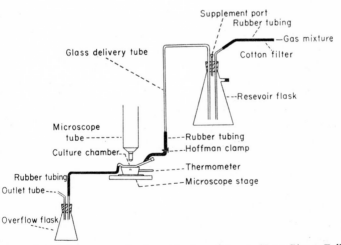

2

FIGURE 7.2 Culture system for the cultivation of *Ascaris*. (From Pitts & Ball, 1958.) **1**. Culture chamber. A. Top and side views; B. Method of mounting on special carrier. **2**. Apparatus used for closed system connection between reservoir flask, culture chamber and overflow flask.

newly hatched larvae) was attained within 42 days. First stage sheaths were shed in most cultures and in good cultures 80% of the larvae exsheathed in 4 days. Supplementing the medium with yeast or liver extract, additional amino acids or pyruvate did not significantly improve the results. Pitts noted that the nutritional requirements of *A.lumbricoides* and *A.lumbricoides* var. *suum* appeared to be the same.

Ascaris lumbricoides var. *suum* Larvae
(Cleeland & Lawrence, 1962; Cleeland, 1963)

MEDIUM

Eagle's medium (p. 355) or medium 199 (p. 355) can be used supplemented with 20% calf or bovine serum. All media are sterilized by filtration after the pH has been adjusted to 7·0 with either 0·5 N NaOH or 0·1 N HCl. Penicillin and streptomycin are added immediately before use (250 units penicillin and 250 μg streptomycin per ml of medium).

TECHNIQUE

1   *Collection of eggs*
Adult *Ascaris* may be obtained from freshly killed pigs at a local slaughterhouse. The uteri of the female worms are removed and washed with water. The anterior two-thirds of the uteri are separated by dissection and homogenized in a Waring Blender. The eggs released by homogenization are collected after low speed centrifugation and resuspended in 0·5 N NaOH containing 10% NaOCl (reagent grade, 5–6% available chlorine) for 16–24 hr at 30°c. This treatment, which removes the entire proteinaceous layer and partially removes the chitinous layer, facilitates microscopic observation and counting of the eggs.

2   *Preparation of infective eggs*
The treated eggs are washed with water to remove the alkaline hypochlorite solution and resuspended in 1% neutral formalin to a concentration of between 10,000 and 20,000 eggs per ml. Twenty millilitres amounts of the formalin-treated eggs are dispensed into 125 ml Erlenmeyer flasks and maintained at 22–26°c with frequent agitation until a majority of the eggs reach the vermiform embryonic state (infective eggs), usually within 30 days.

3 Hatching

Infective eggs are washed several times with 0·9% sodium chloride to remove the formalin. After the last washing the eggs are resuspended in 20 ml of maintenance medium to a concentration of 10,000–20,000 eggs per ml and transferred to 125 ml flasks. A teflon coated bar magnet (1 × $\frac{5}{16}$ in.) with a central teflon coated ring is added to each flask and the flasks immersed in a 37°c constant temperature water-bath. Magnetic stirrers are placed under the water-bath and the contents of the flasks agitated at just under the speed which causes foaming of the medium. If the stirring speed is increased, a sharp decrease in the number of un-damaged viable larvae is observed. The contents of 2 or 3 flasks are combined, centrifuged at 200 × g for 10 min and the supernatant fluid is removed. The sediment is resuspended in 10 ml of fresh medium 199 and transferred to a 15 ml centrifuge tube. After centrifugation at 200 × g for 10 min the supernatant is decanted leaving a sediment consisting of 2 distinct layers. The careful addition of 1 ml of 199 followed by gentle agitation of the tube causes most of the fluffy white upper layer to re-suspend in the medium leaving the light brown lower layer intact. The resuspended material is decanted and the process repeated until only the brown layer remains. This layer, consisting mainly of live hatched larvae free of much of the egg material and all of the shell debris is re-suspended in 199 at room temperature until used (never more than 4–6 hr after hatching).

4 Culture procedure

The freshly hatched larvae are placed in screw-capped tubes (150 × 16 mm) and incubated at 37·5°c in an upright position. At least 20,000 larvae per 10 ml medium per tube should be used.

5 Isolation of growing larvae

Only a small percentage of the larvae in a culture will show significant growth and these can be separated from the bulk of the non-growing ones by adding 1 ml of fresh medium with a Pasteur pipette to the narrow stem portion at the bottom of a Hopkins vaccine tube and then transferring the medium containing the growing larvae to the top part of the vaccine tube. After 5–10 min the original medium is decanted leaving the 1 ml of medium in the stem portion containing the larger larvae (400–1,000 μ in length) mixed with only a few of the smaller ones (200–280 μ in length). The worms may then be removed with a Pasteur pipette and added to the growth medium.

The air in the culture tubes should be replaced at this stage with an atmosphere of 95% nitrogen, 5% carbon dioxide.

Cleeland & Lawrence obtained growth in a small percentage of the larvae. They were maintained for a maximum of 110 days and reached sizes up to $2,300 \times 83 \, \mu$: movement was their criterion of viability.

Ascaris lumbricoides Adults
(Ellison *et al.*, 1960)

MEDIA

Nutrient Medium

	mg/l.		mg/l.
L-Alanine	0·75	Dihydrosteptromycin sulphate	1,000
L-Arginine	0·30	Nystatin	40
L-Asparagine	0·30	Ascorbic acid	10
L-Aspartic acid	0·75	Nicotinamide	5·0
L-Cysteine	0·30	Pyridoxine	1·0
L-Cystine	0·30	Riboflavine	1·0
L-Glutamic acid	0·75	Thiamine	1·0
Glycine	0·30	Calcium pantothenate	0·5
L-Histidine	0·75	Choline chloride	0·5
L-Isoleucine	0·30	Folic acid	0·5
L-Leucine	0·30	*p*-Aminobenzoic acid	0·1
L-Lysine	0·30	Biotin	0·05
L-Methionine	0·75	Cyanocobalamine	0·05
L-Phenylalanine	0·75	Myo-Inositol	0·05
L-Proline	0·30	Glucose	2,000
L-Serine	0·30	NaCl	7,970
L-Threonine	0·75	Na_2HPO_4	865
L-Tryptophan	0·30	KCl	175
L-Tyrosine	0·30	$CaCl_2$	175
L-Valine	0·75	$MgCl_2$	100
Penicillin G, K salt	627	KH_2PO_4	78

The medium is made up in distilled water, adjusted to pH 7·2 and diluted to 1,000 ml.

Basal salts medium

Salt	Concentration	
	%	M
NaCl	0·8	$1·37 \times 10^{-1}$
KCl	0·0175	$2·34 \times 10^{-3}$
$CaCl_2$	0·0175	$1·58 \times 10^{-3}$
$MgCl_2$	0·010	$1·05 \times 10^{-3}$

The medium is adjusted to pH 7·2 with $1·25 \times 10^{-3}$ M phosphate buffer.

Specimens of adult *Ascaris lumbricoides* var. *suum* may be obtained from pigs at the local slaughter house. They are transported to the laboratory in vacuum jugs containing basal salts medium at pH 7·2 and 37°C. In the laboratory the worms are rinsed twice in fresh basal salts medium and then incubated at 37°C in battery jars containing basal salts medium plus 0·2% glucose and antibiotics (penicillin G, potassium salt, 627 mg/l.; dihydrostreptomycin sulphate, 1,000 mg/l.; nystatin, 40 mg/l.). Four litres of medium to every 454 g fresh weight of worms are used. The medium is changed every 4 hr, 4 times. This achieves surface sterilization of the worms. They are further incubated at 37°C for two 24 hr periods in fresh nutrient culture medium (91 g fresh worm weight/l. medium) to sterilize their intestinal contents before being maintained in fresh nutrient medium. The medium should be changed daily.

Ellison *et al.* maintained adult *Ascaris* for 6 days in this way after which time the experiments were terminated.

2. ASCARIDIA

Apart from the work of Ackert *et al.* (1938) who carried out extensive experiments on the culture of *Ascaridia linneata* larvae, little attention has been paid to the culture of *Ascaridia*. These workers made no attempt to hatch eggs artificially but cultured larvae which had hatched from eggs fed to young chicks and had subsequently been recovered from the duodenum. The larvae were maintained in normal saline at bird body temperature (41–42°C); increase in larval length was taken as the criterion of growth. Larvae survived for nearly 2 weeks when kept on a solid glucose-cornmeal agar plate overlaid with sterile normal saline with a pH of 6·9. The addition of various peptone broths did not improve matters, in fact larvae survived for shorter periods in supplemented media but they were observed to ingest food materials.

Ackert *et al.* then turned their attention to older larvae and as possible media they examined hens' eggs, various carbohydroate solutions and isotonic salt-glucose described by Stunkard (1932). Larvae, cultured 19 days after infection of chicks, on plates of glucose-cornmeal agar overlaid with a carbohydrate solution consisting of 20 g starch, and 10 g glucose in 50 ml distilled water with a pH of 6·2 showed a 20% increase in length. Older larvae (23–36 days after infection) showed up to 50% increase in length when cultured in the isotonic salt-glucose solution (Stunkard, 1932). However it is not clear how much the larval reserves and how much the nutrients present in the media contributed to their growth.

Rogers (1961) undertook to study the physiology of hatching of eggs of *A.galli*. The eggs were collected from female worms after they had been incubated for 24 hr in saline at 37°c. They were washed for 1 hr in 0·5 N NaOH or 6 hr in 1% pancreatin (pH 6·8) followed by 28 days incubation at 28°c in 0·5% formalin or 0·1 N H_2SO_4 to allow development to the infective stage. Bicarbonate buffers (without oxygen) containing 0·02 M sodium dithionite gassed with 1% carbon dioxide in nitrogen were tested over a range of pH 5–8. Rogers showed the process to be dependent upon the undissociated carbonic acid concentration, the dissolved gaseous carbon dioxide, the redox potential and the pH of the hatching medium. There was considerable overlap in the hatching conditions required by *A.galli* and *Ascaris*.

In addition to these workers, a few people recently have been interested in the metabolism of *Ascaridia* (e.g. Weatherby *et al.*, 1963) and the uptake of radioactive nutrients *in vitro*.

IV. STRONGYLOIDEA

A ANCYLOSTOMIDAE

ANCYLOSTOMA and *NECATOR AMERICANUS*

Larvae

Several workers have reported methods of culturing the free-living stages of hookworms, the majority of these being faecal cultures or cultures of larvae fed on bacteria (McCoy, 1929a, b; Okada, 1930; Nakajima, 1931, 1932; Lapage, 1933a, b; Marplestone, 1934; Aketogawa, 1938; Kamiko, 1939; Matsusaki, 1939). One of the first attempts to define the nutritional requirements of the free-living stages of *A.caninum* from dogs was that of McCoy (1929a, b) who attempted to grow them on pure strains of bacteria and yeast. He sterilized the eggs recovered from the faeces of heavily infected dogs and used them to inoculate either 24-hour agar plate cultures of the various bacteria or such bacteria suspended in physiological saline. The larvae grew to the infective stage in the normal 7-day period in either type of culture, provided the bacteria were alive; heat-killed bacteria did not support growth of the larvae. McCoy found that

22 species of bacteria were suitable as a sole source of nutrient for the hookworm larvae. Later workers (Sasa *et al.*, 1958; Hsieh *et al.*, 1963) used faecal cultures to facilitate surveys on the prevalence of various species of hookworms in Japan and Taiwan respectively.

The first attempt at the axenic cultivation of hookworms was that of Lawrence (1948) working in Australia on *A.braziliense*, a parasite of dogs and cats. The eggs were sterilized most satisfactorily by a mixture of 10% formalin and 10% 'Milton' (a commercial antiseptic containing 1% sodium hypochlorite); various culture media, including those containing bacteria killed in a variety of ways or even filtrates of *Bacillus coli* cultures were tested. None of these supported development but eventually success was obtained with Glaser & Stoll's medium (1938) for *Haemonchus contortus*. This consisted of a semi-gel agar medium containing ground heat-killed yeast, liver extract and fresh pieces of rabbit kidney; it supported development to the third larval stage when the yeast and liver extract were omitted. Lawrence then undertook to analyse the effective components of this medium and found a heat-stable water-soluble factor to be of importance. However in none of his axenic cultures did he obtain as good growth and development as in those cultures containing living bacteria.

Weinstein (1949, 1953) carried these studies still further when he undertook to confirm that heat-killed bacteria were not a suitable food for the larval stages of *A.caninum* and *A.duodenale* (from a Korean patient) and also to analyse the growth-promoting properties of Glaser & Stoll's medium. He introduced the use of antibiotics which greatly simplified the culture procedures. In fluid cultures consisting of Tyrode's solution and suspensions of dead bacteria with or without liver extract, as recommended by Glaser & Stoll, little development was obtained. However, when small amounts of 50% chick embryo extract were added, approximately 81% of the larvae developed to the infective stage. Weinstein then discovered that he could obtain even greater yields of infective filariform larvae (as shown by the ability of the *A.caninum* larvae to infect puppies) in either 50% chick embryo extract or 20% rat liver extract (p. 275) although there were times when the liver extract was inhibitory to growth; he was unfortunately unable to isolate the growth inhibitor. Bacterial filtration of tissue extracts or their fractionation had markedly deleterious effects on the growth of the larvae. Weinstein (1954) then successfully applied this technique to the culture of *Necator americanus* larvae; 98% of the eggs developed to filariform larvae in 50% chick embryo extract to which formalin-killed *Escherischia coli* had been added.

Sawada *et al.* (1954) reported their attempts to culture *Ancylostoma* larvae in chicken embryos and later Sawada (1961) devised a method of culturing third stage (infective) larvae of *A.caninum*. The larvae were obtained from the lungs and muscles of experimentally infected dogs and were maintained on a variety of media (haemolysed dog, rabbit or human serum, filtrate of dog intestinal contents or filtrate of dog liver homogenate) contained in a glass filter funnel with a rubber cap at one end. He obtained development to the fourth stage only in haemolysed dog serum.

Adults

The first record of maintenance of *A.caninum* adults *in vitro* was that of Komiya *et al.* (1956, 1958). The adult hookworms were recovered from dogs 3–4 weeks after infection and sterilized with antibiotics. Three of each sex were placed in Carell flasks at 37°c and the medium changed every 2 days, motility of the worms being the criterion of survival. Infected dog serum (1 part) diluted with Krebs-Ringer bicarbonate solution (3 parts) maintained males for a maximum of 6 weeks and females up to 12 weeks. Copulation was observed during the first 3 weeks and eggs were deposited throughout the culture period. Larvae hatched from the eggs after periods of up to 30 days *in vitro*. The use of whole serum, serum diluted up to 50% or the addition of red blood cells did not appreciably alter the results, nor did it affect copulation or egg-laying. The worms survived in Krebs-Ringer-bicarbonate for 21 days (female) and 10 days (male) provided 0·5% glucose was added. Ringer's, Locke's and Tyrode's solutions were less efficient.

This work was later continued by Yasuroaka *et al.* (1960) who obtained survival of adult worms for 4 months in human serum, the females surviving for slightly longer periods than the males. During this time the worms increased in length, copulated and laid eggs; these developed into filariform larvae when cultured axenically in chick embryo extract.

An interesting technique, suitable for direct nutritional and metabolic studies on hookworms, has been developed by Roche & Torres (1960). The adult worm is maintained in a double chamber which enables the anterior end of the worm to be separated from its posterior end. The living worm is threaded through a thin rubber membrane which separates the two halves of the chamber and prevents contact between the fluid contents. Worms have been kept alive for periods of several hours during which time these workers have used ^{51}Cr-tagged blood to determine their feeding rates. Later Roche *et al.* (1962) produced a film of their technique.

Ancylostoma caninum Larvae
(Weinstein, 1953)

MEDIUM

Chick Embryo Extract (CEE) (p. 345)
White's Solution

> HgCl₂ . . . . .0·25 g
> NaCl . . . . .6·5 g
> HCl . . . . .1·25 ml
> 95% ethyl alcohol . . . . .250 ml
> Distilled water . . . . .750 ml

Rat Liver Extract (RLE) (p. 345)

Antibiotics. Crystalline penicillin G (300 units/ml) and streptomycin sulphate (200 μg/ml) are dissolved in physiological saline and added to each culture.

TECHNIQUE

1 *Preparation of the egg inoculum*

Eggs are separated from the faeces of a heavily infected dog by mixing them with saturated saline and gently centrifuging to concentrate them. They are washed several times in sterile water before being exposed to White's solution for 20–30 min to surface sterilize them and then re-washed by centrifugation 5 times in 20 ml aliquots of sterile water. The final egg concentration is adjusted to 200–300 eggs per drop.

2 *Setting up cultures*

Cultures are established in 50 ml Erlenmeyer flasks. Either 50% chick embryo extract (CEE₅₀) or 20% rat liver extract (RLE₂₀) may be used together with antibiotics at the above concentration. Three millilitres of medium are placed in each flask and remaining medium (sufficient for a number of transfers, usually 3 for testing a particular medium) stored in Pyrex tubes at −20°c. The eggs (900–1,200/culture) are then added, the flasks sealed with rubber bungs and incubated at 28°c. To subculture (every 48–72 hr), the contents of each flask are centrifuged for 30 secs (700–800 rev/min) under sterile conditions to throw down the larvae, the supernatant is discarded and the larvae transferred to fresh medium in a new flask.

Weinstein obtained good yields of filariform larvae from eggs cultured in either 50% chick embryo extract or 20% rat liver extract, together with antibiotics although more reliable results were obtained with 50% chick embryo extract. These larvae were infective to puppies.

B METASTRONGYLIDAE

1. *ANGIOSTRONGYLUS CANTONENSIS*

This lungworm is transmitted by slugs and other molluscs to its natural definitive host, the rat. When the infective (third stage) larvae are ingested by rats they quickly pass to the central nervous system via the blood stream, and eventually come to lie in the brain. Here they undergo 2 moults, to the fifth or juvenile adult stage, when they migrate to the main branches of the pulmonary artery. Weinstein *et al.* (1962) briefly reported that they were able to maintain adult *A.cantonensis* for 9 weeks in medium NCTC 109 supplemented with 10% horse serum.

The survival of the adults *in vitro* was later extended by Weinstein *et al.* (1963) to 64 days for adult males and 80 days for adult females below. During the culture period the worms copulated and the females deposited eggs; these were fertile for only the first 3–4 days. Weinstein and his colleagues compared the development of the worms *in vivo* (in rats and monkeys) with that *in vitro* and showed that embryonation and hatching of eggs occurred *in vitro* in comparable time and manner to those developing *in vivo*: unfortunately they were not able to obtain growth of any of the larval stages *in vitro*, even after trying a variety of media.

Angiostrongylus cantonensis Adults
(Weinstein *et al.*, 1963)

MEDIUM

NCTC 109 containing 300 units penicillin and 100 μg streptomycin/ml (p. 351) supplemented with 10% horse serum.

TECHNIQUE

A.cantonensis can be maintained in laboratory rats. The intermediate host, the slug (*Limax maximus*), can be infected by feeding for about 1 hr on lettuce leaves smeared with infected faeces. Third stage larvae may be obtained from slug tissue either by cutting it coarsely in a peptic digestion fluid (15 g pepsin, 21 ml concentrated HCl, 3 l. sterile 0·5% NaCl) with scissors or homogenizing it in a Waring blender for 1–2 min in this same fluid (15 large slugs/3 l. of digestion fluid). The digestion is allowed to proceed at 37°c for 2–3 hr, whilst stirring continuously. The liberated larvae are collected by sedimentation in 1 l. Imhoff cones, washed several times in saline and finally transferred to the above medium. Rats are infected by intra-oesophageal inoculation, with a syringe and blunt needle (10–30 larvae per rat). The usual onset of patency occurs between 42–45 days later.

Recovery of worms for culture

Rats are killed in a carbon dioxide chamber and the heart and pulmonary artery and its branches dissected out. The pulmonary artery is carefully slit open and the worms present removed with fine forceps. If the heart-lung preparation is kept warm under a lamp, worms from the branches of the pulmonary artery often migrate rapidly into the slit area from which they also can be removed. The worms are collected into NCTC 109 containing antibiotics and washed several times in this fluid before being transferred into media flasks closed with screw caps or silicone rubber stoppers (2 ml of medium and 1–3 worms per flask) and incubated at 37°c. All flasks are gassed initially with 5% carbon dioxide in air; the medium is changed daily and each time re-gassed.

Weinstein *et al.* maintained adult males for a maximum of 64 days and females for 80 days in this medium. The females during the first 3 days *in vitro*, deposited fertile eggs which embryonated within 5–6 days (comparable with the normal time *in vivo*) but hatching did not occur readily. Eggs deposited after 4 days culture were infertile. Cultures of first-stage larvae were unsuccessful.

2. *DICTYOCAULUS*

The first recorded attempts to culture *Dictyocaulus* were those of Silverman and his colleagues (Silverman, 1962; Silverman & Podger, 1962; Silverman *et al.*, 1962; Silverman, 1963a) who obtained larval development *in vitro* of *D.viviparus*, the lungworm of calves. Initially a variety of media, including tissue homogenates and extracts, sera, protein hydro-lysates and tissue or organ systems, as described by Silverman (1959) for the culture of *Haemonchus contortus*, were tried. Success was eventually obtained with a medium very similar to that used by Weinstein & Jones (1956a) for the cultivation of *Nippostrongylus brasiliensis*, consisting of chick embryo extract, autoclaved sheep liver extract (see Nicholas, 1956), casein hydrolysate and sheep serum in a 2:2:2:1 ratio. Infective larvae, obtained from faecal cultures, were washed and sterilized in antibiotic solutions, exsheathed in 1% gastric pepsin in 1% HCl solution and transferred to the medium in roller cultures at 37°C.

The medium was considerably simplified by systematically eliminating the various undefined components (Silverman *et al.*, 1962) until a final medium was arrived at, consisting of Earle's balanced saline supplemented with the autoclaved liver extract or Bacto-peptone (Difco), which supported the development of larvae from their third to fourth stage *in vitro* (below). This larval development tended to be somewhat erratic until these workers determined the optimum exsheathing stimuli that were required (Silverman, 1963b; Silverman & Podger, 1964). *D.viviparus* larvae can be stored for at least 2–3 weeks in water at 4°C, but only those larvae which had been stored for a maximum of 7 days were found to be suitable for *in vitro* studies.

Dictyocaulus viviparus Larvae
(Silverman, 1962; Silverman *et al.*, 1962)

MEDIUM

Earle's solution (p. 350) containing sodium penicillin G (1,000 units/ml), streptomycin sulphate (1,000 μg/ml) and nystatin (250 units/ml).
Difco Bacto-Peptone made up as a 5% solution in distilled water, Seitz filtered and stored at −20°C.

The culture medium consists of Earle's solution plus 0·05% Difco bacto-peptone solution.

TECHNIQUE

Faecal cultures
Faeces are collected from experimentally infected calves, housed indoors, and are moistened and spread out on trays to a depth of about ¼ in. and incubated at 21°C for about 7 days. A clean suspension of infective third stage larvae of *D. viviparus* in water is prepared from the incubated faeces and the suspension stored for 12 days at 15°C. It is then centrifuged at not more than 1,000 rev/min for 2 min and the supernatant liquid replaced with sterile Earle's solution containing antibiotics. After repeated washings the larvae are exsheathed in 1% pepsin in 1% HCl. The suspension is incubated at 38°C for 30 min with agitation until check counts

indicate that more than 90% of the larvae have been exsheathed (Silverman, 1963b; Silverman & Podger, 1964).

At this stage the larvae are centrifuged, washed 3 times in sterile Earle's solution containing antibiotics and transferred to the culture medium in roller culture tubes. Larvae are cultured at 38°c at a concentration of 5,000/ml to 20,000/ml.

Silverman *et al.* found that after 3–4 days incubation on rollers, up to 70% of the larvae are converted to the early fourth stage.

3. *METASTRONGYLUS*

Sen & Kelley (1960) briefly reported some success in the cultivation of the larval stages of *Metastrongylus apri* and *M. pudendotectus*, lungworms of swine. Third stage larvae were removed from the earthworm by gastric digestion and inoculated into axenic culture. Hanks's medium permitted development to the fifth stage within 192 hr but all larvae were dead by 8 days. Better results were obtained when Hanks's medium was used together with a trypticase medium (designed by Diamond & Douvres, 1960, for the culture of swine strongylid nematodes) consisting of trypticase, yeast extract, glucose, sheep serum and extracts of rabbit embryo and pig's liver. Sixteen and 10% of the larvae had moulted into fourth and fifth stage larvae respectively by the eighth day. Almost all the larvae were alive at this time and some grew to maturity when inoculated directly into the bronchus of the pig.

C STRONGYLIDAE

OSEOPHAGOSTOMUM and *STEPHANURUS*

Diamond & Douvres first reported attempts to culture the larval stages of *Oesophagostomum* in 1960 and since this date they have carried out much work on this parasite (Diamond & Douvres, 1960, 1962; Douvres, 1960a, b; 1962a, b; 1966). Diamond & Douvres (1960, 1962) initially used 8–10 day-old infective larvae of *O. quadrispinulatum* isolated from sphagnum moss cultures which had been seeded with infected swine faeces (infected with *O. quadrispinulatum* and *Hyostrongylus rubidus*). The larvae were exsheathed by hypochlorite treatment and sterilized by washing in antibiotic solutions before being cultured at 38·5°c in a complex medium consisting essentially of trypticase, yeast extract, glucose, sheep serum and extracts of rabbit and pig liver. Within 42 days *in vitro* the *O.quadrispinulatum* larvae had developed to the fourth stage (considerably slower than *in vivo*) and were stunted in form.

Douvres (1960a) modified the medium by using bovine instead of sheep serum and supplementing it with a vitamin mixture and used this to culture the infective larvae of *O.radiatum*, the nodular worm of cattle. These developed to the late fourth stage within 27 days but again were stunted, and growth of the genital primordium was particularly retarded. Still further modifications were tried (Douvres, 1960b) by using extracts and homogenates of intestinal mucosa. Development to the fifth stage within 24 days was achieved when the medium was supplemented with a phosphate buffer extract of the mucosa of the intestine from a young uninfected calf, provided inactivated calf serum replaced the normal calf serum. Douvres (1962a) detailed his previous results on the culture of *O.radiatum* during an extensive series of tests and developed a cell-free, clarified, vitamin supplemented medium which enhanced the rate of growth of the larvae so that the fourth moult occurred after 19 days instead of 24 days *in vitro* (p. 283). A cultivation temperature of 38·5°c was found preferable to 35 or 37°c and the percentage yield of fifth stage larvae was greater in vitamin supplemented media diluted with bovine intestinal mucosa extract than in cultures diluted with buffer alone. This technique was extended to the cultivation of infective third stage larvae of *O.dentatum* (Douvres, 1966) and a maximum of 4% adult worms (alive and dead) were obtained *in vitro*. Cultures were maintained for 125 days and Douvres made the interesting observation that the presence of fifth stage worms and fourth stage larvae inhibited the development of third stage larvae in the same cultures. Douvres also (1962b) used his technique to demonstrate that antibodies can be extracted from intestinal tissues of bovids infected with or resistant to *O.radiatum* and that antigens which react specifically with these antibodies were produced by the larval stages grown *in vitro*.

Douvres & Tromba (1962) adapted the medium that had been previously used for *O. radiatum* (Douvres, 1962a) in order to culture *Stephanurus dentatus* infective larvae obtained from swine faecal cultures. By doubling the amount of swine liver extract and bovine serum and culturing at 39–40°c they succeeded in rearing numbers of early fourth stage larvae within 15 days. However these were stunted and had taken longer to reach the fourth stage than *in vivo*; in addition development of the genital primordium lagged behind somatic differentiation.

Douvres and his colleagues later (Douvres *et al.*, 1966) were more successful when they used stationary swine-kidney cell cultures overlaid with medium NCTC 109 plus other ingredients for growing *S.dentatus*

(p. 284). Not only did development proceed to the late fourth stage (immature adult) but larger numbers of worms were obtained and these were observed to feed on the living kidney cells. Douvres *et al.* showed that the kidney cells were essential for the development of advanced stages of *S.dentatus in vitro*, for when the cells were omitted from the cultures only early fourth stage larvae developed. Their cultures were sufficiently successful to enable them to carry out morphological studies on the parasite and Douvres *et al.* were of the opinion that their *in vitro* system produced worms which were morphologically more 'normal' than those previously described from guinea pigs, an abnormal host.

Leland (1961a, b, 1963a, b, 1965b) cultivated *O.quadrispinulatum* and *O.radiatum* (from sheep) and obtained development to the fifth (adult) stage with roller-drum cultures containing a medium consisting of chick embryo extract, serum, sodium caseinate, vitamins and pig liver extract in balanced saline containing antibiotics. Leland gassed his cultures with carbon dioxide and 5% of the worms reached the adult-stage (containing spermatogonia and oogonia) within 32 days; their maximum survival period was 112 days. He used an interesting device for viewing his cultures, details of which are given below.

Silverman (1963a, 1965) also used carbon dioxide to gas his cultures of an Australian strain of *O.radiatum*. He found that infective larvae exsheathed in balanced saline saturated with carbon dioxide at pH 5 and developed to the fourth stage in Earle's or Hanks's balanced saline solutions saturated with carbon dioxide within 96 hr in roller culture. When the larvae were transferred to a more complex medium of chick embryo extract, bovine liver extract, serum and sodium caseinate they developed to the fifth stage 14–21 days later, a remarkable result in that the development was more rapid than reported by Anataraman (1942) for *in vivo* development.

A simple device for viewing nematode parasites *in vitro*
(Leland, 1961b)

A simple prismatic system for viewing nematode cultures *in situ* has been devised by Leland. It consists of a $\frac{1}{4}$ in. plywood framework for holding glass prisms and providing a suitable supporting surface for culture containers (Fig. 7.3 E). A wing (W) protruding from the right side of the main prism framework holds a culture tube. A slight incline (1°) in the wing restricts the tube contents (2 ml) to the area above the prism and also prevents the medium from contacting the rubber cap or stopper.

The wing is constructed short enough to allow the cap portion of the tube to protrude. The cap can then be used as a knob for revolving or making left and right movements of the tube. Nails at the wing tip restrict the forward or backward movements of the tube.

A length of $\frac{3}{4}$ in. angle iron (A.I., Fig. 7.3, E) acts as a counterweight for stabilizing the wing. The weight provides additional surface for larger flasks and serves as a handle for positioning the device under a stereoscopic microscope.

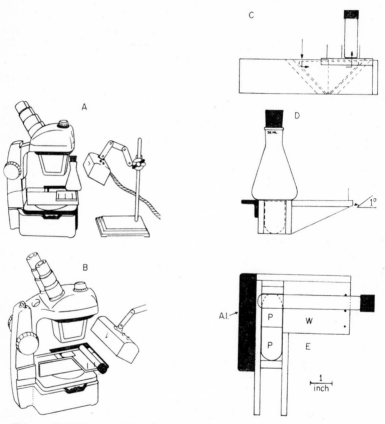

FIGURE 7.3 Prismatic device for viewing nematode parasites *in vitro*. (From Leland, 1961b.) A, prismatic device under stereo-microscope showing flask in position; B, tube in position; C, position of vial over prism (side view); D, flask over prism (front view); E, framework for holding prisms (top view): A.I. three-quarter inch angle iron; P, prism; W, wing. Because the device rests on the stage of the stereo-microscope, it is easily removed and the microscope is then available for other purposes.

The glass container is placed on the distal end of the prism and viewed with a stereomicroscope through the proximal end of the prism (Fig. 7.3, C). At least 2 models of stereoscopic microscopes are known to be satisfactory, giving magnifications up to 45 diameters.

This device has made it possible to follow many characteristics of growth *in vitro* such as increasing size, bursal development from the fourth to the adult stage, buccal capsule changes, vitality and survival. Thus the growth can be assessed before removing the culture from the container. After removal, obscure structures can be verified with a conventional microscope. The device can be used in other ways such as for checking vial-stored specimens or centrifuge tubes for larvae left behind in transferring procedures.

Oesophagostomum radiatum Larvae
(Douvres, 1962a, b)

MEDIA

A variety of culture media were used by Douvres as shown in the following table.

TABLE 7.1. Components of media for the cultivation of *O.radiatum*
(in parts per 100 ml)

Ingredients	Media M-1	SM-1*	SM-2*	SM-3*	SM-4*
Rabbit embryo extract	29·7	29·7	27	27	24·8
Pig liver extract	14·8	14·8	14	14	12·4
Bovine serum	9·9	9·9	9	9	8·3
Nutrient broth	44·6	44·6	40·1	40·1	37·2
Antibiotics	1	1	0·9	0·9	0·8
Phosphate buffer mixture	—	—	9	—	—
Intestinal tissue extract	—	—	—	9	16·5

* Vitamin mixture added to cultures on initial larval inoculation and subsequent transfers to fresh media.

Rabbit embryo extract, pig liver extract (from 3–9 week old pigs), nutrient broth and antibiotics are prepared according to Diamond & Douvres (1962); p. 299.
Bovine serum is obtained from calves or yearlings and sterilized by filtration.
Vitamin mixture (Weinstein & Jones, 1959) in μg/ml of final medium: thiamine hydrochloride, pyridoxine hydrochloride, calcium pantothenate,

nicotinic acid, *p*-aminobenzoic acid, 2·5 each; folic acid, 1·25; riboflavin, 0·75; choline chloride, 10. Prior to use the supplement is sterilized by filtration and then stored in sterile rubber-capped serum bottles at −20°C.

Intestinal tissue extract. The last 6 feet of the small intestine and the caecum and colon of a healthy 4 day old parasite free calf (Holstein) are removed, opened and flushed with 0·7% saline to remove ingesta and faeces. The mucosal and submucosal layers are scraped from each organ with a glass plate, pooled, frozen and stored for 3 days at −40°C. The tissues are then thawed slowly and each 10 g wet weight of tissue is extracted with 100 ml of 0·066 M phosphate buffer (pH 7·2) for 4 days at 5°C. During this time the mixture is agitated daily for several minutes; the slightly viscous serum-coloured extract is then decanted and centrifuged at 2,200 × *g* for 40 min at 4°C. The clear supernatant fluid is passed twice through a Selas 03 filter and stored at −40°C in rubber-capped serum bottles.

Phosphate buffer mixture. Buffer identical to that used for the above extraction is sterilized and stored in the same manner.

The tubing, storage and use in culture of each final medium are identical to the procedures described by Diamond & Douvres (1962); p. 299.

TECHNIQUE

Infective larvae are obtained from sphagnum moss cultures and exsheathed in sodium hypochlorite solution (p. 300). The larvae are added to the culture tubes in numbers varying from 1,000 to 9,500 per culture. Handling and transfers of cultures are detailed on p. 300.

Douvres obtained development of *O.radiatum* to the fifth stage (fourth moult) in all 5 media. Development to each stage was more rapid in media containing the vitamin supplement. Comparisons with *in vivo* development showed that *in vitro* larvae are stunted in the third moult, fourth stage and fourth moult; development of the genital primordium lags behind somatic or cephalic differentiation and in general more time is required to reach the various developmental stages.

Stephanurus dentatus Larvae
(Douvres *et al.*, 1966)

MEDIUM

NCTC 109 (p. 351) 50 ml.

Swine serum (obtained from 3–5 month old males, sterilized by filtration and stored at −20°C) 50 ml.

Yeast extract (obtained from Baltimore Biological Laboratory) 112·5 mg.
Bacto-peptone (Difco) 140·65 mg.
Glucose (obtained from Baltimore Biological Laboratory) 140·65 mg.

The above ingredients are mixed at room temperature with gentle stirring, sterilized by filtration and used as the overlay for the swine kidney cell cultures. The medium may be stored for up to 2 weeks at −20°C. The final pH of the medium should be 7·9.

Fenwick's balanced saline

	mg/l.	
NaCl	8000	
KCl	200	dissolved in 1 litre glass distilled
CaCl$_2$	200	water and sterilized by filtration.
MgCl$_2$	100	

TECHNIQUE

1   *Swine kidney cell cultures*

Trypsinized (Hancock *et al.*, 1959) kidney cells, washed and concentrated to a packed volume of 1 ml, were suspended in 200 ml of growth medium consisting of Hanks's balanced salt solution (p. 350), 80%; 2·5% lactalbumin hydrolysate (Nutritional Biochemicals Corp.), 10% and calf serum, 10%. Approximately 12–14 ml of the suspension are inoculated into prescription bottles (4 oz, with a growth area of approximately 28 cm^2) with screw caps lined with teflon-coated paper. A maintenance medium composed of Earle's balanced salt solution (BSS, p. 350), 85%; lactalbumin hydrolysate, 10%; and calf serum 5% is substituted for the starting medium 3–4 days after inoculation. Antibiotics are added to all media to give a final concentration of 100 units penicillin G potassium, 100 μg dihydrostreptomycin sulphate, and 50 units of nystatin (Mycostatin, Squibb & Sons) per ml of medium. The penicillin and streptomycin are mixed and added to the media separately from the nystatin. The growth and maintenance media contain a final concentration of 0·2% phenol red indicator. The pH is adjusted to 7·0–7·2 by gassing with carbon dioxide. After 5 or 6 days in most cases, the culture chambers contain a confluent sheet of cells. Complete adherence of the cells to the culture vessel is the criterion of viability. Cultures are incubated at 37°C.

2   *Preparation of the larval inoculum*

Eggs are recovered by filtration from the urine of pigs experimentally infected with *S.dentatus* or by dissection from the uteri of sexually mature worms. They are cultured in a shallow layer of tapwater at 21°c. After 7–14 days the infective larvae are recovered with a Baermann apparatus (p. 361) and used immediately either for culture or to infect swine, administered orally in tap water.

The 10–14 day old infective larvae are washed several times with Fenwick's saline, exsheathed in 1·25% solution of Clorox (Clorox Chemical Co.) in Fenwick's saline for 20 min and washed in 6 change of sterile Fenwick's saline before being cultured.

The larvae are cultured in the swine kidney cell cultures overlaid with 10 ml fresh culture medium. About 5,000–6,000 larvae are used per culture. Transfer to fresh cultures overlaid with fresh culture medium are made every 2–3 days. Cultures are maintained at 39°c and held in a horizontal position.

Douvres *et al.* obtained development of morphologically normal late fourth stage larvae in 21 days. The worms were observed to be feeding on the kidney cells *in vitro*.

D   TRICHOSTRONGYLIDAE

1. *NIPPOSTRONGYLUS*

Nippostrongylus brasiliensis (*N.muris* or *Heligmosomum muris*; see Haley, 1961) was the first nematode parasite of vertebrates to be cultured through one complete life-cycle *in vitro* although the culture of successive generations has yet to be achieved (Weinstein & Jones, 1956a, b; see also review by Denham, 1967). *N.brasiliensis*, first described in detail by Yokogawa (1921), is a skin penetrating parasite of rats which undergoes development during migration through the lungs and trachea to the small intestine where it attaches itself to the mucosa and feeds on the tissues and blood. Eggs are passed out in the faeces and undergo development with 2 moults before becoming third stage infective larvae.

Weinstein (1949, 1954) first turned his attention to the cultivation of the free-living stages of *N.brasiliensis* in the absence of living bacteria; workers prior to this had used faecal cultures to provide infective larvae in the laboratory. Weinstein initially obtained development from the egg to the infective third stage in static cultures on a medium consisting of 50% chick embryo extract (CEE_{50}) or rat liver extract, each containing antibiotics (Weinstein, 1949). A higher yield of third stage larvae was obtained when formaldehyde killed *Escherichia coli* were added to cultures in Selas-filtered chick embryo extract (88%) although some third stage larvae could also be obtained from cultures of beef heart infusion broth. Subsequently Weinstein & Jones (1956a) attempted to analyse the growth promoting properties of Weinstein's medium and showed that water soluble vitamins were important components of the medium.

This work was then extended (Weinstein & Jones, 1956b) and resulted in the successful cultivation of sexually mature adult worms. Development from the egg to stages comparable to the advanced lung stages in the rat occurred in roller culture in 50% chick embryo extract alone but further growth and differentiation comparable to fourth and fifth stage worms in the gut occurred only when the chick embryo extract was supplemented with sodium caseinate, liver filtrate, yeast extract and rat serum. However adults of both sexes were stunted although morphologically normal and fertilization did not occur *in vitro*; they took at least 3–4 times longer to develop *in vitro* than in the rat.

Further analysis of their medium (Weinstein & Jones, 1957a, 1959) and attempts to use chemically defined media did not result in copulation of the worms *in vitro* or the production of fertile eggs. Even when these authors removed fourth stage larvae from rats and cultured them *in vitro* the resulting adults did not copulate or produce fertile eggs. However increased yields of sexually mature adults were obtained when a basal medium of chick embryo extract and human serum (human serum gave better results than rat serum on direct comparison) was supplemented with a vitamin mixture, Eagle's medium and liver concentrate. These results were obtained either with or without the inclusion of antibiotics. When they used chemically defined media (199, Eagle's, NCTC 109) alone or with various supplements, the larvae survived but did not grow. Sommerville & Weinstein (1967) have recently investigated the factors concerned with the development *in vitro* of late fourth stage larvae to sexually mature adults. Using a screening procedure based on cultivation in a balanced salt solution (modified Krebs–Ringer saline) containing glucose, they showed that the addition of yeast extract and casein induced sexual development; sperm and eggs were produced by some worms.

One of the most significant features of the above work by Weinstein and his colleagues has been the interest it has stimulated in other workers on the cultivation of worms *in vitro*; also Weinstein & Jones demonstrated the importance of chick embryo extract as a source of nutrient for the cultivation of worms.

Leland (1963a) has repeated Weinstein & Jones's work and cultured *N.brasiliensis* from third stage larvae to sexually mature adults in a specially clarified medium consisting of chick embryo extract, serum, sodium caseinate, vitamins, pig-liver extract, a balanced salt solution and antibiotics. The clarification of the medium enabled him to observe the development of the larvae *in vitro* more readily.

Nippostrongylus brasiliensis (*muris*)   Egg to Adult
(Weinstein & Jones, 1956a, b, 1957a, 1959)

MEDIUM

50% *Chick embryo extract* (CEE_{50}) p. 345.

Serum. Human serum is obtained from whole blood allowed to clot overnight in the refrigerator. The serum is removed, centrifuged at 1°c to remove any cells, sterilized by filtration and stored at −20°c.

Vitamin mixture (II, see Weinstein & Jones, 1956b). Composition in $\mu g/ml$ of final medium: Thiamine hydrochloride, 2·5; pyridoxine hydrochloride, 2·5; calcium pantothenate, 2·5; nicotinic acid, 2·5; *p*-aminobenzoic acid, 2·5; folic acid, 1·25; riboflavin, 0·75; choline chloride, 10·0.

Liver concentrate (202-20) is a powder manufactured by Sigma Chemical Co. It is dissolved in Earle's solution (p. 350) and sterilized by filtration (p. 342).

Antibiotics. 300 units penicillin and 0·3 mg streptomycin per ml of medium.

TECHNIQUE

1   *Maintenance of strain*

N. brasiliensis may be maintained in laboratory rats. Faeces containing eggs are mixed with charcoal on damp filter paper in Petri dishes and the filariform larvae used to infect fresh rats; this is accomplished by suspending the larvae in water in large jars and exposing young rats to the infection for about ½ hr.

2   *Preparation of egg inoculum for culture*

Eggs are concentrated by centrifugal flotation of infected faeces in saturated salt solution (sp. gr. 1·2), after which they are refloated using the same procedure. This double flotation removes virtually all the accompanying faecal debris and greatly facilitates sterilization. The eggs are then sterilized by exposing them to sodium hypochlorite [1·25% solution of 'Clorox' (Clorox Chemical Co.) in 0·7% sterile saline] for 15 min; the hypochlorite is then removed by several washes in sterile saline. 1 ml of the egg suspension may be inoculated into each of 2 tubes of thioglycollate broth for sterility tests.

3   Cultivation of eggs to third stage larvae

Either of two media can be used to rear third stage larvae from eggs *in vitro*, medium 2 yielding slightly larger numbers of larvae; antibiotics may be added if required but perferably should be omitted:

Medium 1 (chick embryo extract-vitamin mixture II), composed of 50% chick embryo extract supplemented with vitamin mixture II.

Medium 2 (chick embryo extract-liver concentrate), composed of 50% chick embryo extract supplemented with 2·6 mg liver concentrate per millilitre of medium.

Since large numbers of third stage larvae are needed for cultivation to the adult stage, mass cultures of eggs are prepared in 125 ml Erlenmeyer flasks. Flasks containing 10 ml of either medium are set up and the sterilized eggs are inoculated; the flasks are rubber stoppered and incubated at 26°c (7 days in medium 1 or 14 days in medium 2).

Preparation of faeces-reared third stage larvae for cultivation

A clean suspension of third stage larvae obtained from charcoal-faecal cultures is surface sterilized by exposure to 0·25% 'Clorox' solution in 0·7% sterile NaCl for 10 min. The larvae are then thoroughly washed in several changes of sterile saline before being transferred to culture.

Preparation and handling of cultures of third stage larvae

All cultures are prepared in 16×150 mm test-tubes containing 2 ml of medium. Approximately 7% of the larvae develop to the fifth stage in a medium consisting of 70% chick embryo extract (CEE_{70}), 20% human serum, 10% Earle's solution (p. 350). Supplementing this medium with vitamin mixture II increases the yield of adult worms to about 25%. Following inoculation of approximately 500 third stage larvae, and after each transfer, tubes are gassed for 30 sec with a mixture of 5% carbon dioxide in air and then rubber stoppered. Cultures are incubated at 37·5°c in a roller drum rotating at 12 rev/hr. Transfers are made 3 times a week. Cultures are carried through 7–10 transfers, the usual number being 7.

Weinstein & Jones used third stage larvae, from either axenic or charcoal-faecal cultures, for the initiation of cultures to the adult stage. They obtained development from the egg to the sexually mature adult (male and female) within about 3 weeks, but all eggs were infertile, probably because the worms did not copulate *in vitro*. Strict axenic conditions were maintained throughout without the use of antibiotics, although these were used in some experiments.

2. HAEMONCHUS CONTORTUS

Glaser & Stoll (1938), using a medium which had been developed by Glaser & Coria (1935) for culturing *Paramoecium* under sterile conditions, succeeded in rearing *H.contortus* larvae from the egg to the infective stage and showed that these cultivated larvae were, although stunted, still capable of infecting lambs. The medium they used was a semi-solid agar gel containing 0·5% liver extract. Sterile test-tubes (100 × 13 mm) were used and 0·2–0·3 g of fresh sterile rabbit kidney were placed in the bottom of each tube over which the liver extract-agar was poured. Two drops of an aqueous yeast extract were added to each tube which was cotton-plugged after inoculation with sterilized *H.contortus* eggs. The cultures were held at 22–27°c in a darkened humidor; the optimum pH was found to be 7·0. Fourteen days after sowing the eggs, well nourished and active infective larvae were recovered from the surface of the agar but they were stunted in comparison with larvae reared on faecal cultures.

Stoll later (1940) showed that third stage larvae of *H.contortus* were able to develop from their third to fourth stage without an exogenous supply of food. He incubated third stage larvae in a variety of balanced salt solutions and obtained good yields of exsheathed larvae in Ringer's or Tyrode's solutions; normal saline appeared to be toxic. Ecdysis was accelerated by the addition of an aqueous liver extract and by sealing the culture tubes, but even so it did not occur until 3–5 weeks had passed *in vitro* (cf. the appearance of fourth stage larvae within 48–72 hr *in vivo*).

Silverman (1959, 1962) attempted to use Weinstein & Jones's (1957a) *Nippostrongylus brasiliensis* medium for the cultivation of the parasitic stages of *H.contortus*. In addition a variety of nutrients was tried but all ended in failure until a medium, very similar to that of Weinstein & Jones's medium but differing particularly in the method of preparation of liver extract (Nicholas, 1956), was devised consisting of chick embryo extract, autoclaved sheep liver extract, casein hydrolysate and sheep serum in a 2:2:2:1 ratio. Silverman claimed that the use of this medium in roller culture resulted in growth and metamorphosis from the third to adult (fifth) stage within 24–30 days but the adults were stunted and infertile; unfortunately other workers have as yet been unable to repeat these results (Denham, 1967; Robinson, 1967).

The exsheathing stimulus appears to be of importance for the subsequent culture of the parasitic stages. Lapage (1933a, b) and Glaser & Stoll

(1940) used hypochlorite solution to sterilize and induce exsheathment of the third stage larvae, but subsequently Sommerville (1957), Taylor & Whitlock (1960) and Silverman & Podger (1964) have shown the importance of carbon dioxide and certain reducing agents for ecdysis of third stage nematode larvae.

Douvres (1960a) obtained exsheathed third stage *H.contortus* by treatment with hypochlorite and these developed further in a medium consisting principally of trypticase, yeast extract, glucose, cattle serum, rabbit embryo extract, pig liver extract and antibiotics. Third stage *H.contortus* larvae developed to the fourth stage within 9 days in this medium and had undergone the fourth moult within a further 7 days. No improvement upon this result was obtained by supplementing the medium with vitamins.

Leland (1961a, 1963b), in his studies on the cultivation of gastro-intestinal nematodes of sheep and cattle, obtained development of *H.contortus* larvae only, from the third to the fourth stage in a medium resembling that of Weinstein & Jones for *N.brasiliensis* (p. 293). Like Silverman, he used roller-drum cultures of these larvae but his medium was slightly more complex and consisted of chick embryo extract, serum, sodium caseinate, vitamins, pig liver extract, balanced saline and antibiotics. This development to the fourth stage was not as good as the result previously claimed by Silverman who, in 1965, attributed Leland's lack of success to the fact that he used a different liver extract and exsheathed the larvae with sodium hypochlorite solution. It is interesting to note that Hansen and her colleagues (Hansen *et al.*, 1966; Silverman *et al.*, 1965) have had limited success in culturing *H.contortus* in a medium designed for the cultivation of the free-living nematode *Caenorhabditis briggsae*. They obtained development up to the beginning of the fourth moult in 5 days and maintained that their success was due to the addition of a proteinaceous growth factor (derived from liver) which they had included in their chemically defined medium (Sayre *et al.*, 1963).

Robinson (1967) reported a technique for the culture of *Haemonchus* in a complex medium consisting of chick embryo extract, sheep liver extract, sodium caseinate, sheep serum and antibiotics (p. 292). Infective third stage larvae developed to the late fourth stage in this medium, the males growing to a maximum length of 1·3 mm and the females to a maximum of 2·76 mm.

Further experiments on the requirements of *H. contortus* larvae for development from the third to the fourth stage *in vitro* have been carried out by Sommerville (1966). Third stage larvae were successfully exsheathed with sodium hypochlorite solution according to the method of Weinstein

20

& Jones (1956a) and cultured in a balanced saline solution gassed with a variety of gas mixtures (p. 295). The greatest number of fourth stage larvae were obtained from solutions gassed with 40% carbon dioxide; up to 90% of them developed to stage four within 72 hr. Once the larvae had commenced to develop, carbon dioxide was withdrawn and development proceeded readily under air. Sommerville also showed that third stage larvae were unable to ingest the medium under these conditions since serum labelled with a fluorochrome was not detected in the intestine of such larvae cultured *in vitro*. The larvae obtained by this technique were morphologically identical with those that had developed *in vivo*; their developmental times were more or less comparable.

Haemonchus contortus Larvae
(Robinson, 1967)

MEDIUM

Chick embryo extract (CEE 50), p. 345 . . . . 25 ml
Sheep liver extract, see below . . . . 30 ml
5% sodium caseinate solution . . . . 30 ml
Inactivated sheep serum (56°c for $\frac{1}{2}$ hour) . . . . 15 ml
Sodium penicillin G . . . . 1,000 units/ml
Streptomycin sulphate . . . . 1,000 μg/ml
Nystatin . . . . .100 units/ml

Sheep liver extract is prepared by homogenizing fresh liver (50 g) in 50 ml Tyrode's solution (p. 350), autoclaving the extract twice and Seitz filtering it before use.

TECHNIQUE

Infective larvae are harvested from 7–14 days old cultures of sheep faeces. They are cleaned and sedimented in tap water before being transferred (in 1 ml portions containing 250,000 larvae) into 19 ml 0·05% sodium hypochlorite solution at 38°c. After 15 min, with occasional shaking, exsheathment is complete and the larvae are washed in Earle's solution containing antibiotics (p. 350) before being cultured in the above medium. Optimum development occurs in roller culture (250 ml Soxhlet bottles containing 25 ml cultures) at 38°c at a concentration of 10,000 larvae per ml. The medium is changed twice weekly.

Robinson found that late fourth stage larvae developed under the above conditions in about 14 days.

Cooperia, Haemonchus, Oesophagostomum, Ostertagia, Nippostrongylus and Nematodirus Larvae
(Leland, 1963a, b)

MEDIUM

Earle's salt solution (p. 350). The pH is adjusted to 7 by gassing with sterile carbon dioxide and 5 ml antibiotic mixture (400 units penicillin, 0·4 mg dihydrostreptomycin and 100 units nystatin per 0·01 ml sterile distilled water) per l. salt solution are then added. The pH is further adjusted to 7·2–7·3 with sterile sodium bicarbonate or carbon dioxide. All containers are kept tightly sealed and exposure to air kept at a minimum.

The antibiotic mixture is added at a concentration of 0·01 ml/ml of medium in addition to the volume included in Earle's solution above.

Fifty per cent chick embryo extract; preparation is based on Weinstein & Jones (1956a) method (p. 345) but modified as follows: 11 day old chick embryos are used and placed in Earle's saline in a bottle embedded in crushed ice. They are again rinsed in chilled Earle's saline before being homogenized for 3 min with an equal volume (w/v) of Earle's saline. The homogenate is dispensed into screw-capped centrifuge tubes and held at 4°c for 1 hr. Following the extraction period the homogenate is spun at $900 \times g$ for 20 min at 4°c and the supernatants pooled and distributed to screw-capped Erlenmeyer flasks in amounts desired for a particular experimental medium. All chick embryo extract (CEE_{50}) is made the same day it is incorporated into a medium (Leland considered that storage decreased its activity).

Serum. Blood is obtained aseptically from ruminants by venipuncture, or from rats by cardiac puncture. The harvested serum may be stored at − 20°c in 10–15 ml quantities.

Cysteine-fortified 2% sodium caseinate, based on Weinstein & Jones (1956a); 4 g of 'vitamin free' casein (Nutritional Biochemical Corp.), and 50 mg cysteine are suspended in 150 ml distilled water. N NaOH is added until solution is complete (pH 11·0) and back-titrated to pH 7·2 with N HCl at 37·5°c and the volume adjusted to 200 ml. It is stored at − 20°c in 10 ml aliquots.

Vitamin mixture (100 × concentration). 0·1 mg/ml biotin, choline, folic acid, nicotinamide, pantothenic acid, pyridoxal and thiamine plus 0·01 mg/ml of riboflavin.

Liver concentrate (supplied by Sigma Chemical Company: No. 202–20). This material is dissolved in Earle's saline (0·1 g/5 ml) and sterilized by filtration.

Preparation of medium (Ae). Manipulations are carried out in chilled containers and following combination the pH is adjusted to 7·2–7·3 with sterile carbon dioxide or sodium bicarbonate. The medium is then quickly dispensed in 2 ml aliquots to screw-capped culture tubes (16 × 125 mm), quickly frozen in a dry ice-alcohol mixture and stored at −20°c.

Composition in parts/100 ml

50% Chick embryo extract (CEE_{50})..............50·0
Serum (from helminth-free lambs or calves)........15·0
Cysteine-fortified 2% sodium caseinate..........15·0
2% Sigma liver concentrate......................5·0
Vitamin mixture (100 × concentrate)..............5·0
Antibiotic mixture ....1·0
Earle's salt solution............................9·0

TECHNIQUE

Leland used larvae which were cultured from infected faeces of sheep with mixed infections (*Ostertagia, Oesophagostomum, Nematodirus, Haemonchus, Nippostrongylus*) or cattle with mixed infections (*Cooperia, Ostertagia, Haemonchus, Oesphagostomum, Trichostrongylus axei*) or rabbits (*T.axei*) or rats (*Nippostrongylus brasiliensis*): third stage infective larvae are isolated from sphagnum moss cultures (sheep, cattle and rabbit faeces) and charcoal cultures (rat faeces) by the Baermann technique (p. 361). To remove any free-living nematodes that may be present the resulting larval suspension is diluted with an equal volume of 1/30 HCl in distilled water and left for 10–15 min. The larvae are then washed 4 times with distilled water and exsheathed by the sodium hypochlorite technique (p. 300) for 10 min followed by 5 min centrifugation (100 × *g*). The larvae are washed 3 times in sterile distilled water before being suspended in Earle's saline and their concentration adjusted so that 500–1,000 larvae are contained in the 0·2 ml inoculum.

Culture manipulation. Tubes of medium required for cultures are thawed at 37·5°c, the larval inoculum added, the tubes tightly sealed and placed in a roller culture (1 rev/5 min) at 37·5–38·5°c. The cultures are examined twice weekly (routine examinations may be made with a prismatic device; Leland, 1961b, p. 282), the old medium removed from the culture, the worms washed and fresh medium added as follows: the contents of the culture tube are poured into a sterile screw-capped centrifuge tube and the culture tube rinsed with 5 ml Earle's saline which is added to the culture in the centrifuge tube. This is tightly capped and spun at 100 × *g* for 5 min. The worms are then removed in a minimum of medium with a

Pasteur pipette, returned to the culture tube and 2 ml of fresh medium added, the culture sealed and reincubated.

Leland obtained development to the fourth stage of all species cultured, except *T.axei*, and in some cases (see Table 7.2) moulting to the fifth stage occurred with development to egg-laying adults (*C.punctata, O.ostertagi, O.circumcincta* and *N.brasiliensis*). Sperm was demonstrated from males of *C.punctata* and *O.ostertagi* grown *in vitro*. The adult worms were smaller and required a longer period of development *in vitro* than is commonly observed *in vivo*.

TABLE 7.2. Extent of *in vitro* development of the various nematode species from artificially exsheathed third stage larvae in medium Ae

Third stage larvae	Moult	Fourth stage	Moult	Fifth stage	Eggs	Sperm
From Cattle						
Cooperia punctata	+	+	+	+	+	+
Cooperia onchophora	+	+	+	+		
Ostertagia ostertagi	+	+	+	+	+	+
Haemonchus sp.	+	+				
Oesophagostomum radiatum	+	+				
Trichostrongylus axei	−					
From Swine						
Ostertagia circumcincta	+	+	+	+	+	
Ostertagia trifurcata	+	+	+	+	?	
Oesophagostomum sp.	+	+				
Nematodirus tp.	+	+				
Haemonchus sp.	+	+				
Ostertagia ostertagi	+	+	+	+		
From Rat						
Nippostrongylus brasiliensis	+	+	+	+	+	

Haemonchus contortus Larvae

(Sommerville, 1966)

MEDIUM

g/l.

NaCl	8·23	
KCl	0·42	dissolved in distilled water.
CaCl$_2$	0·33	NaHCO$_3$ is added to yield a pH of 6.
MgSO$_4$.7H$_2$O	0·34	

All components are sterilized by filtration before use and the final medium should contain 500 mg streptomycin and 500 units penicillin G (sodium salt) per ml.

TECHNIQUE

Infective larvae of *H.contortus* are harvested from 7–14 day old cultures of sheep faeces, and stored in tap water at 5°c for about 1 week before use. They are prepared for culture by passage through 3 layers of lens tissue in a sterile Baermann apparatus (p. 361) containing sterile 0·4% sodium chloride at 38°c. Larvae are subsequently washed twice by suspension in 0·4% sterile sodium chloride and centrifuged at 350 × *g*. They are exsheathed by rinsing for 10 min in 20 ml of sterile 0·4% sodium chloride to which has been added 1 ml of 'Milton' (1% sodium hypochlorite: Milton Pharmaceuticals Ltd). They are then washed 6 times in sterile 0·4% sodium chloride and counted. These procedures are essentially those followed by Weinstein & Jones (1956a).

Larvae are incubated in screw-capped roller tubes which contain either 2 or 3 ml of the medium and 1,000 larvae, i.e. about 350–500 larvae per ml of medium. The roller drum must be kept in an incubator in the dark and rotated 12 times each hr. The temperature is 40 ± 0·5°c. The temperature inside the tubes is checked periodically with thermocouples inserted in the tube and connected to an automatic recorder.

Commercially prepared gas mixture containing 40% carbon dioxide, 10% oxygen, 50% nitrogen is used. The mixture is passed through sterile cotton wool and cultures are gassed for 2 min in a water bath at the same temperature as for subsequent incubation. Tubes are sealed with a screw top containing a silicone rubber lining. Larvae are incubated under the gas mixture for 72 hr.

Sommerville showed that 90% of these larvae had developed to the fourth stage within 72 hr *in vitro*, after which time the experiments were terminated. The larvae so obtained were identical morphologically with those that had developed *in vivo* and their development times were more or less comparable.

3. COOPERIA, HYOSTRONGYLUS, NEMATODIRUS, OSTERTAGIA and TRICHOSTRONGYLUS

Extensive studies have been made on the exsheathing mechanism of trichostrongyle infective larvae (Lapage, 1935; Sommerville, 1957; Rogers & Sommerville, 1957, 1960; Wilson, 1958; Fairbairn, 1960; Silverman & Podger, 1964; Christie & Charleston, 1965) and in particular Rogers & Sommerville have carried out some elegant experiments showing that the exsheathing fluid is produced in a region 70–130 μ from the anterior extremity (*Trichostrongylus axei*). This fluid dissolves the inner layer of the cuticle 19 μ from the anterior extremity leaving the outer layer as a refractile ring which subsequently ruptures, thus separating a cap from the remainder of the cuticle, allowing the larva to escape. The stimulus which induces the production of exsheathing fluid varies according to the species concerned and readers are recommended to consult the original papers on this subject.

Lapage (1933a, b, 1935) was one of the first workers to try to determine the nutritional requirements of nematode larvae (*T.retortaeformis*, *Ostertagia*, *Chabertia* and *Graphidium strigosum*); he cultured eggs, externally sterilized in formalin, on broth cultures of *Bacillus coli* previously isolated from the intestine of a nematode and obtained development to the third stage. Hanging drop cultures of artificially exsheathed larvae were used to test about 200 different media and in some cases development to the fourth stage occurred. Other culture techniques were also tried but with similar lack of success.

Leland (1961a, 1963a) using mixed as well as monospecific cultures of swine and bovine species of *Trichostrongylus* (p. 293), *Cooperia punctata*, *C.onchophora*, *Ostertagia ostertagi*, *O.circumcincta*, *Oesophagostomum radiatum*, *Nematodirus* sp., *Haemonchus* sp. and *Trichostrongylus axei* obtained varying degrees of larval development using carbon dioxide gassed roller cultures and a complex medium consisting principally of chick embryo extract, serum, sodium caseinate, vitamins and pig liver extract in Earle's balanced saline with antibiotics. *C.punctata*, *O.ostertagi* and *O.circumcincta* were cultured to the egg-laying stage and the eggs produced by *C.punctata* were very numerous but infertile, as were the smaller numbers of eggs observed from the other species. Sperm were developed in the adults of *C.punctata* and *O.ostertagi*. However these worms were smaller and took longer to develop than those grown *in vivo*. *Nematodirus* sp. were grown to the fourth stage only. In contrast to his success with *Cooperia* and *Ostertagia*, Leland was unable to obtain any development of *Trichostrongylus axei* in this medium. However a most important result was obtained with cultures of *C.punctata*. Leland (1962, 1963a) cultured fertile eggs *in vitro* in a variety of media and obtained development of adults, bearing eggs or sperm, although all the eggs deposited were infertile. Furthermore development from the fertile eggs through the 5 stages to the sexually mature adults was accomplished with unbroken sequence in the same culture. These experiments were subsequently (1965a, 1967) repeated with *C.pectinata*, yielding the same degree of success. Leland considered that the exsheathing stimulus was unnecessary for initiating the parasitic stages in his *in vitro* system. Leland & Wallace (1966) went on to show that third stage, fourth stage and adult worms (*C.punctata*) grown *in vitro* were all infective to rabbits and when introduced surgically, reproducible prepatent periods were obtained. Also antibiotics used in 'sterilizing' larvae and suppressing bacterial growth *in vitro* did not irreverisbly affect the reproductive potential of *C.punctata*.

Douvres & Alicata (1962) also reported on attempts to grow *C.punctata in vitro*. They used artificially exsheathed third stage larvae and a culture technique originally designed by Diamond & Douvres (1962) for the culture of *Oesophagostomum radiatum*. The culture medium (SM-1; Douvres, 1962a, b) consisted of rabbit embryo extract, pig liver extract, bovine serum, nutrient broth and antibiotics (p. 283). The larvae were exsheathed with sodium hypochlorite and cultured in tubes at 38·5°c held horizontally. In all tests stunted but sexually mature adults were obtained within 14–19 days but longer time was required to reach the fourth and fifth stages *in vitro* than *in vivo* and, as with *Hyostrongylus*, the development of the genital primordium lagged behind somatic differentiation.

Hyostrongylus rubidus was cultured by Diamond & Douvres (1960, 1962) with the object of making available for laboratory study a trichostrongyle of economic importance (p. 299) particularly because the parasite was readily available and the normal *in vivo* morphology was already known. Infective larvae were artificially exsheathed by sodium hypochlorite and cultured at 38·5°c in a medium consisting essentially of trypticase, yeast extract, glucose, ascorbic acid, salts, rabbit embryo extract, pig liver extract and serum. The majority of the larvae did not undergo any changes during 35–42 days *in vitro*. However some individuals in the third moult were recovered after the thirty-fifth day (as compared to 5 days *in vivo*) and fourth stage larvae after 42 days *in vitro*. The larvae were stunted and the genital primordium lagged behind somatic differentiation. Leland (1965c), using a similar culture system to that used for other trichostrongyles (Leland, 1963a), successfully reared third stage larvae of *H.rubidus* to egg-bearing adults in 60 days. He substituted pig serum for calf serum in these cultures, since the parasites were of porcine origin.

Ostertagia ostertagi larvae were first cultured by Silverman (1959, 1965) in a medium used for *Haemonchus* larvae consisting of chick embryo extract, autoclaved sheep liver extract, casein hydrolysate and sheep serum in a 2:2:2:1 ratio. Roller culture techniques were used and development of exsheathed third stage larvae to the adult stage in 24–30 days was obtained but the adults were decidedly stunted.

Douvres (1960a) in his experiments on the gastro-intestinal nematodes of sheep, reported successful cultivation of exsheathed third stage larvae of *O.ostertagi* to the fourth stage in his trypticase medium, unsupplemented with vitamins, within 9 days whereas larvae of *O.radiatum* had carried out only their third moult in this medium within 14 days. No further development of either species was obtained.

Hyostrongylus rubidus and *Oesophagostomum quadrispinulatum* Larvae
(Diamond & Douvres, 1962)

MEDIUM

Nutrient broth

Trypticase (Baltimore Biological Laboratory) ....2·0 g	Ascorbic acid..................0·02 g
Yeast extract (Baltimore Biological Laboratory) ....1·0 g	NaCl ....0·5 g
	KH_2PO_4 ....0·08 g
Glucose ....0·5 g	K_2HPO_4 (anhyd.).............0·08 g
L-Cysteine hydrochloride ....0·1 g	Distilled water to............90·0 ml

The pH is adjusted to 7·2 with N NaOH and the broth is sterilized by autoclaving for 10 min at 15 lb pressure (121°c).

Tissue extracts: Rabbit embryos (22–24 days old) or pig liver obtained from donor animals immediately after slaughter by exsanguination, are washed in physiological saline (0·9%) and stored for 24 hr at −20°C. After thawing and quick rinsing in distilled water the tissues are sliced into chunks, placed in an Erlenmeyer flask and 100 ml of 0·02 N HCl are added to each 10 g of tissue (each type of tissue being extracted separately).

Extraction is carried out at 5°c for 96 hr, the extract poured off and filtered through 2 layers of filter paper (Whatman No. 2). The filtrate is then sterilized by filtration and stored at −20°c.

To prepare the complete medium 60 ml of rabbit embryo extract, 30 ml of pig liver extract and 20 ml of sheep serum (inactivated at 56°c for 30 min) are added aseptically to 90 ml portions of nutrient broth. The medium is then dispensed in 10 ml aliquots into 16 × 125 mm screw-capped tubes and chilled overnight at 5°c to hasten the formation of a flocculent precipitate which forms in this medium. It may safely be stored for 2 weeks at this temperature.

Immediately before use the medium is thawed and centrifuged for 3 min at 1,000 × *g*. The clarified supernatant is then aspirated and redistributed in 3 ml portions to screw-capped culture tubes (16 × 125 mm). Antibiotics are added (penicillin G potassium 500 units, dihydrostreptomycin sulphate 0·5 mg and nystatin 100 units/ml of medium respectively).

TECHNIQUE

Infective third stage larvae (8–9 days old) are used to initiate the cultures. The larvae are isolated from faecal sphagnum moss cultures, prepared as follows: about 2·5 kg of faeces from infected pigs are mixed with steam sterilized sphagnum moss (7·5–10 g/100 g of faeces) in 2·5 gal pails and allowed to stand for 8–9 days. The larvae are recovered by means of a Baermann apparatus (p. 361).

Before inoculation into culture, the larvae are first exsheathed and at the same time freed of many microbes by treatment with dilute sodium hypochlorite saline solution (0·25 ml 'Clorox' solution, containing 5·25% sodium hypochlorite by weight, added to 17·75 ml 0·7% NaCl) followed by 5 rinses in sterile 0·7% saline. About 400–800 larvae are introduced into each culture (see above). These are incubated at 38·5°c in a horizontal position and gently agitated twice daily. Transfers are made every 48 hr during the first 6 days and every 5–7 days thereafter. Larvae to be transferred are resuspended in the medium by gentle shaking, transferred with a pipette to a conical screw-capped centrifuge tube and spun at 700 × g for 3 min. The supernatant fluid is replaced by fresh medium and the larvae in this medium transferred to clean culture tubes for further incubation.

Diamond & Douvres found that third stage infective larvae of *H.rubidus* reached the fourth moult within 42 days at 38·5°c whilst those of *O.quadrispinulatum* reached the fourth stage. Stunting was noted in all stages of *H.rubidus* beginning with the third moult and was likewise noted in the fourth stage of *O.quadrispinulatum*.

E OTHER STRONGYLOIDEA

NEMATOSPIROIDES

Jones & Weinstein (1957) were the first workers successfully to culture *Nematospiroides dubius*, parasitic in mice, from the egg to the fifth stage under axenic conditions. Fresh chick embryo extract supported good development of the free-living stages and when supplemented with liver concentrate, yields of more than 90% filariform larvae were obtained

These larvae developed to the fifth stage *in vitro* in high concentrations of chick embryo extract and rat serum but sexual maturity was not achieved.

These results were later used by Sommerville & Weinstein (1964) in their experiments comparing the reproductive behaviour of *N.dubius in vitro* and *in vivo*. The chick embryo extract and rat serum medium was supplemented with a vitamin mixture and in this medium (based on that of Weinstein & Jones, 1956a, b, 1959) copulation and fertilization were observed *in vitro*. Cultures were initiated with worms taken from infected mouse intestines 7 days and 11 days (late fourth and early fifth stage larvae) after infection. Many of these worms became sexually mature and produced sperm and ova which were apparently normal but the ova, although fertilized *in vitro*, failed to develop further. This reproductive behaviour was similar to that occurring *in vivo* although slower with poorer yields of eggs and sperm and for shorter periods of time (egg production lasted only 10 days *in vitro* but continues for 10 weeks *in vivo*).

More recently Christie & Charleston (1965) have studied the exsheathing stimulus required by infective larvae of *N.battus*. When they suspended the larvae in open vials containing acidified 0·6% NaCl solution (pH 2·0 with HCl) for 3 hr at 39°c, 90% exsheathment of the larvae was obtained. Saturation of the saline with carbon dioxide had no effect and these workers considered that the main exsheathing stimulus was HCl, not carbon dioxide as had been found with *Haemonchus contortus* larvae.

V. FILAROIDEA

The cultivation of filariae *in vitro* was initially directed towards the maintenance of microfilariae in whole blood, in fact Hobson (1948) credits the microfilariae with some of the longest survival records *in vitro* of any nematode species parasitic in warm blooded hosts. This early work is well reviewed by Earl (1959). During the last decade interest in the culture of all stages in the life-cycles of filariae has developed, and it is to this work that we now direct our attention.

1. *DIROFILARIA*

Larval stages

Earl (1959) carried out a series of experiments on the maintenance of the microfilariae of *Dirofilaria immitis*, the dog heartworm, *in vitro* in a variety of media, using static Soxhlet (milk dilution) bottles incubated at 37°c on their sides (p. 308). He found that microfilariae would survive for

4 days in medium 199 alone but when supplemented with 10% inactivated dog serum, medium 199 supported the microfilariae for 43 days at 37°C or 18 days at room temperature; they survived for 61 days when the serum supplement was increased to 30%. Similar results were obtained when he replaced the dog serum with ox or horse sera. Kidney tissue cultures overlaid with medium 199 plus 10% inactivated dog serum did not improve these results (40 days survival) and in none of his cultures did Earl obtain any growth or development of the microfilariae.

Taylor (1960a) working independently without the knowledge of Earl's results, attempted to grow *D.immitis* microfilariae in a variety of media, and cultures of mosquito whole gut. She used medium 199 supplemented with horse serum, raw liver or mosquito extracts, red blood cells or dilute Tyrode's solution and her cultures were maintained at 22°C in an attempt to induce development of the mosquito stages *in vitro*. Unfortunately, although the microfilariae survived for a maximum of 14 days *in vitro*, no growth or development occurred in this species.

The following year (1961) Sawyer & Weinstein briefly reported on their preliminary attempts to determine the importance of various inorganic ions for the *in vitro* survival of *D.immitis* microfilariae. The inorganic components of Earle's, Gey's, Krebs–Ringer–phosphate and Locke's solutions were tested and maximum survival in such simple solutions (35 hr at 37°C and 55 hr at 27°C) was obtained in a modified Locke's solution. Krebs–Ringer–phosphate with 0·25% glucose and 1·5% sodium caseinate buffered at pH 7·2 with Tris buffer permitted survival for 5 days at 27°C but only 40 hr at 37°C.

This work was later considerably extended by Sawyer & Weinstein (1962, 1963a, b, c). Successful development of microfilariae to the late first stage (early 'sausage stage') was obtained initially (1962, 1963b) in cultures of heparinated whole blood maintained in upright conical tubes at 22 or 27°C. Although such development occasionally occurred as early as 3 days *in vitro*, no further development was obtained throughout the 21 day culture period. They also used the same method to culture *Dipetalonema* microfilariae but only obtained 'sausage' stages *in vitro* after 12 days (cf. 3 days for *D.immitis*).

Sawyer & Weinstein (1963b) then developed a technique for separating the microfilariae from red blood cells before culture. This was accomplished by lysing the red cells with saponin (0·2%) and enzymes (streptolysin O 0·33% and trypsin 0·1%) leaving the microfilariae intact and viable for culture. Incubation of these embryos at 22 or 27°C in human or rabbit blood or in Locke's solution containing a suspension of dog blood cells, resulted in the development of first stage ('sausage') larvae

(1963a, c). Survival for several weeks without development occurred in dog plasma or horse serum but when a chemically defined culture medium (NCTC 109) was used, the survival time was limited to 7 days and similarly no development occurred. Sawyer & Weinstein (1963c) then went on to find the optimum concentration of horse serum which would promote growth to the 'sausage' form in NCTC 109. Maximum yields (30%) of 'sausage' larvae were obtained at 27°c with 5–10% inactivated serum in NCTC 109 and the survival time of the larvae was increased to 8 days; in some cases definite increase in width occurred in less than 30 hr *in vitro* (p. 305). They found that gassing the cultures every 2–3 days with 5% carbon dioxide in air was beneficial even though they did not attempt to change the medium during culture. No development occurred at 37°c and survival time was reduced to 4 days at this temperature. Unfortunately these workers were unable to induce further development of the mosquito stages.

Taylor (1960a) first reported development of the infective third stage larvae of *D.immitis in vitro* and she obtained moulting and exsheathing of such larvae in several media; dog serum alone or horse serum, Tyrode's solution with 0·1% glucose and chick embryo extract in a 1:1:0·75 ratio supported the larvae for 3 days during which time exsheathing occurred. Results were improved in tissue cultures of puppy skin and heart tissue where the larvae exsheathed and survived for 7 days and in the heart tissue cultures slight increase in length was obtained.

Later workers (Sawyer, 1963, 1965; Yoeli *et al.*, 1964) have obtained exsheathment and partial development of this stage *in vitro*. Sawyer (1963, 1965) cultivated third stage infective larvae of *D.immitis* isolated from *Anopheles quadrimaculatus* in medium NCTC 109 alone and with various serum supplements. In serum-free medium the larvae became vacuolated and survived without exsheathing for about 3 days. When 10% human or horse serum was included in the cultures and these were gassed with 5% carbon dioxide in air, the larvae survived from 12–15 days and approximately 100% of the healthy larvae exsheathed within about 72 hr. The optimum pH was found to be 7·2–7·6 at a temperature of 37°c. However maintaining the larvae at 21–25°c increased their survival period to 22 days. Normal dog serum and still more, infected dog serum were inhibitory (6–9 days survival and 25% exsheathment); oral precipitates formed on the larvae, very few of them exsheathed and they were mostly inactive during their 3–5 days survival *in vitro*. The maximum development of exsheathed larvae corresponded to that occurring after 5 days *in vivo*.

Yoeli *et al.* (1964) tried a different method of approach to this problem in that they used a perfusion apparatus instead of static cultures, as described previously by other workers. Third stage larvae from *A.quadrimaculatus* were maintained for 30 days at 37°C in this apparatus containing a medium consisting of 10% normal inactivated dog plasma, 50% Ringer's solution, 40% medium 1066 and antibiotics; 2 ml normal dog's heparinized blood was included per 100 ml of culture medium (p. 306). Moulting and exsheathment occurred under these conditions and increases in size comparable to those occurring *in vivo* after the same time were observed (1059 μ length, 27·69 μ width to 1,510 μ length, 34·7 μ width after 12 days and 1,825 μ length, 38·70 μ width after 30 days). Blunting and rounding of the anterior ends of the growing larvae were conspicuous and the caudal papillae were prominent (6–7 days *in vitro*) and throughout the culture period the larvae were motile and very active.

Adults

Earl (1959) maintained adult *D.immitis* for a maximum of 65 days in a modified Eagle's HeLa medium plus 10% inactivated horse serum but the worms also survived well in medium 199 supplemented with 10% inactivated horse serum. During the culture period acid metabolites were produced and the females were observed to be more active than the males. Females produced microfilariae for the first 4–7 days of culture and Earl observed all the developmental stages from the 4 cell embryo to the microfilaria in his cultures; he considered that these microfilariae had developed *in vitro*. However the more likely situation is that the ova were extruded from the females because either the culture conditions were unfavourable or the rich medium induced unnatural activity in the worms. Only microfilariae are extruded *in vivo*, the embryonic stages all developing within the body of the female (Taylor, 1960b). Earl also claimed that anaerobic culture was lethal to the worms.

Taylor (1960a) attempted to culture adult *D.immitis* in Kolle flasks (2 females and 1 male/50 ml of medium) containing 1 of 2 media consisting of either Ringer's or Tyrode's solution with dog serum and chick embryo extract plus 0·1% glucose in a 3:1:1 ratio. Although the females produced large numbers of microfilariae for 2 days, the adults only survived for 8 days but, like the worms cultured by Earl, they were active and produced acid metabolites. Since both Earl's and Taylor's culture conditions were 'semi-anaerobic' ['semi-anaerobic' since although the gas phase in the culture vessels was initially air, the oxygen present would soon be used up by the metabolism of the worms (Taylor *et al.*, 1966)] differences in the worms' survival times must have been due to variations in the composition of the media used.

In 1961 Weinstein & Sawyer turned their attention to the cultivation of adult *D.uniformis*, a subcutaneous parasite of rabbits. The medium of choice was NCTC 109 alone or supplemented with various amounts of serum. In medium NCTC 109 alone the filariae survived 10 days, whereas those cultured in the serum supplemented (5, 10 or 20%) medium survived 21 days; the concentrations of serum tested were equally effective in prolonging survival. Peak microfilarial production occurred during days 2 and 3 but gradually declined thereafter and ceased by days 13–16.

In an interesting series of experiments on the metabolism of *D.uniformis in vitro* von Brand *et al.* (1963) extended the survival period of these worms to 24 days in medium NCTC 109 plus 10% rabbit serum. They compared the glucose utilization and survival of the worms in this and more simple media showing that the worms used considerable amounts of glucose and produced large amounts of lactic acid which accounted for most of the glucose consumed. In all experiments however the glucose consumption and lactic acid production was at a maximum during the first 4 days *in vitro* and declined steadily after this, indicating that optimum culture conditions have not yet been determined for this parasite.

Dirofilaria immitis Larvae
(Sawyer & Weinstein, 1963a, b, c)

MEDIUM

Five to ten per cent inactivated horse serum (56°c for $\frac{1}{2}$ hr) in NCTC 109 (p. 351) containing 200 units penicillin and 100 μg streptomycin sulphate per ml of medium.

Lytic enzymes

Saponin: 0·2 g in 100 ml 0·85% NaCl.

Trypsin (Difco 1·250): 0·1% in balanced saline (NaCl 0·85g, NaHCO$_3$ 0·02 g, Na$_2$HPO$_4$ 0·115 g, KH$_2$PO$_4$ 0·02 g, glucose 0·15 g, phenol red 0·002 g all dissolved in 100 ml distilled water).

Streptolysin O: Difco streptolysin O, supplied as '2-test' bottles each containing approximately 130–135 μg lyophilized enzyme. One bottle rehydrated in 30 ml 0·85% NaCl at time of use and sterilized by filtration.

TECHNIQUE

The microfilariae of *D.immitis* can be separated from fresh, heparinated, whole blood prior to culture by haemolysis of the blood cells as follows: (1) Add 1 ml heparinated whole blood to 10 ml of warm saponin solution and incubate at 37°c for 15 min. (2) Centrifuge and wash sediment twice in Ringer-Locke saline (p. 350), 10 ml each wash. (3) Resuspend sediment in 30 ml streptolysin O, incubate at 37°c for 15 min. (4) Centrifuge and wash sediment once in 10 ml Ringer-Locke, resuspend in 20 ml 0·85% NaCl, and incubate at room temperature for 5 min. (5) Centrifuge and resuspend sediment in 20 ml of trypsin, incubate at 37°c for 15 min. (6) Centrifuge and resuspend sediment in 20 ml 0·85% NaCl, incubate at room temperature for 5 min. (7) Wash 4 times in Ringer-Locke, 10 ml each wash. (8) Resuspend final sediment in graduated conical tube containing known volume of 0·85% NaCl or culture medium and count samples to estimate the number of microfilariae per unit volume.

During the procedure suspensions are incubated in 125 or 250 ml Erlenmeyer flasks capped with sterile beakers and agitated frequently to resuspend the blood cells. After each incubation period the suspensions are centrifuged at $400 \times g$ for 2–3 min in conical centrifuge tubes, the supernatant fluids are removed by aspiration to approximately 1 cm from the bottom of the tubes, and the pellets containing microfilariae then resuspended in the next solution.

One hundred to three hundred microfilariae are added to 1 ml of culture medium contained in 15×125 mm test tubes and incubated at 27°c. The medium is not renewed during culture but each tube is gassed initially and every 2–3 days thereafter with 5% carbon dioxide in air.

Sawyer and Weinstein obtained development to the 'sausage' stage within 8 days in the above medium.

Dirofilaria immitis Infective Larvae
(Yoeli *et al.*, 1964)

MEDIUM

Inactivated dog plasma 10%
Ringer's solution (p. 350) 50%
Medium CMRL 1066 (p. 356); also supplied by Baltimore
    Biological Laboratories Inc.............................40%
Heparinized normal dog's blood.........2 ml/100 ml of medium

Antibiotics:
    Chloromycetin ....100 mg/ml of medium
    Penicillin G ....100 units/ml of medium
    Dihydrostreptomycin ....50 mg/ml of medium
    Nystatin ....24 mg/ml of medium

Dissecting Fluid (See Earl, 1959)
    Inactivated dog plasma 10%
    Ringer's solution......................................50%
    Eagle's solution (see p. 354)..........................40%

Antibiotics in the same concentration as culture medium as above.

TECHNIQUE

Laboratory bred *A.quadrimaculatus* or *A.freeborni* are allowed to engorge on an infected dog. The engorged mosquitoes are transferred to cages and kept in an insectary at 27°c and 90–96% relative humidity. They are allowed to imbibe a 10% glucose-antibiotic solution, to reduce bacterial contamination.

Under these experimental conditions invasive third stage *D.immitis* larvae reach the head and proboscis of their intermediate hosts within 16–19 days.

Eighteen days after their infective blood meal, batches of *A.quadri-maculatus* or *A.freeborni* are transferred to test-tubes, anaesthetized with carbon dioxide and dissected. The heads of the mosquitoes are severed from the bodies in a pool of dissecting fluid and only third stage invasive larvae obtained from the proboscis and the head are used. The liberated larvae are sucked up with fine capillaries and transferred to Maximow slides. The harvesting of the larvae lasts 2–4 hr, during which time the parasites must be kept at room temperature.

The harvested larvae exhibit very vigorous and continuous coiling and recoiling movements. They are transferred to a 10 cm glass boat (made of tubing) containing the culture medium. The fine capillary ends of the boat are connected by means of polyethylene tubing to a dual

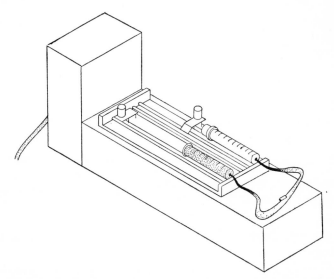

FIGURE 7.4 Dual infusion withdrawal apparatus with culture boat used in maintaining larvae of *D.immitis in vitro*. (From Yoeli *et al.*, 1964.)

infusion withdrawal apparatus (model 600–920, Harvard Apparatus Company). The pump is adjusted for slow run, and fresh medium replacing the old is fed to the boat (Fig. 7.4) in 50 ml syringes at 48 hr intervals. The infusion apparatus with the boat is placed in an incubator at 37°c. One hundred to 200 invasive larvae are deposited in the boat for each experiment. The boat contains between 8 and 9 ml of fluid medium.

Yoeli *et al.* maintained the larvae in a healthy condition for periods of up to 30 days. Moulting was observed and an increase in size from an initial mean length of 1,059 μ and 27·68 μ width to an average 1,825 μ length and 38·70 μ width within 30 days. Blunting and rounding of the anterior ends of the larvae were conspicuous as were the caudal papillae and were comparable to the changes found in larvae of similar age *in vivo*.

Dirofilaria immitis   Microfilariae and Adults
(Earl, 1959)

MEDIUM

Dog or horse serum inactivated by heating at 56°c for 30 min.
Eagle's HeLa medium (p. 354); contains modified Earle's balanced saline (i.e. g/l. NaCl, 6·80; KCl, 0·40; CaCl$_2$, 0·20; MgSO$_4$.7H$_2$O, 0·20; Na$_2$HPO$_4$, 1·40; Glucose, 2·50).
Medium 199 (p. 355).
Antibiotics; 100 units of penicillin G, 50 μg dihydrostreptomycin and 12 mg nystatin per ml of medium.

TECHNIQUE

1   *Microfilariae*
Clean microfilariae may be obtained by adding surface-active agents to blood and centrifuging. Samples of blood taken from dogs having severe infections of *Dirofilaria immitis* are allowed to clot at 37°c and the serum, containing blood elements and many of the microfilariae is drawn off and diluted 1:1 with warmed medium 199. Ten-millilitre portions of the 1:1 mixture are placed in 15 ml centrifuge tubes to which are added 1 ml aliquots of 10% autoclaved saponin. Saponin forms a precipitate during cooling after autoclaving that is easily shaken into solution. The resultant mixtures are allowed to stand at room temperature for 5–10min in order to lyse most of the blood cells, and then centrifuged at 220–230 × g for 3–5 min. The supernatants are decanted and 10 ml of medium 199 added to each tube to resuspend the deposits, which are then centrifuged

again. This operation is repeated several times until microfilariae are harvested that are free or nearly free from blood elements.

Suspensions of microfilariae are incubated at 37°c in rubber-stoppered test-tubes or Soxhlet (milk dilution) bottles placed on their sides.

Earl found that survival of microfilariae varied as follows: 43 days in medium 199 plus 10% inactivated dog serum; 61 days in medium 199+ 30% inactivated dog serum; 40 days in medium 199 plus 10% inactivated dog serum layered over sheets of dog kidney cells.

2   Adult worms

Adult *D.immitis* are aseptically removed from the heart of an infected dog. 1–3 worms are placed in 25 × 200 mm screw-capped tubes containing 50 ml medium and incubated in the dark at 37°c. The medium is changed every 1–2 days.

Earl found that Eagle's HeLa medium (containing antibiotics plus 10% inactivated horse serum supported the adult worms for 65 days *in vitro*. No growth was obtained of microfilariae or adults.

2. *LITOMOSOIDES CARINII*

Larval stages

Weinstein (1963) applied his technique for the culture of the mosquito stages of *D.immitis* to the microfilariae of *L.carinii*. Exsheathment of the embryos was induced by treatment of infected blood with lytic enzymes (p. 305, omitting saponin which was toxic) and development to a 'sausage' stage, corresponding to 6 days in the mite, was achieved in medium NCTC 109 containing 20% inactivated human serum and antibiotics supplemented with the amino acids, sugars and organic acids of Grace's medium (1962).

Adults

Hawking (1954) was the first to culture adult filariae *in vitro*. He placed adult *L.carinii* in Carrel flasks containing 25% horse serum and 75% Ringer's solution (containing 0·2% glucose); they survived for 2 days and the females produced microfilariae (4,000–43,000/worm/19–22 hr). During this time some ova were extruded, probably indicating sub-optimal culture conditions since only microfilariae are extruded by adult worms *in vivo* (Taylor, 1960b). Taylor (1960a) maintained adult *L.carinii* in medium 199 and fresh rat serum (2:1) for a maximum of 23 days (p. 310). During this time the females continued to produce microfilariae for 18 days (1,000–9,660 microfilariae/female/day, in different experiments) and the changing of the medium (on alternate days) appeared to stimulate microfilaria production.

Litomosoides carinii Larvae
(Weinstein, 1963)

MEDIUM

NCTC 109 (p. 351.)

Human serum. Inactivated at 56°c for $\frac{1}{2}$ hr and added to NCTC 109 to yield 20% solution.

Grace's medium supplements. Amino acids, sugars and organic acids in GMA medium (p. 312).

Lytic enzymes: see p. 305 but omit saponin as this is toxic to *L.carinii.*

TECHNIQUE

Microfilariae are obtained from infected cotton rats (*Sigmodon hispidus,* see Hawking & Sewell, 1948 for technique) and fresh, heparinated, whole blood is treated in the same manner as for *D.immitis* culture (p. 305) with the omission of saponin treatment. The culture medium is not changed but no details are given of period of cultivation.

Weinstein obtained development to the 'sausage' stage (approximately $123 \times 7 \cdot 6 \mu$) corresponding to 4–5 days development in the mite and a few developed to about $155 \times 10 \cdot 5 \mu$ corresponding to day 6 in the mite.

Litomosoides carinii Adults
(Taylor, 1960a)

MEDIUM

Medium 199 (p. 355) and fresh rat serum are combined in the ratio 2:1 using sterile techniques.

TECHNIQUE

Adult *L.carinii* may be maintained in the laboratory in a colony of cotton rats according to the technique of Hawking & Sewell (1948). Worms should be removed aseptically from the pleural cavity and washed in culture medium in a Petri dish. Groups of worms (approximately 5 males and 5 females) are then transferred to Carrel flasks each containing

2 ml of culture medium and incubated at 37°c. The medium is changed every 24–48 hr.

Taylor maintained the adult worms for 23 days in the above medium and active microfilariae were produced for a maximum of 18 days.

3. OTHER FILARIAE

Taylor (1960a) maintained the microfilariae of *Wuchereria bancrofti* and *Loa loa* for 10–14 days *in vitro* in a variety of media containing serum, blood cells and chemically defined components. Although the microfilariae of *W.bancrofti* exsheathed *in vitro* no development occurred whereas there was indication of the first stages of development of *L.loa* in that the G cells 1 and 2 were seen to have divided.

Weinstein (1963) had more success with the microfilariae of *W.bancrofti* in that he obtained the 'sausage' stage in about 4–7% of his organisms cultured in a similar manner to the microfilariae of *D.immitis* (p. 305) but with additional amino acids, sugars and organic acids to supplement the medium. Although 40% of the microfilariae of *W.bancrofti* showed some signs of development *in vitro*, the time of development was considerably prolonged compared to the period required in the normal insect host.

Sawyer & Cheever (1962) reported that microfilariae found in the Columbian marmoset (*Oedipomidas*) survived for 22 days in a suspension of marmoset kidney cells in medium 199 plus calf serum. During this time the microfilariae showed an increase in length of 25% but this development was probably abnormal since the *in vivo* development of microfilariae to the 'sausage' stage is accompanied by a shortening and fattening process.

The most successful cultivation of microfilariae has been achieved by Wood and Suitor (1966) using microfilariae of *Macacanema formosana* from the blood of a Taiwan monkey *Macaca cyclopis*. These workers used a strain of *Aedes aegypti* cells (Grace, 1966) which had been maintained in serial culture for 3 years. The cells were adpated by Wood and Suitor to grow in a medium consisting of 0·5% haemolymph from *Philosamia cynthia* plus 10% foetal bovine serum in Grace's insect cell culture medium GMA (see p. 312 for details; Grace, 1958, 1962). Microfilariae were separated from heparinated blood by treatment with saponin before being cultured. Development to the third stage took place at 22°c but not 28°c; the medium was not changed throughout the 33 day culture period (p. 312).

Within 5 days the larvae had reached the 'sausage' stage and movement during this period was minimal. On the sixth to ninth days the larvae grew rapidly in length and narrowed slightly and by 14–19 days the maximum development had occurred i.e. the larvae had reached the third stage but had incompletely moulted. Unfortunately no tests have yet been made to determine whether the larvae were infective. One point of interest is that in some experiments where the growth of the insect cells was retarded (because of a lack of sufficient growth promoting substances) that of the filariae was also retarded, possibly indicating similar growth requirements of the 2 species.

Macacanema formosana Larval Stages
(Wood & Suitor, 1966)

MEDIUM

Insect tissue culture medium GMA (Grace, 1958, 1962).

Salts (A)	mg/100 ml
$NaH_2PO_4.2H_2O$	114
$NaHCO_3$	35
KCl	224
$CaCl_2$ (separate)	100
$MgCl_2.6H_2O$	228
$MgSO_4.7H_2O$	278

Amino Acids (B)

L-Arginine hydrochloride	70
L-Aspartic acid	35
L-Asparagine	35
L-Alanine	22·5
β-Alanine	20
L-Cystine hydrochloride	2·5
L-Glutamic acid	60
L-Glutamine	60
L-Glycine	65
L-Histidine	250
L-Isoleucine	5
L-Leucine	7·5
L-Lysine hydrochloride	62·5
L-Methionine	5
L-Proline	35
L-Phenylalanine	15
DL-Serine	110
L-Tyrosine (dissolved in N HCl)	5
L-Tryptophan	10
L-Threonin	17·5
L-Valine	10

Sugars (C)	mg/100 ml
Sucrose	2,668
Fructose	40
Glucose	70

Organic Acids (D)	
Malic acid	67
α Ketoglutaric acid	37
Succinic acid	6
Fumaric acid	5·5
(neutralize organic acids with KOH)	

Antibiotics	
Penicillin G (sodium salt)	3
Streptomycin sulphate	10

Vitamins	
Thiamine hydrochloride	0·002
Riboflavin	0·002
Calcium pantothenate	0·002
Pyridoxine hydrochloride	0·002
p-Aminobenzoic acid	0·002
Folic acid	0·002
Niacin	0·002
Inositol	0·002
Biotin	0·001
Choline chloride	0·02

A is dissolved in 20 ml, B in 30 ml, C in 20 ml and D in 20 ml distilled water. The calcium chloride is dissolved separately in a small amount of water and is added after A, B, C and D have been thoroughly mixed. The vitamins are then added and the pH adjusted to 6·5 with potassium hydroxide. Streptomycin and penicillin are added and the volume made up to 100 ml just before the medium is sterilized by filtration. The final culture medium consists of GMA medium plus sterile insect haemolymph (0·5%; see below) and sterile foetal bovine serum (10%).

Preparation of insect haemolymph (Philosamia cynthia)
Diapausing pupae are bled into sterile centrifuge tubes packed in ice. Immediately after collection the blood is heated to 60°C for 5 min and then deep frozen for 24 hr to inhibit the action of the enzyme tyrosinase. After thawing and centrifugation to remove the blood cells and precipitated proteins, the clear yellow supernatant is added to the above medium.

TECHNIQUE

Preparation of mosquito cells for culture
The tissues are obtained from axenically grown *Aedes aegypti* larvae about to pupate. The larvae are placed in GMA medium and their heads, tails and alimentary canals removed. After discarding the peritrophic membranes, the alimentary canals and bodies are washed twice in fresh medium. The tissues are torn apart before cultivation. Each culture consists of the bodies and alimentary canals from 3 larvae in 1·0 ml of medium GMA containing 1% insect haemolymph (*Anthera eucalypti*) in a $3 \times \frac{1}{4}$ inch round-bottomed tube slanted about 20° from the horizontal and incubated at 30°C.

Two days after the cultures are made, the cells have migrated from several masses of tissue. The number of cells increases over the next 14 days and most of the cells float in the medium. After 4 weeks of culture, free-floating cells are transferred to an equal volume of fresh medium. Sub-cultures of these cells had been made weekly for 3 years before Suitor adapted the cells to growing in the modified medium (0·5% *Philosamia cynthia* haemolymph, 10% foetal bovine serum in GMA medium). The cells were also adapted to grow at 22°C instead of 30°C before being used successfully for microfilaria culture.

Preparation of microfilariae for culture
Five-millilitre samples of infected blood (70–80 microfilariae/cu mm) are drawn into tubes containing heparin and held at 30°C for approximately

12–16 hr until used. One millilitre samples are diluted in 10 ml of 0·02% saponin in Ringer's solution at pH 7·2. Complete lysis of red cells occurs, with intermittent shaking at 37°c, within 15 min. The samples are washed twice in GMA by centrifuging at 1,500 rev/min for 4 min each time and finally resuspending them in complete insect growth medium (10% bovine foetal serum, 0·5% haemolymph in GMA) containing *A.aegypti* cells in static 2 oz glass or plastic screw-capped bottles. The cultures are maintained at 22°c and the medium is not changed at all.

Wood & Suitor obtained development of the first, second and third stage larvae in their cultures in a time comparable with that required *in vivo*. The third stage larvae had undergone incomplete exsheathment in 19 days but although they survived for a total of 33 days no further development occurred. Unfortunately no evidence as to their infectivity has been recorded.

VI. SPIRUROIDEA

GNATHOSTOMA SPINIGERUM

Oba (1959) working in Japan reported on the maintenance of *Gnathostoma spinigerum*, a spiruroid parasite of cats. He was able to maintain the third stage larvae in cultures of cat liver slices in Ringer's solution for 69 days at 38°c. Supplementing the medium with chick embryo extract promoted survival of the adult worms *in vitro*.

TABLE 7.3. Cultivation of Nematoda

Species	Stage	Survival (days)	Author	Date
Ancylostoma	—	—	Miyagawa & Okada	1930
	—	—	Sasa *et al.*	1958
	—	—	Sawada *et al.*	1954
Ancylostoma braziliense	L	—	Lawrence	1948
Ancylostoma caninum	—	—	Kamiko	1939
	A	48	Komiya *et al.*	1956
	—	—	Komiya *et al.*	1958
	—	—	Matsusaki	1939
	—	—	Okada	1930
	—	—	Roche *et al.*	1962
	—	—	Warren *et al.*	1962
	A & L	—	Weinstein	1953

TABLE 7.2—*contd.*

Species	Stage	Survival (days)	Author	Date
Ancylostoma duodenale	—	—	Aketogawa	1938
	—	—	Hsieh *et al.*	1963
	—	—	Nakajima	1931
	—	—	Nakajima	1932
	L	—	Weinstein	1953
	A & L	3 mths.	Yasuraoka *et al.*	1960
Hookworms	—	—	Harada & Mori	1955
	—	—	Lamy & Bénex	1956
	—	—	McCoy	1929a, b
	—	—	Marplestone	1934
	—	—	Roche & Torres	1960
	L	—	Sawada	1961
	—	—	Shirasaka	1959
Angiostrongylus cantonensis	A	63	Weinstein *et al.*	1962
	A	80	Weinstein *et al.*	1963
Ascaridia lineata	L	—	Ackert *et al.*	1938
Ascaris	—	—	Harpur	1962a, b
	—	—	Hoeppli *et al.*	1938
	—	—	Izumi & Nakamura	1952
	—	—	Kovalevsky & Kurlov	1927
	—	—	Stewart	1934
Ascaris acus	—	—	Hoeppli *et al.*	1938
Ascaris decipens	—	—	Hoeppli *et al.*	1938
Ascaris suilla	—	—	Adam	1932
Ascaris lumbricoides	—	—	Beames & Read	1962
	—	—	Cavier & Savel	1953
	—	—	Ellison *et al.*	1960
	—	—	Fairbairn & Ressal	1950
	—	—	Harpur	1962a, b
	—	—	Hobson *et al.*	1952a, b
	—	—	Hoeppli *et al.*	1938
	L	—	Pitts	1963
	Ova	—	Rogers	1958
	—	—	Toikawa	1957a, b
Ascaris lumbricoides var. *suum*	A	—	Benediktov	1962
	—	—	Cleeland	1963
	—	—	Cleeland & Lawrence	1962
	L	—	Crandall & Arean	1964
	A	—	Doran	1961
	L	—	Fenwick	1939
	—	—	Ichii *et al.*	1958
	—	—	Ichii *et al.*	1959
	Ova	—	Pitts	1948
	L	—	Pitts	1960

TABLE 7.2—*contd.*

Species	Stage	Survival (days)	Author	Date
Ascaris lumbricoides var. *suum*—contd.	L	—	Pitts	1962
	L	49	Pitts	1963
	L	—	Pitts & Ball	1953
	L	—	Pitts & Ball	1955
	L	—	Salmenkova	1962
Ascaris megalocephala	Ova	—	Pick	1948
Brugia malayi	—	—	Bergman	1932
	—	—	Bergman	1933
Capillaria hepatica	Ova	20	Sato & Shimatani	1961
Chabertia	—	—	Lapage	1933b
Cooperia pectinata	L & A	—	Leeland	1965a
Cooperia punctata	L	4	Douvres	1960a
	—	—	Douvres & Alicata	1962
	—	36	Leeland	1961a
	L & A	—	Leeland	1962
	A	—	Leeland	1963a
	—	—	Leeland & Wallace	1966
Cooperia onchophora	L & A	—	Leeland	1961a
	A	—	Leeland	1963a
Dictyocaulus viviparus	—	—	Silverman & Podger	1962
	—	—	Silverman & Podger	1964
Dirofilaria immitis	L & A	61, 65	Earl	1959
	—	—	Hoeppli *et al.*	1938
	L	12	Joyeaux & Sautet	1937
	L	18	Mazzotti	1953
	L	15	Sawyer	1963
	L	—	Sawyer	1965
	—	—	Sawyer & Weinstein	1961
	L	—	Sawyer & Weinstein	1962
	L	21	Sawyer & Weinstein	1963a, b, c
	L & A	—	Taylor	1960a
	—	—	Yoeli *et al.*	1964
Dirofilaria uniformis	—	—	von Brand *et al.*	1963
	—	—	Weinstein & Sawyer	1961
Dipetalonema	—	21	Sawyer & Weinstein	1963a
Gnathostoma spinigerum	L	69	Oba	1959
Haemonchus	L	—	Leland	1963a
Haemonchus contortus	—	—	Douvres	1960a
	L	—	Glaser	1940
	—	—	Glaser & Stoll	1938
	L & A	30	Silverman	1959
	L	—	Silverman	1965
	—	—	Silverman *et al.*	1965
	L	72 hr	Sommerville	1964

TABLE 7.2—*contd.*

Species	Stage	Survival (days)	Author	Date
Heamonchus contortus	L	72 hr	Sommerville	1966
—cont.	—	—	Stoll	1940
	L	—	Taylor & Whitlock	1960
Hyostrongylus rubidus	L	—	Diamond & Douvres	1960
	—	—	Diamond & Douvres	1962
Icossiella neglecta	L	15	Coutelen	1928
	—	—	Hoeppli *et al.*	1938
	L & A	2	Hawking	1954
Litomosoides carinii	L & A	21	Taylor	1960:
	L	5	Weinstein	1963
Loa loa	L	—	Laas	1934
	L	10	Taylor	1960a
Macacanema formosana	L	—	Wood & Suitor	1966
Microfilariae	—	—	Fülleborn	1912
	—	—	Johns & Querens	1914
	—	—	Low	1921
	—	—	Nagano	1923
	—	22	Sawyer & Cheever	1962
	—	—	Wellman & Johns	1912
Metastrongylus apri	L	—	Sen & Kelley	1960
Metastrongylus pudendotectus	L	—	Sen & Kelley	1960
Necator	L	—	Sasa *et al.*	1958
	L	—	Shirasaka	1959
Necator americanus	—	—	Hsieh *et al.*	1963
Nematospiroides	—	—	Leland	1963a
Nematodirus dubius	A	—	Sommerville & Weinstein	1964
Neoaplectana chresima	—	—	Glaser *et al.*	1942
Neoaplectana glaseri	L & A	—	Dropkin	1950
	L & A	5	Glaser	1931
	L & A	—	Glaser	1940a, b, c
	L & A	—	Glaser & Fox	1930
	—	—	Jackson	1961
	L & A	—	Jackson	1962a, b,
	—	—	Jackson	1965
	—	—	Jackson & Siddiqui	1965
	L	—	Stoll	1948
	L & A	21	Stoll	1951
	—	—	Stoll	1953a, b
	—	—	Stoll	1954
	L	—	Stoll	1956
	—	—	Stoll	1959
	—	—	Stoll	1961

TABLE 7.2—*coutd.*

Species	Stage	Survival (days)	Author	Date
Nippostrongylus brasiliensis	L	—	Barakat	1951
	—	—	McCoy	1929a, b
	—	—	Sarles	1938
	L	—	Weinstein	1954
	L & A	—	Weinstein & Jones	1956a, b
	L & A	10	Weinstein & Jones	1957a
Oesophagostomum dentatum	L & A	—	Douvres	1966
Oesophagostomum quadrispinulatum	L	42	Diamond & Douvres	1960
	—	—	Diamond & Douvres	1962
	L	—	Leland	1963b
Oesophagostomum radiatum	—	—	Anataraman	1942
	L	14	Douvres	1960a, b
	—	—	Douvres	1962a, b
	L	—	Leland	1963b
Ostertagia circumcincta	L & A	—	Leland	1961a
Ostertagia ostertagi	L & A	—	Leland	1961a
Stephanurus dentatus	L	15	Douvres & Tromba	1962
	L	21	Douvres *et al.*	1966
Strongyloides	L	—	Lamy & Bénex	1956
	L	—	Sasa *et al.*	1958
	L	—	Shirasaka	1959
Strongyloides fuellerborni	L	—	Chung	1936
Strongyloides papillosus	—	—	Silverman & Podger	1962
Strongyloides ratti	—	—	Weinstein & Jones	1957b
Trichinella spiralis	L & A	—	Berntzen	1962
	L & A	—	Berntzen	1965
	—	—	Chipman	1957
	—	—	Haskins & Weinstein	1957
	L	17 hr	Kim	1961
	L	1–2	Kim	1962
	L	11	Levin	1940
	L	5	McCoy	1936
	L	—	Meerovitch	1962
	L	1–2	Meerovitch	1965a, b
	L	65 hr	Weller	1943
Trichostrongylids	—	—	Lapage	1935
Trichostrongylus	L	—	Lapage	1933a, b
	L	—	Sasa *et al.*	1958
Trichostrongylus colubriformis	—	—	Silverman & Podger	1964
Trichostrongylus retortaeformis	L	—	Lapage	1933a, b
	Ova	—	Wilson	1958
Wuchereria bancrofti	L	32	Coutelen	1929
	L	23	Takeshita & Okuda	1925
	L	—	Weinstein	1963

TABLE 7.2—*contd.*

Species	Stage	Survival (days)	Author	Date
MISCELLANEOUS	—	—	Fairbairn	1960
	L	—	Glaser & Stoll	1940
	L	—	Grainger	1959
	—	—	Hobson	1948
	—	—	Krotov	1958
	L	—	Lapage	1933a, b
	—	—	Lee	1965
	—	—	Leland	1961b
	—	—	Silverman	1963a, b
	L	—	Silverman	1965
	L	—	Silverman *et al.*	1962
	—	—	Silverman *et al.*	1966
	—	—	Sommerville	1957
	—	—	Stunkard	1932
	L	—	Weinstein	1949
	—	—	Weinstein & Jones	1959
	L	—	Whitlock	1956

A=Adult; L=Larva.

REFERENCES

ACKERT J.E., TODD A.C. & TANNER W.A. (1938). Growing larval *Ascaridia lineata* (Nematoda) *in vitro. Trans. Am. microsc. Soc.* **57**: 202–296.

ADAM W. (1932). Ueber die Stoffwechselprozesse von *Ascaris suilla* Duj. I Teil. Die Aufnahme von Sauerstoff aus der Umgebung. *Z. vergl. Physiol.* **26**: 229–251.

AKETOGAWA H. (1938). Some experimental contributions on oral and cutaneous infection of hookworms. *Jap. J. exp. Med.* **16**: 85–107.

ANATARAMAN M. (1942). The life-history of *Oesophagostomum radiatum*, the bovine nodular worm. *Indian J. vet. Sci.* **12**: 187–132.

BARAKAT M.R. (1951). A new procedure for the cultivation of nematode parasites. *J. Egyp. med. Ass.* **34**: 323–326.

BEAMES C.G. & READ C.P. (1962). Neutral and phospholipids of *Ascaris lumbricoides* with special reference to the fatty acids and fatty aldehydes. *J. Parasit.* **48** (2 sect. 2, suppl.): 27.

BENEDIKTOV I.I. (1962). Proteins in the body fluid of *Ascaris suum* kept in a protein deficient medium. *Medskaya Parazit.* **31**: 660–664 (Russian, English Summary).

BERGMAN R.A.M. (1932). Microfilarien in Bloedculturen. *Geneesk. Tijdschr. Med.—Indie* **72**: 973–981.

BERGMAN R.A.M. (1933). Mikrofilarien und Blutleukozyten in Kulturen *in vitro. Arch. exp. Zellforsch.* **13**: 491–509.

BERNTZEN A.K. (1962). *In vitro* cultivation of *Trichinella spiralis. J. Parasit.* **48** (2 sect. 2, suppl.): 48.

BERNTZEN A.K. (1965). Comparative growth and development of *Trichinella spiralis in vitro* and *in vivo*, with a redescription of the life-cycle. *Expl Parasit.* **16**: 74–106.

BERNTZEN A.K. (1966). A controlled culture environment for axenic growth of parasites. *Ann. N.Y. Acad. Sci.* **139**: 176–189.

BRAND T. VON, BOWMAN I.B.R., WEINSTEIN P.P. & SAWYER T.K. (1963). Observations on the metabolism of *Dirofilaria uniformis. Expl Parasit.* **13**: 128–133.

CAVIER R. & SAVEL J. (1953). Les conditions de vie de l'Ascaris du porc *Ascaris lumbricoides*, Linné 1758, hors de l'organisme de l'hote in milieu aseptique. *Annls Sci. nat.* (zool.) (11) **15**: 57–70.

CHIPMAN P.B. (1957). The antigenic role of the excretions and secretions of adult *Trichinella spiralis* in the production of immunity in mice. *J. Parasit.* **43**: 593–598.

CHRISTIE M.G. & CHARLESTON W.A.G. (1965). Stimulus to exsheathing *Nematodirus battus* infective larvae. *Expl Parasit.* **17**: 46–50.

CHUNG H.L. (1936–37). Observations on the filariform larvae of *Strongyloides fuellerborni* in different media as well as in tissue cultures. *Z. Parasitkde* **9**: 28–49.

CLEELAND R. (1963). The effects of different atmospheres and various supplements on the *in vitro* survival and growth of *Ascaris suum* larvae. *J. Parasit.* **49**: 64–68.

CLEELAND R. & LAURENCE K.A. (1962). *In vitro* cultivation of *Ascaris lumbricoides* var. *suum* larvae. *J. Parasit.* **48**: 35–38.

COUTELEN F. (1928). Contribution aux essai de culture *in vitro* d'embryons de filaires. *Bull. Soc. Path. exot.* **29**: 316–322.

COUTELEN F. (1929). Essai de culture *in vitro* de microfilaires de Bancroft. *Annls Parasit. hum. comp.* **7**: 399–409.

CRANDALL C.A. & AREAN V.M. (1964). *In vivo* studies of *Ascaris suum* larvae planted in diffusion chambers in immune and non-immune mice. *J. Parasit.* **50**: 685–688.

DENHAM D.A. (1967). *In vitro* culture of nematodes, especially *Nippostrongylus* and *Trichinella. Symp. Br. Soc. Parasit.* No. 5: 49–60.

DIAMOND L.S. & DOUVRES F.W. (1960). Cultivation of parasitic stages of the swine nematodes *Hyostrongylus rubidus* and *Oesophagostomum quadrispinulatum* free of microbial associates. *J. Parasit.* **46** (5 sect. 2, Suppl.): 25.

DIAMOND L.S. & DOUVRES F.W. (1962). Bacteria-free cultivation of some parasitic stages of the swine nematodes *Hyostrongylus rubidus* and *Oesophagostomum quadrispinulatum* (*O. longicaudum*). *J. Parasit.* **48**: 39–42.

DORAN D.J. (1961). *In vitro* survival of germinal cord tissue of *Ascaris lumbricoides* var. *suum. J. Parasit.* **47**: 890.

DOUVRES F.W. (1960a). The *in vitro* cultivation of some gastrointestinal nematodes of cattle and sheep. *J. Parasit.* **46** (5. Sect. 2, Suppl.): 25.

DOUVRES F.W. (1960b). Influence of intestinal extracts and sera from cattle infected with *Oesophagostomum radiatum* on the *in vitro* cultivation of this nematode: preliminary report. *J. Parasit.* **46** (5. Sect. 2, Suppl.): 25–26.

DOUVRES F.W. (1962a). The *in vitro* cultivation of *Oesophagostomum radiatum*, the nodular worm of cattle. I. Development in vitamin supplemented and non-supplemented media. *J. Parasit.* **48**: 314–320.

DOUVRES F.W. (1962b). The *in vitro* cultivation of *Oesophagostomum radiatum*, the nodular worm of cattle. II. The use of this technique to study immune responses of host tissue extracts against the developing nematode. *J. Parasit.* **48**: 852–864.

DOUVRES F.W. (1966). *In vitro* growth of *Oesophagostomum dentatum* (Nematoda: Strongyloidea) from third stage larvae to adults with observations on inhibited larval development. *J. Parasit.* **52**: 1033–1034.

DOUVRES F.W. & ALICATA J.E. (1962). Development *in vitro* of the parasitic stages of *Cooperia punctata*, an intestinal nematode of cattle. *J. Parasit.* **48** (2. Sect. 2, Suppl.): 35.

DOUVRES F.W. & TROMBA F.G. (1962). Development of *Stephenurus dentatus*, Diesing 1839, to the fourth stage *in vitro*. *J. Parasit.* **48:** 269.

DOUVRES F.W., TROMBA F.G. & DORAN D.J. (1966). The influence of NCTC 109, serum and swine kidney cell cultures on the morphogenesis of *Stephanurus dentatus* to fourth stage *in vitro*. *J. Parasit.* **52:** 875–889.

DROPKIN V.H. (1950). Isolation cultures of *Neoaplectana glaseri*. *J. Parasit.* **36** (6. Sect. 2, Suppl.): 34.

EARL P.R. (1959). Filariae from the dog *in vitro*. *Ann. N.Y. Acad. Sci.* **77:** 163–175.

ELLISON T., THOMPSON W.A.B. & STRONG F.M. (1960). Volatile fatty acids from axenic *Ascaris lumbricoides*. *Archs Biochem. Biophys.* **91:** 247–254.

FAIRBAIRN D. (1957). The biochemistry of *Ascaris*. *Expl Parasit.* **6:** 491–554.

FAIRBAIRN D. (1960). Physiologic aspects of egg hatching and larval exsheathment in nematodes. In *Host influence on parasite physiology*. L.A.Stauber (ed.). New Brunswick, New Jersey: Rutgers University Press.

FAIRBAIRN D. (1961). The *in vitro* hatching of *Ascaris lumbricoides* eggs. *Can. J. Zool.* **39:** 153–162.

FAIRBAIRN D. & RESSAL M.R. (1950). The preparation of bacteria-free helminth parasites. *Proc. Trans. R. Soc. Can. Ser.* 3 **44** (List of officers): 241.

FELLER A.E., ENDERS J.F. & WELLER T.H. (1940). The prolonged coexistence of vaccinia virus in high titre and living cells in roller cultures of chick embryonic tissues. *J. exp. Med.* **72:** 367–388.

FENWICK D.W. (1939). Studies on the saline requirements of the larvae of *Ascaris suum*. *J. Helminth.* **17:** 211–218.

FÜLLEBORN F. (1912). Beitrage zur Biologie der Filarien. I. Mikrofilarien. *Zentbl. Bakt. ParasitKde* **66:** 255–267.

GLASER R.W. (1931). The cultivation of a nematode parasite of an insect. *Science, N.Y.* **73:** 614.

GLASER R. W. (1940a). Continued culture of a nematode parasitic in the Japanese beetle. *J. exp. Zool.* **84:** 1–12.

GLASER R.W. (1940b). The bacteria-free culture of a nematode parasite. *Proc. Soc. exp. Biol. Med.* **43:** 512–514.

GLASER R.W. (1940c). The culture of parasitic nematodes. *Int. Congr. Microbiol.* **3:** 431–432.

GLASER R.W. (1943). The germ-free culture of certain invertebrates. In Reynier J. A. *Micrurgical and germ free methods:* 164–184. Springfield, Ill. and Baltimore, Md.

GLASER R.W. & CORIA N.A. (1935). The culture and reactions of purified protozoa. *Am. J. Hyg.* **21:** 111–120.

GLASER R.W. & FOX H. (1930). A nematode parasite of the Japanese beetle (*Popillia japonica*). *Science, N.Y.* **71:** 16–17.

GLASER R.W., McCOY E.E. & GIRTH H.B. (1942). The biology and culture of *Neoaplectan chresima* a new nematode parasitic in insects. *J. Parasit.* **28:** 123–126.

GLASER R.W. & STOLL N.R. (1938). Sterile culture of free-living stages of the sheep stomach worm, *Haemonchus contortus*. *Parasitology* **30:** 324–332.

GLASER R.W. & STOLL N.R. (1940). Exsheathing and sterilizing infective nematode larvae. *J. Parasit.* **26:** 87–94.

GRACE T.D.C. (1958). The prolonged growth and survival of ovarian tissue of the promethea moth (*Callosamia promethea*) *in vitro*. *J. gen. Physiol.* **41**: 1027–1034.

GRACE T.D.C. (1962). Establishment of four strains of cells from insect tissues grown *in vitro*. *Nature, Lond.* **195**: 788–789.

GRACE T.D.C. (1966). Establishment of a line of mosquito (*Aedes aegypti*) cells grown *in vitro*. *Nature, Lond.* **211**: 366–367.

GRAINGER J.N.R. (1959). The identity of the larval nematodes found in the body muscles of the cod (*Gadus callarias* L.). *Parasitology* **49**: 121–131.

GURSCH O.F. (1948). Effects of digestion and refrigeration on the ability of *Trichinella spiralis* to infect rats. *J. Parasit.* **34**: 394–395.

HALEY A.J. (1961). Biology of the rat nematode *Nippostrongylus brasiliensis* (Travassos, 1914). 1. Systematics, hosts and geographical distribution. *J. Parasit.* **47**: 727–732.

HALL, M. C. (1917). The longevity of adult ascarids outside the body of the host. *J. Am. med. Ass.* **68**: 772–773.

HANCOCK B.B., BOHL E.H. & BRIKLAND J.M. (1959). Swine kidney cell cultures—susceptibility to viruses and use in isolation of enteric viruses of swine. *Am. J. vet. Res.* **20**: 127–132.

HANSEN E.L., SILVERMAN P.H. & BUECHER E.JR. (1966). Development of *Haemonchus contortus* in media designed through studies with *Caenorhabditis briggsae*. *J. Parasit.* **52**: 137–140.

HARADA Y. & MORI O. (1955). A new method for culturing hookworm. *Yonago Acta med.* **1**: 177–179.

HARPUR R.P. (1962a). Metabolism of *Ascaris* muscle as an index of *in vitro* health. *J. Parasit.* **48** (2. Sect. 2, Suppl.): 34–35.

HARPUR R.P. (1962b). Maintenance of *Ascaris lumbricoides in vitro*: a biochemical and statistical approach. *Can. J. Zool.* **40**: 991–1011.

HASKINS W.T. & WEINSTEIN P.P. (1957). The amine constituents from the excretory products of *Ascaris lumbricoides* and *Trichinella spiralis* larvae. *J. Parasit.* **43**: 28–32.

HAWKING F. (1954). The reproductive system of *Litomosoides carinii*, a filarial parasite of the cotton rat. III. The number of microfilariae produced. *Ann. trop. Med. Parasit.* **48**: 382–385.

HAWKING F. & SEWELL P. (1948). The maintenance of a filarial infection (*Litomosoides carinii*) for chemotherapeutic investigations. *Br. J. Pharmacol.* **3**: 285.

HOBSON A.D. (1948). The physiology and cultivation in artificial media of nematodes parasitic in the alimentary tract of animals. *Parasitology* **38**: 183–227.

HOBSON A.D., STEPHENSON W. & BEADLE L.C. (1952a). Studies on the physiology of *Ascaris lumbricoides*. I. The relation of the total osmotic pressure, conductivity and chloride content of the body fluid to that of the external environment. *J. exp. Biol.* **29**: 1–21.

HOBSON A.D., STEPHENSON W. & EDEN A. (1952b). Studies on the physiology of *Ascaris lumbricoides*. II. The inorganic composition of the body fluid in relation to that of the environment. *J. exp. Biol.* **29**: 22–29.

HOEPPLI R., FENG L.C. & CHU H.J. (1938). Attempts to culture helminths of vertebrates in artificial media. *Chin. med. J.* **2**: 343–374.

HSIEH H.C., KON M. & SHIH C.C. (1963). Studies on the relative prevalence of *Ancylostoma duodenale* and *Necator americanus* in Taiwan with reference to employment of test-tube filter-paper cultivation method. *Publ. Hlth Pap. W.H.O.* No. 24: 1–13.

ICHII S., SUGIURA K. & MATSUMOTO K. (1958). Metabolic changes in *Ascaris lumbricoides* var. *suum* during the culture *in vitro*. *Jap. J. Parasit.* **7**: 661–665 (English summary).

ICHII S., MATSUMOTO K. & SUGIURA K. (1959). Metabolic changes in *Ascaris lumbricoides* var. *suum* culture *in vitro*. 2. Digestive enzymes. *Jap. J. Parasit.* **8**: 19–21 (English summary).

IZUMI S. & NAKAMURA S. (1952). Biological studies on *Ascaris* eggs. I. Comparative study of various culture methods of *Ascaris* eggs. *Jap. J. med. Sci. Biol.* **5** (1): 7–12.

JACKSON G.J. (1961). The parasitic nematode *Neoaplectana glaseri* in axenic culture. I. Effects of antibiotics and anthelminthics. *Expl Parasit.* **11**: 241–247.

JACKSON G.J. (1962a). The parasitic nematode *Neoaplectana glaseri* in axenic culture. II. Initial results with defined media. *Expl Parasit.* **12**: 25–32.

JACKSON G. J. (1962b). On axenic cultures of certain protozoan and worm parasites of insects. *Trans. N.Y. Acad. Sci.* Series II **24**: 954–965.

JACKSON G.J. (1965). Differentiation of three species of *Neoaplectana* (Nematoda: Rhabditida) grown axenically. *Parasitology* **55**: 571–578.

JACKSON G.J. (1966). Helminth physiology: stage and species differences in culture. *Ann. N.Y. Acad. Sci.* **139**: 91–97.

JACKSON G.J. & SIDDIQUI W.A. (1965). Folic acid in axenic cultures of *Neoaplectana glaseri*. *J. Parasit.* **51**: 727–730.

JOHNS F.M. & QUERENS P.L. (1914). Further note on the growth of filarial embryos *in vitro*. *Am. J. trop. Dis. prev. Med.* **1**: 620–624.

JONES M.F. & WEINSTEIN P.P. (1957). The axenic cultivation of *Nematospiroides dubius*. *J. Parasit.* **43** (Sect. 5, suppl.): 46.

JOYEUX C. & SAUTET J. (1937). Contribution à l'étude de la culture des microfilaires. *C.r. Séanc. Soc. Biol.* **126**: 361–362.

KAMIKO K. (1939). On the development of *Ancylostoma caninum* in the heterogenous host. *Jap. J. exp. Med.* **23**: 301–318.

KIM C.W. (1961). The cultivation of *Trichinella spiralis in vitro*. *Am. J. trop. Med. Hyg.* **10**: 742–747.

KIM C.W. (1962). Further study on the *in vitro* cultivation of *Trichinella spiralis*. *Am. J. trop. Med. Hyg.* **11**: 491–496.

KOMIYA Y., YASURAOKA K. & SATO A. (1956). Survival of *Ancylostoma caninum in vitro*. *Jap. J. med. Sci. Biol.* **9**: 283–292.

KOMIYA Y., YASURAOKA K. & SATO A. (1958). Survival of *Ancylostoma caninum in vitro*. I. Survival in various physiological saline solutions and dog serum without blood cells. *Jap. J. Parasit.* **7**: 103–107 (English summary).

KOVALEVSKY A. & KURLOV A.V.M. (1927). Versuch einer Zuchtung von Ascaridenlarven und dei Wege ihrer weiteren Enturklung beim Infizieren von Tieren (Russian text). *Sib. arch. teoret. Klin. medit.* **2**: 27–41.

KROTOV A.I. (1958). Maintenance and cultivation of worms under artificial conditions. *Usp. sovrem. Biol.* **46**: 230–239.

LAAS E. (1934). Blutzellen und Mikrofilarien bei Auspflanzung. *Arch. exp. Zellforsch.* **16**: 260–274.

LAMY L. & BÉNEX J. (1956). Modification de technique de coproculture pour helminthes et protozoaires. *Bull. Soc. Path. exot.* **49**: 43–44.

LAPAGE G. (1933a). Cultivation of parasitic nematodes. *Nature, Lond.* **131**: 583–584.

LAPAGE G. (1933b). The cultivation of infective nematode larvae on cultures of *Bacillus coli*. *Rep. Inst. Anim. Path. Univ. Camb.* **3**: 237–271.

LAPAGE G. (1935). The behaviour of sterilized exsheathed infective trichostrongylid larvae in sterile media resembling their environment in ovine hosts. *J. Helminth.* **13**: 115–128.

LAWRENCE J.J. (1948). The cultivation of the free-living stages of the hookworm *Ancylostoma braziliensis* de Faria under aseptic conditions. *Aust. J. exp. Biol. Med. Sci.* **26**: 1–8.

LEE D.L. (1965). *The physiology of nematodes.* Edinburgh: Oliver & Boyd.

LELAND S.E. JR. (1961a). The *in vitro* cultivation of the parasitic stages of *Cooperia punctata, C. onchophora, Ostertagia ostertagi* and *O. circumcincta.* A preliminary report. *J. Parasit.* **47** (5. Sect. 2, Suppl.): 21.

LELAND S.E. JR. (1961b). A simple prismatic device for viewing nematode parasites *in vitro* cultures. *J. Parasit.* **47**: 623–624.

LELAND S.E. JR. (1962). The *in vitro* cultivation of *Cooperia punctata* from egg to egg. *J. Parasit.* **48** (2. Sect. 2, Suppl.): 35.

LELAND S.E. JR. (1963a). Studies on the *in vitro* growth of parasitic nematodes. I. Complete or partial parasitic development of some gastro-intestinal nematodes of sheep and cattle. *J. Parasit.* **49**: 600–611.

LELAND S.E. JR. (1963b). *In vitro* cultivations of fourth and fifth stages of the swine nodular worm *Oesophagostomum quadrispinulatum. J. Parasit.* **49** (5. Sect. 2, Suppl.): 58–59.

LELAND S.E. JR. (1965a). *Cooperia pectinata. In vitro* cultivation of the parasitic stages including egg production. *J. Parasit.* **51** (No. 2, Suppl.): 46.

LELAND S. E. JR. (1965b). *Oesophagostomum quadrispinulatum. In vitro* cultivation of parasitic adults including the formation of spermatogonia and oogonia. *J. Parasit.* (2. Sect. 2, Suppl.): 47.

LELAND S. E. JR. (1965c). *Hyostrongylus rubidus. In vitro* cultivation of the parasitic stages including the production and development of eggs through five cleavages: a preliminary report. *J. Parasit.* (2. Sect. 2, Suppl.): 47.

LELAND S. E. JR. (1967). The *in vitro* development of *Cooperia pectinator*, a nematode parasite of cattle, from third stage to adults, including egg production. *J. Parasit.* **53**: 630–633.

LELAND S.E. JR. & WALLACE L.J. (1966). Development to viable egg production in the rabbit duodenum of parasitic stages of *Cooperia punctata* grown *in vitro. J. Parasit.* **52**: 280–284.

LEVIN A.J. (1940). Culturing *Trichinella spiralis in vitro.* I. Preliminary experiments. A basic medium to sustain larvae unchanged for long periods *in vitro. J. Parasit.* **26** (No. 6, Suppl.): 31.

LOW G.C. (1921). The life of filarial embryos outside the body. *J. trop. Med. Hyg.* **15**: 338–339.

MCCOY E.E. & GLASER R.W. (1936). Nematode culture for Japanese beetle control. *Circ. New Jers. Dept. Agri.* **285**: 1–10.

MCCOY E.E. & GLASER R.W. (1938). The culture of *Neoaplectana glaseri* on veal pulp. *Circ. New Jers. Dept. Agric.* No. 285: 1–12.

MCCOY O.R. (1929a). The growth of hookworm larvae on pure cultures of bacteria. *Science, N.Y.* **69**: 74–75.

MCCOY O.R. (1929b). The suitability of various bacteria as food for hookworm larvae. *Am. J. Hyg.* **10**: 140–156.

MCCOY O.R. (1936). The development of Trichinae in abnormal environments. *J. Parasit.* **22**: 54–59.

MARPLESTONE P.A. (1934). A simple method of growing hookworm larvae. *Indian J. med. Res.* **22**: 203–214.

MATSUSAKI G. (1939). Studies on the development of *Ancylostoma caninum* in the normal host. I. Development and migration after oral infection. *J. Keio Med. Soc.* **19**: 483–498.

MAZZOTTI L. (1953). Superivencia de las microfilarias de *Dirofilaria immitis* y de *Onchocerca reticulata* a la temperatura de 25°c bajo cero. *Revta Inst. Salubr. Enferm. trop. Mex.* **13**: 289–291.

MEEROVITCH E. (1962). *In vitro* development of *Trichinella spiralis* larvae. *J. Parasit.* **48** (2. Sect. 2, Suppl.): 34.

MEEROVITCH E. (1965a). Studies on the *in vitro* axenic development of *Trichinella spiralis*. I. Basic culture techniques, pattern of development and the effects of the gaseous phase. *Can. J. Zool.* **43**: 69–79.

MEEROVITCH E. (1965b). Studies on the *in vitro* axenic development of *Trichinella spiralis*. II. Preliminary experiments on the effects of farnesol, cholesterol and an insect extract. *Can. J. Zool.* **43**: 81–85.

MIYAGAWA Y. & OKADA R. (1930). Biological significance of the lung journey of *Ancyclostoma* larvae in the normal host. *Jap. J. exp. Med.* **14**: 224–242; 951–995.

NAGANO K. (1923). Beitrag zur Kultur der Mikrofilarien ausserhall des Wirtskörpers. *Arch. Schiffs-u. TropenHyg.* **27**: 178–85.

NAKAJIMA K. (1931). Experimental studies on the development of *Ancylostoma duodenale*. I, II and III. *Jap. J. exp. Med.* **15**: I (755–781) II (843–878) III (1054–1102).

NAKAJIMA K. (1932). Experimental studies on the development of *Ancylostoma*. IV. On the condition of development in rabbits of *A. duodenale* larvae collected from puppy lungs after percutaneous infection. *Jap. J. exp. Med.* **16**: 65–78.

NICHOLAS W.L. (1956). The axenic culture of *Turbatrix aceti* (the vinegar eelworm). *Nematologica* **1**: 337–340.

OBA N. (1959). Studies on *Gnathostoma spinigerum*. 3. Studies on the survival of *Gnathostoma spinigerum in vitro*. *J. Kurume med. Ass.* **22**: 3012.

OKADA R. (1930). Experimental studies on the oral and percutaneous infection of *Ancylostoma caninum*. Reports 1–4. *Jap. J. exp. Med.* **14**: 686–695; 696–708.

PICK F. (1948). Essai de development des oeufs d'*Ascaris megalocephala* sur des milieux solides. *Bull. Soc. Path. exot.* **41**: 208–212.

PITTS T.D. (1948). Experimental hatching of the eggs of *Ascaris suum. Proc. Soc. exp. Biol.* **69**: 348–351.

PITTS T.D. (1960). *In vitro* culture of the larvae of *Ascaris lumbricoides suum.* A report on progress. *J. Parasit.* **46** (5. Sect. 2, Suppl.): 24.

PITTS T.D. (1962). *In vitro* culture of the larvae of *Ascaris lumbricoides suum.* Continued studies with newly hatched larvae. *J. Parasit.* **48** (2. Sect. 2, Suppl.): 37.

PITTS T.D. (1963). *In vitro* cultivation of newly hatched larvae of *Ascaris* from man and swine. *J. Parasit.* **49**: 1034–1035.

PITTS T.D. & BALL G.H. (1953). *In vitro* culture of the larvae of *Ascaris lumbricoides suum. J. Parasit.* **39** (4. Sect. 2, Suppl.): 42.

PITTS T.D. & BALL G.H. (1955). Further studies on the *in vitro* culture of the larvae of *Ascaris lumbricoides suum. J. Parasit.* **41** (6. Sect. 2, Suppl.): 47–48.

PITTS T.D. & BALL G.H. (1958). A chamber for helminth cultures. *Trans. Am. microsc. Soc.* **77**: 280–283.

ROBINSON D.L.H. (1967). *In vitro* studies on nematodes and their application to experimental immunology with special reference to *Haemonchus contortus*. *Symp. Br. Soc. Parasit.* No. 5: 61–70.

ROCHE M., MARTINEZ C. & MACPHERSON L. (1962). *In vitro* studies on *Ancylostoma caninum*. Motion picture. *J. Parasit.* **48** (2. Sect. 2, Suppl.): 49.

ROCHE M. & TORRES C.M. (1960). A method for the *in vitro* study of hookworm activity. *Expl Parasit.* **9**: 250–256.

ROGERS W.P. (1958). Physiology of the hatching of eggs of *Ascaris lumbricoides*. *Nature, Lond.* **181**: 1410–1411.

ROGERS W.P. (1961). The physiology of hatching of eggs of *Ascaridia galli*. *J. Helminth.* R.T.Leiper Suppl.: 151–156.

ROGERS W.P. & SOMMERVILLE R.I. (1957). Physiology of nematode exsheathment. *Nature, Lond.* **179**: 619–621.

ROGERS W.P. & SOMMERVILLE R.I. (1960). The physiology of the second ecdysis of nematodes. *Parasitology* **50**: 329–348.

SALMENKOVA E.A. (1962). The composition of free amino acids in the body fluid of *Ascaris suum* and its changes during cultivation under conditions of protein deficiency. *Medskaya Parazit.* **31**: 664–668. (In Russian: English summary).

SARLES M.P. (1938). The *in vitro* action of immune rat serum on the nematode *Nippostrongylus muris*. *J. infect. Dis.* **62**: 337–348.

SASA M., HAYASHI S., TANAKA H. & SHIRASAKA R. (1958). Application of test-tube cultivation method on the survey of hookworms and related human nematode infections. *Jap. J. exp. Med.* **28**: 129–137.

SATO A. & SHIMATANI T. (1961). Studies on *Capillaria hepatica*. III. On the culture method of the egg of *C. hepatica*. *Igaku Seibutfugaku* **58**: 27–31. (In Japanese).

SAWADA J. (1961). Biological studies on the third-stage larvae of canine hookworm. *Jap. J. Parasit.* **10**: 398–409. (In Japanese).

SAWADA T., SANO M. & VENO T. (1954). Studies on the development of *Ancylostoma* larvae in chicken embryos. *Gunma J. med. Sci.* **3**: 21–28.

SAWYER T.K. (1963). *In vitro* culture of third-stage larvae of *Dirofilaria immitis*. *J. Parasit.* **49** (5. sect. 2, Suppl.): 59.

SAWYER T.K. (1965). Molting and exsheathment *in vitro* of third stage *Dirofilaria immitis*. *J. Parasit.* **51**: 1016.

SAWYER T.K. & CHEEVER A.W. (1962). Some intestinal parasites of the cotton-topped pinch (Colombian marmoset), *Oedipomidas*, with a note on the survival *in vitro* of microfilariae of one of the parasites. *Proc. helminth. Soc. Wash.* **29**: 159–162.

SAWYER T.K. & WEINSTEIN P.P. (1961). Survival of *Dirofilaria immitis* microfilariae in modified physiological saline solutions. *J. Parasit.* **47** (No. 5, Suppl.): 24.

SAWYER T.K. & WEINSTEIN P.P. (1962). Development *in vitro* to the sausage stage of microfilariae of the dog heartworm, *Dirofilaria immitis*. *J. Parasit.* **48** (2. Sect. 2, Suppl.): 35–36.

SAWYER T.K. & WEINSTEIN P.P. (1963a). Morphologic changes occurring in canine microfilariae maintained in whole blood cultures. *Am. J. vet. Res.* **24**: 402–407.

SAWYER T.K. & WEINSTEIN P.P. (1963b). Studies on the microfilariae of the dog heartworm *Dirofilaria immitis:* separation of parasites from whole blood. *J. Parasit.* **49**: 39–45.

SAWYER T.K. & WEINSTEIN P.P. (1963c). The *in vitro* development of microfilariae of the dog heartworm *Dirofilaria immitis* to the 'sausage form'. *J. Parasit.* **49**: 218–224.

SAYRE F.W., HANSEN E.L. & YARWOOD E.A. (1963). Biochemical aspects of the nutrition of *Caenorhabditis briggsae. Expl Parasit.* **13**: 98–107.

SEN H.G. & KELLEY G.W. JR. (1960). Attempts at axenic culture of lungworms of swine. *J. Parasit.* **46** (5. sect. 2, Suppl.): 24.

SHIRASAKA R. (1959). Studies on the bionomics of infective larvae of parasitic nematodes. 2. Researches for the optimum conditions in the test tube cultivation of hookworm and *Trichostrongylus* larvae. *Jap. J. Parasit.* **8**: 62–68.

SILVERMAN P.H. (1959). *In vitro* cultivation of the histotrophic stages of *Haemonchus contortus* and *Ostertagia* spp. *Nature, Lond.* **183**: 197.

SILVERMAN P.H. (1962). Improvements in or relating to vaccines. *Br. Patent Specification* No. 894,603.

SILVERMAN P.H. (1963a). *In vitro* culture of parasites. *Symp. Br. Soc. Parasit.* No. 1: 49–68.

SILVERMAN P.H. (1963b). Exsheathment mechanisms of some nematode infective larvae. *J. Parasit.* **49** (5. sect. 2, Suppl.): 50.

SILVERMAN P.H. (1965). *In vitro* cultivation procedures for parasitic helminths. *Adv. Parasit.* **3**: 159–222.

SILVERMAN P.H. & PODGER K.R. (1962). Larval antigens derived by cultivation of some parasitic nematodes in simple media. *J. Parasit.* **48** (2. sect. 2, Suppl.): 15.

SILVERMAN P.H. & PODGER K.R. (1964). *In vitro* exsheathment of some nematode infective larvae. *Expl Parasit.* **15**: 314–324.

SILVERMAN P.H., ALGER N.E. & HANSEN E.L. (1966). Axenic helminth cultures and their use for the production of antiparasitic vaccines. *Ann. N.Y. Acad. Sci.* **139**: 124–142.

SILVERMAN P.H., HANSEN E.L. & BUECHER E. (1965). Development of larval *Haemonchus contortus* in supplemented chemically defined media. *J. Parasit.* **51** (No. 2, Suppl.): 46.

SILVERMAN P.H., POYNTER D. & PODGER K.R. (1962). Studies on larval antigens derived by cultivation of some parasitic nematodes in simple media: protection tests in laboratory animals. *J. Parasit.* **48**: 562–571.

SOMMERVILLE R.I. (1957). The exsheathing mechanism of nematode infective larvae. *Expl Parasit.* **6**: 18–30.

SOMMERVILLE R.I. (1964). Effect of carbon dioxide on the development of third stage larvae of *Haemonchus contortus in vitro. Nature, Lond.* **202**: 316.

SOMMERVILLE R.I. (1966). The development of *Haemonchus contortus* to the fourth stage *in vitro. J. Parasit.* **52**: 127–136.

SOMMERVILLE R.I. & WEINSTEIN P.P. (1964). Reproductive behavior of *Nematospiroides dubius in vivo* and *in vitro. J. Parasit.* **50**: 401–409.

SOMMERVILLE R.I. & WEINSTEIN P.P. (1967). The *in vitro* cultivation of *Nippostrongylus brasiliensis* from late fourth stage. *J. Parasit.* **53**: 116–125.

STEWART F.H. (1934). A method of incubating *Ascaris* eggs. *Ind. J. med. Res.* **22**: 1.

STOLL N.R. (1940). *In vitro* conditions favouring ecdysis at the end of the first parasitic stage of *Haemonchus contortus* (Nematoda). *Growth* **4**: 383–405.

STOLL N.R. (1948). Axenic cultures of *Neoaplectana glaseri* Steiner, in fluid media. *J. Parasit.* **34** (6. Sect. 2, Suppl.): 12.

STOLL N.R. (1951). Axenic *Neoaplectana glaseri* in fluid cultures. *J. Parasit.* **37** (5. Sect. 2, Suppl.): 18.

STOLL N.R. (1953a). Continued infectivity for Japanese beetle grubs of *Neoaplectana glaseri* (Nematoda) after seven years axenic culture. Thaper Commemoration

Volume: 259–268. Dayal J. & Singh K.S. (eds.). Lucknow University, Dept. Zoology.

STOLL N.R. (1953b). Axenic cultivation of the parasitic nematode *Neoaplectana glaseri* in a fluid medium containing raw liver extract. *J. Parasit.* **39**: 422–444.

STOLL N.R. (1954). Improved yields in axenic fluid cultures of *Neoaplectana glaseri* (Nematoda). *J. Parasit.* **40** (5. Sect. 2, Suppl.): 14.

STOLL N.R. (1956). Axenic cultivation of the parasitic nematode *Neoaplectana glaseri*, Steiner, 1929, in fluid media. *Int. Congr. Zool.* **14**: 382.

STOLL N.R. (1959). Conditions favouring the axenic culture of *Neoaplectana glaseri*, a nematode parasite of certain insect grubs. *Ann. N.Y. Acad. Sci.* **77**: 126–136.

STOLL N.R. (1961). Favored RLE for axenic culture of *Neoaplectana glaseri*. *J. Helminth*. R.T. Leiper Suppl.: 169–174.

STUNKARD H.W. (1932). Attempts to grow cestodes *in vitro*. *J. Parasit.* **19**: 163.

TAKESHITA S. & OKUDA M. (1925). On the cultivation of Bancroft's filarial larvae and animal inoculation experiments. *Japana cent. Revuo med.* **23**: 3. Summary in *Japan med. Wld* 1925, **5**: 296.

TAYLOR A. & WHITLOCK J.H. (1960). The exsheathing stimulus for infective larvae of *Haemonchus contortus*. *Cornell Vet.* **50**: 339–344.

TAYLOR A.E.R. (1960a). Maintenance of filarial worms *in vitro*. *Expl Parasit.* **9**: 113–120.

TAYLOR A.E.R. (1960b). The spermatogenesis and embryology of *Litomosoides carinii* and *Dirofilaria immitis*. *J. Helminth.* **34**: 3–12.

TAYLOR A. E. R., McCABE M. & LONGMUIR I. S. (1966). Studies on the metabolism of larval tapeworms (Cyclophyllidea: *Taenia crassiceps*). II. Respiration, glycogen utilization and lactic acid production during culture in a chemically defined medium. *Expl Parasit.* **19**: 269–275.

TOIKAWA M. (1957a). Biological studies on *Ascaris lumbricoides*. I. An attempt to keep live *Ascaris* larvae in a bacterially sterile medium. *Jap. J. Parasit.* **6**: 145–154. (English summary).

TOIKAWA M. (1957b). Biological studies on *Ascaris lumbricoides*. II. Experiments on the survival of hatched out *Ascaris* larvae in the sterilized medium and their migration into animal tissues added in the medium. *Jap. J. Parasit.* **6**: 542–545. (English summary).

WARREN L.G., GUEVARA A. & PATZREK D. (1962). Respiration and carbohydrate metabolism of *Ancylostoma caninum*: effect of carbohydrates, acid intermediates and electron transport inhibitors. *J. Parasit.* **48** (2. Sect. 2, Suppl.): 25–26.

WEATHERBY N.F., HANSEN M.F. & MOSER H.C. (1963). *In vitro* uptake of ^{14}C labelled alanine and glucose by *Ascaridia galli* (Nematoda) of chickens. *Expl Parasit.* **14**: 37–48.

WEINSTEIN P.P. (1949). The cultivation of the free-living stages of parasitic nematodes in the absence of living bacteria. *J. Parasit.* **35** (6. Sect. 2, Suppl.): 14.

WEINSTEIN P.P. (1953). The cultivation of the free-living stages of hookworms in the absence of living bacteria. *Am. J. Hyg.* **58**: 352–376.

WEINSTEIN P.P. (1954). The cultivation of the free-living stages of *Nippostrongylus muris* and *Necator americanus* in the absence of living bacteria. *J. Parasit.* **40** (5. Sect. 2, Suppl.): 14–15.

WEINSTEIN P.P. (1961). The specific concentration of a reddish pigment in the coelomocytes of some nematodes exposed to vitamin B_{12} *in vitro*. *J. Parasit.* **47** (4. Sect. 2, Suppl.): 23.

WEINSTEIN P.P. (1963). Development *in vitro* of the microfilariae of *Wuchereria bancrofti* and of *Litomosoides carinii* as far as the sausage form. *Trans. R. Soc. trop. Med. Hyg.* **57:** 236.

WEINSTEIN P.P. & JONES M.F. (1956a). The *in vitro* cultivation of *Nippostrongylus muris* to the adult stage. *J. Parasit.* **42:** 215–236.

WEINSTEIN P.P. & JONES M.F. (1956b). The effects of vitamins and protein hydrolysates on the growth *in vitro* of the free-living stages of *Nippostrongylus muris* under axenic conditions. *J. Parasit.* **42** (4. Sect. 2, Suppl.): 14.

WEINSTEIN P.P. & JONES M.F. (1957a). The development of a study on the axenic growth *in vitro* of *Nippostrongylus muris* to the adult stage. *Am. J. trop. Med. Hyg.* **6:** 480–484.

WEINSTEIN P.P. & JONES M.F. (1957b). The axenic cultivation of *Strongyloides ratti* and *Strongyloides* spp. from the rhesus monkey. *J. Parasit.* **43** (5. Sect. 2, Suppl.): 45.

WEINSTEIN P.P. & JONES M.F. (1959). Development *in vitro* of some parasitic nematodes of vertebrates. *Ann. N.Y. Acad. Sci.* **77:** 137–162.

WEINSTEIN P.P., ROSEN L., LACQUEUR G. L. & SAWYER T.K. (1962). *Angiostrongylus cantonensis* infection in rats and rhesus monkeys and survival of the parasite *in vitro. J. Parasit.* **48** (2. Sect. 2, Suppl.): 51–52.

WEINSTEIN P.P., ROSEN L., LACQUEUR G.L. & SAWYER T.K. (1963). *Angiostrongylus cantonensis* infection in rats and rhesus monkeys and observations on the survival of the parasite *in vitro. Am. J. trop. Med. Hyg.* **12:** 358–377.

WEINSTEIN P.P. & SAWYER T.K. (1961). Survival of adults of *Dirofilaria uniformis in vitro* and their production of microfilariae. *J. Parasit.* **47** (4. Sect. 2, Suppl.): 23.

WELLER T.H. (1943). The development of the larvae of *Trichinella spiralis* in rollertube cultures. *Am. J. Path.* **19:** 503–513.

WELLMAN C. & JOHNS F.M. (1912). The artificial culture of filarial embryos. A preliminary note. *J. Am. med. Ass.* **59:** 1531–1532.

WHITLOCK H.V. (1956). An improved method for the culture of nematode larvae in sheep faeces. *Aust. vet. J.* **32** (6): 141–143.

WILSON P.A.G. (1958). The effect of weak electrolyte solutions on the hatching rate of the eggs of *Trichostrongylus retortaeformis* (Zeder) and its interpretation in terms of a proposed hatching mechanism of strongylid eggs. *J. exp. Biol.* **35:** 585–601.

WOOD D.E. & SUITOR E.C. (1966). *In vitro* development of microfilariae of *Macacanema formosana* in mosquito cell cultures. *Nature, Lond.* **211:** 868–870.

YASURAOKA K., HOSAKA Y. & OGAWA K. (1960). Survival of *Ancylostoma duodenale in vitro. Jap. J. med. Sci. Biol.* **13:** 207–212.

YOELI M., UPMANIS R.S. & MOST H. (1964). Studies on Filariasis. III. Partial growth of the mammalian stages of *Dirofilaria immitis in vitro. Expl Parasit.* **15:** 325–334.

YOKOGAWA S. (1921). A new nematode from the rat. *J. Parasit.* **7:** 29–33.

CHAPTER 8

ACANTHOCEPHALA

Few attempts have been made to culture species of Acanthocephala *in vitro* and these in the main have been restricted to the maintenance of the adults. Von Brand (1940) was unable to keep *Macracanthorhyncus hirudinaceus* alive *in vitro* for more than a few hours, but Gettier (1942) reported that *Neoechinorhyncus emydis* lived a maximum of 25 days (mean 20·3 days) in a sodium chloride (0·5%) and calcium chloride (0·02%) solution. Van Cleave & Ross (1944) found that *N.emydis* survived 15 days in 0·85% sodium chloride, but after 13 days the worms became swollen. In 0·7% sodium chloride few lived more than 10 days and all were turgid in 3–4 days; in 0·8% sodium chloride the worms became turgid in 6 days and died in 10–14 days. No attempt was made by these workers to devise media in which the life of the worms could be prolonged under sterile conditions.

It was not until Ward (1951) became aware of the need for sterile conditions of culture for these worms (*Macracanthorhyncus hirudinaceus*) and devised a technique using antibiotics, that axenic culture was attempted. He maintained sterile cultures for 6 days by pre-washing the worms several times in Ringer-Tyrode solution containing penicillin and streptomycin (140 mg and 50 mg/l. medium respectively) before culturing them in this medium. During his experiments the worms were incubated at 38°c and the medium was not changed during the 6 days.

More recently Dunagan (1962) has attempted the cultivation of *N.emydis* in a variety of media. Mature worms were recovered from the small intestines of infected turtles and sterilized before culture by washing several times in sterile solutions containing antibiotics. The survival of the worms in Tyrode's solution was 19–21 days and was unaffected by alterations in pH between 7·2 and 8·2. The use of nutrient media had the effect of prolonging the worms' survival. The worms, after being surface sterilized, were able to survive for 66 days (mean survival period=51 days) in turtle serum alone, but when they were placed in dialysis tubing immersed in Tyrode's solution (pH 8·2) plus 11% turtle serum and 0·1% glucose they survived for 71–75 days, provided the medium was changed weekly. The replacement of Tyrode's solution with medium 199 supplemented with only 3% turtle serum (pH 7·8) induced 90 days survival (mean=64 days) and much the same result was obtained with Eagle's HeLa medium (pH 8·0) supplemented with 20% calf serum (96 days maximum, mean=61 days) provided the medium was changed at least once during the period. Throughout the study, though, no indication of growth was noted but copulation and egg maturation was achieved. Regardless of the length of survival time, all the worms gradually became swollen *in vitro* leading to their subsequent immobilization. Female worms, examined during the 51st to 73rd days *in vitro*, contained motile sperm which were attached to developing ovarian balls. The eggs were apparently normal but unfortunately their viability was not tested.

Harms (1963), working with adult *Octospinifer macilentis*, an intestinal parasite of the common sucker *Catostomus commersoni*, has attempted cultivation in 28 different media. Small adults (3–5 mm in length) were found to be the most useful for *in vitro* experiments and the medium showing the greatest potential (assessed by noting survival, increase in length, and maintenance of normal turgor and body movements) contained neopeptone, yeast extract, horse serum, glucose, inorganic salts, water soluble vitamins and essential amino acids. Harms noted that *O.macilentis* appeared to have strict nutritional and environmental requirements *in vitro* and postulated that this was the reason for the strict host specificity of this species.

Nicholas & Grigg (1965) have attempted to define the culture requirements of both adult and acanthor stages of *Moniliformis dubius* taken from the intestine of laboratory infected rats. They treated the worms with a mixture of antibiotics for 24 hr before culture, which suppressed bacterial contamination, but there was some doubt as to whether this suppression was complete, even during the 8 day observation period. Experiments were made with Hanks's saline, Eagle's medium and inactivated bovine serum at different hydrogen ion concentration and with different gas mixtures. Eagle's medium (pH 7·5) or inactivated bovine serum, each gassed with 5% carbon dioxide in nitrogen, gave the best results. However although the worms survived and produced viable acanthors *in vitro* they were abnormal in appearance. The development of the acanthors stopped or slowed down within the females, and the reproductive tracts released partially developed acanthors as well as infective ones. With immature worms there was little if any growth. These results, together with the failure of young worms to develop, suggest that the culture media may be nutritionally deficient and that the eggs contain too little yolk to sustain their development *in vitro*.

Neoechinorhyncus emydis
(Dunagan, 1962)

MEDIUM

Turtle serum. Turtles are bled aseptically at weekly intervals by puncture of the ventricle after a hole has been drilled through the plastron. At such intervals 10–15 ml of blood can be removed from a 10 in. turtle and the hole in the plastron closed with a collodion coated cork stopper. Serum not used immediately can be stored at −20°c.

Eagle's HeLa medium (p. 354).

Medium 199 (p. 355).

Washing solution. Tyrode's solution (p. 350) with a sodium chloride concentration of 0·9% containing 200 units/ml of penicillin G potassium and 1 mg/ml of streptomycin sulphate.

TECHNIQUE

On removal from the host (*Pseudemydis scripta*), the worms are washed 3 times in 0·7% sodium chloride followed by 3 times in washing solution. Cultures can be made either in 8 ml screw-capped test-tubes containing 2 ml medium or better still in dialysis tubing in an apparatus similar to that used by Smyth (p. 202). The cultures are incubated at 22–23°c and the worms can survive a pH range of 7·0–8·2.

Dunagan found the maximum period of survival to be 71 days in turtle serum alone (test tube culture), 90 days in medium 199 (pH 7·8) containing 3% turtle serum or 96 days in Eagle's HeLa Medium (pH 8·0) containing 20% calf serum.

Moniliformis dubius
(Nicholas & Grigg, 1965)

MEDIUM

Sterilizing solution. Hanks's saline (p. 350) containing 5 mg penicillin, 5 mg streptomycin, 2 mg nystatin, 7 mg crude tetracycline, and gassed with 5% carbon dioxide in nitrogen.

Eagle's medium (p. 355).

Serum. Inactivated bovine serum (heated to 56°c for ½ hr to destroy complement).

TECHNIQUE

A laboratory strain of *Moniliformis dubius* can be maintained in rats (definitive host) and cockroaches, *Periplaneta americana* (intermediate host). Rats can be infected by feeding 10–12 cystacanths taken from the haemocoel of the cockroach. Cockroaches are infected by feeding them large numbers of acanthors taken from a chopped up female worm.

Worms are obtained 6–12 weeks after the rats have been infected, incubated for 24 hr in the sterilizing solution and rinsed in sterile Ringer's solution before being cultured in 160 ml screw-capped flasks containing 11 ml of medium (either serum or Eagle's medium), 1 worm per flask. The flasks are gassed with a mixture of 5% carbon dioxide in nitrogen. The worms are transferred to new flasks containing fresh culture medium, daily throughout the 8 day experimental period, with a platinum wire hook and the flasks re-gassed. The flasks, square in section, are incubated (37–39°c) in a horizontal position to facilitate gaseous exchange.

In Nicholas & Grigg's experiments the worms survived and produced viable acanthors in these two media throughout their 8 day experimental period.

TABLE 8.1. Cultivation of Acanthocephala

Species	Stage	Maximum survival (days)	Author	Date
Macracanthorhynchus hirudinaceus	A	4 hr	von Brand	1940
	A	6	Ward	1951
Moniliformis dubius	A & L	8	Nicholas & Grigg	1965
Neoechinorhynchus emydis	A	15	van Cleave & Ross	1944
	A	96	Dunagan	1962
	A	25	Gettier	1942
Neoechinorhynchus pseudemydis	A	90	Dunagan	1962
Octospinifer macilentis	A	—	Harms	1963

A=Adult; L=Larva.

REFERENCES

BRAND T.VON (1940). Further observations upon the composition of Acantho-cephala. *J. Parasit.* **26**: 301–307.

CLEAVE H.J. VAN & ROSS E.L. (1944). Physiological responses of *Neoechinorhyncus emydis* (Acanthocephala) to various solutions. *J. Parasit.* **30**: 369–372.

DUNAGAN T.T. (1962). Studies on the *in vitro* survival of Acanthocephala. *Proc. helminth. Soc. Wash.* **29**: 131–135.

GETTIER D.A. (1942). Studies on the saline requirements of *Neoechinorhyncus emydis*. *Proc. helminth. Soc. Wash.* **9:** 75–78.

HARMS C.E. (1963). The development and cultivation of the acanthocephalan *Octospinifer maculentis* (Sic) Van Cleave, 1919. *Dissert. Abstr.* **23:** 2632–2633.

NICHOLAS W.L. & GRIGG H. (1965). The *in vitro* culture of *Moniliformis dubius* (Acanthocephala). *Expl Parasit.* **16:** 332–340.

WARD H.L. (1951). The use of antibiotics in artificial media for *in vitro* experiments with Acanthocephala. *J. Parasit.* **37:** 319.

PART THREE
APPENDIX

APPENDIX

GENERAL TECHNIQUES AND MEDIA
FOR CULTIVATION *IN VITRO*

Many techniques and media have been designed for the cultivation of parasites *in vitro* and several of these have been reviewed by Silverman (1963). Technical details will be found under the sections dealing with the relevant parasites. However, certain basic procedures are common to all methods of growing organisms *in vitro* and these will be dealt with briefly in this appendix. Further information can be obtained by consulting standard works on tissue culture (e.g. Hanks, 1955; Parker, 1961; Paul, 1965). In addition, for those interested in the cultivation of animal parasites of plants, the following are recommended: Chen *et al.*, 1961; Dropkin, 1966; Khera & Zuckerman, 1963; Krusberg, 1961; Sanwal, 1959; Tiner, 1966; Wallace, 1963; Webster & Lowe, 1966; White, 1954.

I. PREPARATION OF APPARATUS

One of the greatest hazards besetting *in vitro* cultivation is contamination with bacteria or fungi or with toxic chemicals. Consequently, great care must be taken to ensure that *all* parts of the culture apparatus are scrupulously clean and that they are properly sterilized before use.

1. GLASSWARE

Culture vessels can be made of many substances such as Perspex and other plastics, but glass is the material most commonly used because it is readily available and can be sterilized by heat.

Glass varies considerably in composition and may contain materials such as lead and arsenic, which are highly toxic to cells; these substances may be brought into solution slowly by the action of slightly alkaline media used in culture. There are, however, two types of glass which appear to be most satisfactory for culture work and these are the borosilicate glass made by Pyrex and the soda glass used for the production of most medical prescription bottles in England.

Cleaning of general glassware

After cotton wool plugs etc. have been removed, all glassware should be soaked in water as soon as it has been used so that deposits of protein do not dry on the glass. Glassware may be cleaned with either oxidizing acids, alkalies or detergents.

(a) Cleaning with oxidizing acids

Many workers clean glassware with strongly oxidizing acids. It is not absolutely necessary to use them for biological materials, but they certainly can be relied upon to remove all organic material and they probably etch glass less than alkalies. The ones most commonly used are sulphuric, nitric and in particular chromic acid. The great disadvantage of these is that they are highly corrosive and dangerous to handle. Chromic acid is prepared by placing 40 g of potassium dichromate into a large (5 l.) Pyrex beaker and adding a little water to dissolve it. Concentrated sulphuric acid is then added to a total volume of 1 l.: this produces a yellow-brown solution; when it has turned green the acid has become reduced, is no longer useful and should be discarded. Glassware should always be well rinsed before soaking for several hours in chromic acid (preferably overnight). Subsequent rinsing should be very thorough and final washing should be in glass distilled water.

Nitric acid is often used for cleaning small objects such as cover slips, after which they must be very thoroughly rinsed in distilled water. Finally cover slips should be rinsed in 95% alcohol, dried and polished before use.

Oxidizing acids are especially suitable for the cleaning of sintered glass bacterial filters. Such filters can be cleaned by allowing concentrated sulphuric acid (to which has been added a few crystals of sodium nitrate and sodium chlorate) to percolate through, after which they must be rinsed very thoroughly by passing large volumes of distilled or deionized water through them before they are dried and sterilized.

(b) Alkali cleaning

Cleaning with sodium metasilicate solution is probably the most popular method since it introduces no foreign ions to the glass and if a monolayer remains after cleaning it is deposited as glass on neutralization. However, soft soap, sodium triphosphate or sodium carbonate can be used equally well. It is best to have several large containers so that the glassware can be transferred from one to the other during the following cleaning procedure.

(i) Glassware should be scrubbed in water to remove debris and then transferred to boiling dilute metasilicate solution for 20 min.

Concentrated Metasilicate Solution ($\times 100$) is prepared as follows: sodium metasilicate 360 g and Calgon (Albright & Wilson) 40 g are dissolved in a gallon of water and filtered; *dilute* 1 part in 100 parts tapwater for boiling glassware.

(ii) After cooling, the glassware should be soaked for several hours in dilute (N/100) hydrochloric acid.

(iii) Glassware is then rinsed thoroughly, first in tapwater and second in deionized water, before being dried in an oven and prepared for sterilization.

(c) *Detergent cleaning*

The advantage of using detergents instead of alkalies is that no boiling or neutralization by hydrochloric acid is necessary, otherwise the procedure is the same as for alkali cleaning. Detergents are quite often used for cleaning glassware, but they should be used cautiously as they are difficult to remove and may be toxic to cells, so that very thorough washing indeed is required. Microsole (Microbiological Associates Inc.) is a detergent that has been developed especially for cleaning tissue culture glassware and is practically non-toxic. Other detergents that can be used are Haemosol (Meinecke & Co. Inc.), Alconox (Alconox Inc.), and 7x (Limbro Chemicals).

Cleaning pipettes

Cotton wool plugs should be removed from pipettes which can then be well washed in a siphon type pipette washer. After this they can *either* be soaked for several hours in chromic acid and thoroughly rinsed, *or* soaked for 24 hr in sodium metasilicate, quickly rinsed, soaked in N/100 hydrochloric acid and quickly rinsed again. To speed drying they can be rinsed finally in 95% ethyl alcohol.

Cleaning paraffined glassware

Most of the paraffin should be scraped off with a knife or it will most likely form a layer on the washing solution which may ultimately be deposited on all other glassware. Paraffined glassware should be soaked in a beaker (with a layer of gauze in the bottom to prevent damage) of sodium metasilicate solution and boiled. The scum of liquid paraffin can then be poured off and the partially cleaned articles cleaned in either of the ways described above for glassware.

23

Cleaning siliconed glassware

Silicone can be removed by heating in 0·5 N sodium hydroxide or by treating with alcoholic potassium hydroxide. In either case it is best to float the scum off as with paraffined objects, or the silicone may be disseminated to all the other material being cleaned at the same time. The glassware can then be cleaned by the chosen method.

2. VESSEL STOPPERS

Rubber bungs (or screw caps with rubber liners) are suitable for sealing culture vessels. Corks are not satisfactory because they cannot be easily sterilized and do not form a perfectly air-tight seal. Rubber bungs or screw cap liners however, contain toxic impurities and therefore have to be subjected to very thorough cleansing to remove all surface impurities. Thus if these have not been used for *in vitro* culture before, they should be boiled in dilute alkali (5% sodium carbonate) followed by exhaustive rinsing in distilled water. Even this treatment does little more than remove surface impurities and the rubber remains toxic. Great care therefore must be taken to ensure that culture media do not come into prolonged contact with the rubber by using culture vessels designed to prevent it (most vessels are so designed). As a further precaution either non-toxic white rubber stoppers (Esco (Rubber) Ltd.) or stoppers of silicone rubber may be used, but they are more expensive and are rarely necessary so long as care is taken when using rubber stoppers.

Rubber stoppers (unless of silicone rubber) cannot be sterilized by dry heat. They should be boiled in water for 5–10 min before use and then allowed to dry by evaporation in a sterile environment.

3. FLEXIBLE TUBING

In many cases where tubing is used the medium is exposed to it only briefly (e.g. in a dispensing apparatus) so that in these circumstances rarely is any trouble experienced from this source. However, continuous flow cultures are becoming increasingly popular and where these are used, silicone rubber tubing is to be recommended. This type of tubing can be sterilized by dry heat which is an added advantage.

4. INSTRUMENTS

All protective grease should be removed from new instruments by wiping with carbon tetrachloride followed by a wet cloth before they are dried and sterilized. Used instruments should be wiped clean and dry immediately after use and should be kept scrupulously clean. They can be sterilized either by dry heat or by boiling in water and allowing them to dry by evaporation in a sterile environment.

5. PREPARATION OF APPARATUS FOR STERILIZATION

Wherever possible, all pieces of apparatus should be plugged with non-absorbent cotton wool. Any apertures that are too large to be thus plugged should be covered with a tightly fitting piece of aluminium foil. If the apparatus is to be steam sterilized a further precaution of wrapping a piece of greaseproof paper or aluminium foil around the outside of the plug is often necessary to prevent the condensation of moisture within the apparatus. If bottles closed with screw caps or rubber bungs are to be heat sterilized they should be loosened during sterilization but closed immediately afterwards.

Bulky or specialized apparatus may be prepared for autoclaving by wrapping either in gauze or paper (this is especially necessary if the equipment is to be stored for any length of time). Pure kraft paper or aluminium foil may be used to wrap the apparatus or better still a paper (Patapar) specially designed for this purpose. The packages may be sealed with special autoclave adhesive tape (e.g. Scotch hospital autoclave tape No. 222, Minnesota Mining and Manufacturing Co. Ltd). Apparatus may be also wrapped in envelopes of nylon film (e.g. 'Portex' autoclave film, Portland Plastics Ltd). This is supplied in the form of a tube $\frac{1}{4}$–20 in. wide (0·6–50 cm) and may be sealed with autoclave tape to form bags; it is permeable to steam but not bacteria so that after removal from the autoclave the contents remain sterile until required.

The mouth-pieces of graduated pipettes should be plugged with non-absorbent cotton wool. Their tips can be rolled in aluminium foil and they can then be placed in metal canisters ready for sterilization. The canisters help to keep the pipettes clean and sterile before use. Pasteur pipettes need not be rolled in foil but can be sterilized in glass pipette holders ready for use.

Petri dishes should be sterilized in special canisters. If such a container is not available they may be sterilized in biscuit tins; however before using these for sterilizing glassware, they should be placed open in the oven and heated to sterilization temperatures for 2 or 3 hr. This drives off various volatile materials which would otherwise be transferred to the glassware. (N.B. some tins are lacquered inside and these are not suitable since the lacquer is burned or volatilized and the products are deposited on the glassware.)

II. STERILIZATION

One of the chief difficulties when culturing parasites *in vitro* is to avoid contamination with other micro-organisms (bacteria, fungi) which not only grow rapidly in the highly nutritious media used for culture but also may produce toxins which are lethal to parasites or animal cells. In work of this nature the chief sources of contamination are (i) the culture medium, (ii) the apparatus, (iii) the parasite to be cultured, (iv) the environment in which cultures are manipulated. Aseptic technique is an essential part of *in vitro* culture and is detailed in standard works such as Paul (1965) and Parker (1961). Media and equipment must also be sterile and it should be noted that some media, especially natural media, cannot be sterilized without damage and must therefore be prepared aseptically (e.g. chick embryo extract, p. 345).

Sterilization can be achieved either by the physical destruction of micro-organisms (e.g. by dry heat, moist heat, or irradiation), by the physical removal of micro-organisms (e.g. by filtration, centrifugation or washing), or by the chemical inhibition or destruction of micro-organisms (e.g. by antibiotics). These methods are briefly described below but further details can be obtained from standard works (e.g. Sleigh, 1965).

1. STERILIZATION BY DRY HEAT

In general, apparatus which is not damaged by high temperature can be sterilized in this way. This method cannot be used for liquid media or for rubber or plastic materials. The temperature and time of sterilization vary with the size of apparatus and expected type of contaminant but for general purposes 60 min at 160°C or 20 min at 180°C are effective (N.B. the apparatus must be held at the sterilization temperature for the full period).

2. STERILIZATION BY MOIST HEAT

This is usually carried out by autoclaving (sterilizing by steam under pressure) and is frequently used for solutions, rubber, cloth etc. Sterilization can be carried out in an autoclave at 15 lb pressure per sq. in. $(1 \cdot 05 \text{ kg/cm}^2)$ for 20 min $(121°\text{c})$, but 15 min should be used for solutions. The pressures and times vary with the size of apparatus or volume of liquid to be sterilized and large volumes should be autoclaved for longer periods (see Sleigh, 1965).

Liquids are usually autoclaved in partially filled vessels closed with cotton-wool plugs: if screw caps or rubber bungs are used they must be loosened during autoclaving and closed immediately afterwards.

It should be noted that bicarbonate solutions will lose carbon dioxide when autoclaved. Thus small volumes must be autoclaved in either small thick walled bottles (e.g. 30 ml Universal containers) which are filled completely and screwed up tightly before treatment or normal containers (with a loosely fitting cap) and the carbon dioxide replaced after autoclaving by bubbling the gas through a saturation flask containing 1% copper sulphate solution (to suppress moulds), then passing it through a sterile cotton filter (about 9×2 cm) and introducing it into the solution through a sterile pipette. Glucose solutions are also thermolabile but will withstand autoclaving at 10 lb pressure $(0 \cdot 7 \text{ kg})$ for 10 min. Protein solutions should never be sterilized by heating.

Boiling water (or normal saline) can also be used for moist heat sterilization and is convenient for rapid sterilization of syringes and instruments.

3. STERILIZATION BY IRRADIATION

Irradiation with ultra-violet light is often used to sterilize the atmosphere of a culture laboratory but it must be used with care since shadowed areas are unaffected. Also it is harmful to the eyes and skin and workers should use protective clothing or glasses.

Ionizing radiations (β, γ and X-rays) are used for sterilizing apparatus such as plastic syringes, plates and dishes but this is generally carried out at source and not in the laboratory.

4. STERILIZATION BY FILTRATION

Various filters are available; these should be sterilized by autoclaving before use:

(i) Kieselguhr (diatomaceous earth: e.g. Berkefeld W).

(ii) Porcelain filters (e.g. Selas 03).

(i) and (ii) are useful general purpose filters.

(iii)   Sintered (or fritted) glass filters are useful for small quantities of material but they have the disadvantage of filtering slowly and are difficult to clean.

(iv)   Asbestos filters (e.g. Seitz) have the advantage of effectively removing all micro-organisms whilst at the same time permitting a fairly high rate of filtration. They have the disadvantage that they sometimes release toxic substances into the filtrate and change its pH (House, 1964; Nydegger & Manwell, 1962). Thus these filters should be very thoroughly washed before use and often it is best to discard the initial filtrate (e.g. the first litre of solution passing through a 14 cm diameter pad).

(v) Membrane filters (e.g. 'Millipore' filters, Millipore Corporation) can be used instead of Seitz filters. They have the advantage of providing rapid filtration rates, they are completely inert and may be obtained with defined pore size. Also they are disposable and thus present no cleaning difficulties.

It is desirable to use positive pressure filtration for biological materials rather than negative pressure (suction) as the latter causes carbon dioxide to be evolved from solutions thus causing radical pH changes. Also protein solutions froth badly when a vacuum is applied. Both difficulties are avoided by using positive pressure.

The other physical methods of removing contaminants such as centrifugation and washing, although relatively inefficient, are not to be despised on occasions, particularly before filtration of contaminated solutions.

5. STERILIZATION WITH ANTIBIOTICS

To facilitate the handling of cultures, antibiotics are often included in culture media. Much work has been done on the effect of antibiotics on tissue cultures and has been summarized by Paul (1965, Chapter IX). In addition, parasites from unsterile environments can often be surface sterilized before *in vitro* culture by washing them several times in balanced saline solutions containing antibiotics.

III. PREPARATION OF MEDIA

Ideally the media used for culturing parasites, or any cells *in vitro* should be precisely defined. However, this ideal has seldom been achieved and the majority of workers in this field have been forced to use either entirely undefined media or defined media to which 'natural' products, such as serum, have been added. These media will be dealt with in the following two sections.

NATURAL MEDIA

1. TISSUE EXTRACTS

Many different media have been used together with extracts of tissues which appear to have enhanced the growth of the cells or organisms being cultured. The most popular of the tissue extracts has been chick embryo extract, and in addition to this various extracts of adult tissues have been used to good effect. The method of preparing such extracts is outlined below.

1 Chick embryo extract
Chick embryo extract varies considerably in composition depending upon the age of the embryos extracted, the diluent used for extracting them and the ratio of diluent to embryos. It is therefore important when using embryo extract to state precisely how it has been made. Since Weinstein & Jones (1956) were the first to use chick embryo extract for the successful cultivation of *Nippostrongylus*, their technique of preparation is cited below:
(i) The egg shell (containing a 9–12 day chick embryo) is wiped carefully with alcohol (70%).
(ii) The blunt end of the shell is cracked by gentle taps using a sterile instrument such as a scalpel handle.
(iii) Using a sterile pair of forceps, the shell is removed above the air sac to expose the membrane.
(iv) With another pair of sterile forceps the membrane is removed carefully to expose the embryo.
(v) A sterile curved pair of forceps is slipped under the neck of the embryo and it is gently lifted out of the shell and dropped into a covered sterile beaker embedded in dry ice to freeze it rapidly.
(vi) When the required number of embryos has been collected, chilled Earle's balance salt solution (p. 350) is added (1:1 ratio w/v) and they are homogenized for 60 sec in a Waring blender.
(vii) The homogenate is centrifuged at $1,000 \times g$ for 20 min at 0°c. The supernatant is dispensed into small sterile bottles and is known as 50% chick embryo extract (50% CEE; CEE_{50}). It may be stored frozen at −20°c (up to 6 weeks) and should first be tested for sterility by inoculation into suitable bacteriological media.

Slightly different techniques have been used for tissue culture as follows:

(i) The whole procedure is carried out at room temperature.

(ii) The embryos are washed three times in the balanced saline, to remove all blood and yolk, before homogenizing the embryos alone (without any diluent) in a stainless steel tissue extractor or failing that 2–3 embryos may be placed in the barrel of a 20 ml syringe and their juice gently expressed into a sterile centrifuge tube.

(iii) The embryo juice is diluted with the balanced saline of choice, stirred with a sterile glass rod and left to stand for 30 min.

(iv) The embryo extract is centrifuged at $2,000 \times g$ for 20 min.

(v) Before use it is thawed slowly and recentrifuged at $2,000 \times g$ for 10 min to remove the precipitate which will have been formed by freezing and thawing (N.B. Weinstein & Jones make no mention of recentrifuging their extracts before use).

2 Other tissue extracts

(a) Raw liver extract (Weinstein, 1953).
Livers of 3–4 month old rats are processed in the same way as for the preparation of Weinstein & Jones's chick embryo extract, and the concentration of the final extract is expressed in a similar manner.

(b) Alternative methods of preparation
It should be noted that tissue extracts may be of 2 types according to their method of preparation. They can be prepared either with a minimum of damage to the cells, by using the syringe technique or a stainless steel tissue extractor, or with complete destruction of the cells by homogenizing them in a Waring blender or a glass tissue homogenizer (Potter Elvehjem type). The latter type of tissue homogenate should be used with care since in high concentrations it can be quite toxic. In addition to this tissues have been extracted with acid for the cultivation of the nematodes Hyostrongylus and Oesophagostomum (Diamond & Douvres, 1962; p. 299).

Other supplements such as yeast extract, lactalbumin or casein hydrolysate and meat broths have been used in culture media. Generally these have been obtained commercially and will be mentioned under the relevant culture techniques.

2. BLOOD PRODUCTS

Blood and its various fractions are widely used in undefined culture media. The donor species most commonly used in the laboratory are the rabbit and the chicken. Blood of larger mammals (horse, ox, sheep) can be obtained commercially (e.g. from Burroughs Wellcome & Co.).

1 *Whole blood*

This must be collected aseptically, using sterile equipment since the composition of blood will be altered by sterilization. Clotting can be prevented in two ways:

(i) *Anticoagulants* such as heparin should be added to the collection vessel before use and may be used in powder form or dissolved in saline. One international unit of heparin is sufficient to prevent clotting of 5 ml of blood but concentrations of 1, 10 or 100 units/ml of blood are often used.

(ii) *Defibrination* of the blood prevents clotting and can be achieved by gently rotating the blood in a sterile vessel containing small glass beads for 10–15 min.

Blood may be collected by heart or venepuncture:

(i) Heart puncture. Chickens or rabbits should be anaesthetized with pentobarbitone sodium* at 25 mg/kg body weight by intravenous or intramuscular inoculation.

Rabbits but not chickens may also be anaesthetized with ether. The procedure for chickens is illustrated in Fig. A.1, and described in detail by Paul (1965): the skin must first be plucked and sterilized with tincture of iodine followed by ethanol. A similar technique can be used with rabbits.

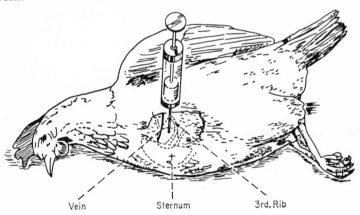

Vein   Sternum   3rd. Rib

FIGURE A.1 Illustration of method of obtaining blood from a chicken by heart-puncture. (From Paul, 1965.)

* Nembutal (Abbott Laboratories) or Sagatal (May and Baker).

(ii) *Venepuncture*. With chickens the vein of choice is the brachial or jugular vein, with rabbits the marginal ear vein (see Paul, 1965 for full details). A convenient way of adding rabbit blood to a series of small bottles has been described by Wenyon (1926). The rabbit is held on a sack on a table (or if necessary it can be restrained in a special box, see Fig. A.2) and the skin over the marginal vein shaved, sterilized and thinly coated with molten paraffin wax (melting point 45°c). The vein is then opened with a sterile scalpel blade or Hagedoorn needle and the blood allowed to drip into the collecting vessels.

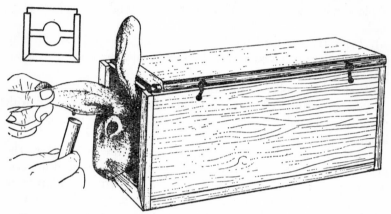

FIGURE A.2 Method of obtaining blood from marginal ear vein of rabbit. The inset shows the end of the box with hole for passage of rabbit's neck: the upper piece is removable. A spring-loaded false inner back to the box is a convenient way of accommodating rabbits of different sizes. (From Wenyon, 1926, slightly modified.)

The sterility of the collected blood should be tested by inoculating small portions into tubes of nutrient broth, or other bacterial growth medium, and incubating for 24 hr at 37°c and 28°c. Bacterial contamination is evidenced by cloudiness or precipitation.

Whole blood may be stored at 4°c, but it is preferable to use it within 2–7 days (2 days for heparinated blood; 7 days for defibrinated blood).

Inactivation of blood is achieved by heating at 56°c for ½ hr: this results in the denaturing of complement.

2 Plasma

Plasma is obtained from whole blood by centrifugation to remove the blood cells. To prevent clotting, anticoagulant must be added to the blood (see 1) but if the plasma is to be used later to form a clot then the blood must either contain a *minimum* quantity of anticoagulant or it can be collected carefully in siliconed tubes without any anticoagulant, preferably on ice. It may be stored at −20°c or freeze-dried (Strumia, 1954).

3 *Serum*

The collection of serum is straightforward for whole blood is simply allowed to coagulate and the supernatant fluid removed. Clotting may be accelerated by keeping the blood at 37°c for 1 hr; when the clot has formed it is gently separated from the sides of the vessel with a sterile glass rod and then held at 4°c overnight to contract the clot. The supernatant fluid may be centrifuged to remove blood cells and increase the yield of serum.

Serum may be inactivated as for whole blood. It may be stored at −20°c or freeze-dried (Strumia, 1954).

DEFINED MEDIA

Only the purest chemicals should be used in the preparation of culture media and the use of double or even triple glass-distilled water is generally recommended.

1. BALANCED SALT SOLUTIONS BSS

The balanced salt solutions used for *in vitro* cultivation have three main functions: (a) to serve as diluting and irrigating fluids while maintaining tonicity in the cells: (b) to provide buffers to bring the medium to and maintain it in the physiological pH range (7·2–7·6) and (c) to provide the water and inorganic ions needed for normal cell metabolism. *Phenol red* is usually added at 1–5 mg % w/v.

To simplify pH control, sodium bicarbonate is often omitted from balanced salt solutions when they are prepared and is added later to the medium as required. For this purpose a 3% solution of sodium bicarbonate is filtered by positive pressure (to retain the carbon dioxide) and stored in tightly stoppered containers. This may then be used to adjust the pH of the culture medium after preparation.

Calcium and magnesium chloride should be dissolved separately from the other ingredients to avoid risk of precipitation.

Ringer's frog solution (Ringer, 1895; see Parker, 1961, p. 55).

	g/l.
NaCl	6·5
KCl	0·14
$CaCl_2$	0·12
$NaHCO_3$	0·20

Dissolved in 1 l. double distilled water and sterilized by filtration.

Ringer-Locke solution (Locke, 1901)

	g/l.
NaCl	9·0
KCl	0·42
$CaCl_2$	0·24
$NaHCO_3$	0·2
Glucose	1·0

Dissolved in 1 l. double distilled water and sterilized by filtration.

Tyrode's solution (1910)

	g/l.
NaCl	8·0
KCl	0·2
$CaCl_2$	0·2
$MgCl_2.6H_2O$	0·1
$NaH_2PO_4.H_2O$	0·05
$NaHCO_3$	1·0
Glucose	1·0

Dissolved in 1 l. double distilled water and sterilized by filtration. Tyrode's solution is designed for use saturated with oxygen.

Earle's solution (1943)

	g/l.
NaCl	6·8
KCl	0·4
$CaCl_2$	0·2
$MgSO_4.7H_2O$	0·2
$NaH_2PO_4.H_2O$	0·14
$NaHCO_3$	2·2
Glucose	1·0

All except $NaHCO_3$ are dissolved in 1 l. double distilled water (solution 1) and $NaHCO_3$ made up as 10% (w/v) solution in double distilled water (solution 2). Both solutions are sterilized by filtration. Solution 2 ($NaHCO_3$) is adjusted to pH 7·0 with sterile CO_2 and 22 ml then added to solution 1.

Hanks's solution (Hanks & Wallace, 1949)

	g/l.
NaCl	8·0
KCl	0·4
$CaCl_2$	0·14
$MgSO_4.7H_2O$	0·2
$Na_2HPO_4.12H_2O$	0·15
KH_2PO_4	0·06
$NaHCO_3$	0·35
Glucose	1·0

Dissolved in 1 l. double distilled water and sterilized by filtration.

2. CHEMICALLY DEFINED CULTURE MEDIA

Chemically defined media are usually very complicated; culture medium NCTC-109 has been chosen as a typical complex medium and full preparatory details are given below. Other culture media are cited with their ingredients only and the original publications must be consulted for preparatory details.

Culture medium NCTC-109
(Evans *et al.*, 1956a, b; McQuilkin *et al.*, 1957)

Amino acids	mg/100 ml
L-Alanine	3·148
L-α-Aminobutyric Acid	0·551
L-Arginine	2·576
L-Asparagine	0·809
L-Aspartic Acid	0·991
L-Cystine	1·049
L-Glutamine	13·573
L-Glutamic Acid	0·826
Glycine	1·351
L-Histidine	1·973
L-Hydroxyproline	0·409
L-Isoleucine	1·804
L-Leucine	2·044
L-Lysine	3·075
L-Methionine	0·444
L-Ornithine	0·738
L-Phenylalanine	1·653
L-Proline	0·613
L-Serine	1·075
L-Taurine	0·418
L-Threonine	1·893
L-Tryptophan	1·750
L-Tyrosine	1·644
L-Valine	2·500

Enzymes and co-enzymes	
DPN Diphosphopyridine nucleotide (Cozymase, Co-enzyme 1)	0·70
TPN Triphosphopyridine nucleotide (sodium salt)	0·10
Co-enzyme A	0·25
Cocarboxylase	0·10
Flavin adenine dinucleotide	0·10
Uridine triphosphate (sodium salt)	0·10

Reducing agents	mg/100 ml
Cysteine hydrochloride	25·99
Glutathione (monosodium salt)	1·01
Ascorbic acid (Vitamin C)	4·99

Nucleic acid derivatives	
Deoxyadenosine	1·00
Deoxycytidine-HCl	1·00
Deoxyguanosine	1·00
Thymidine	1·00
5-Methylcytosine	0·01

Vitamins	
Thiamine-HCl (B_1)	0·0025
Riboflavin (B_2)	0·0025
Pyridoxine-HCl (B_6)	0·00625
Pyridoxal-HCl	0·00625
Niacin	0·00625
Niacinamide (Nicotinamide)	0·00625
Calcium pantothenate (D)	0·0025
Biotin	0·0025
Folic acid	0·0025
Choline chloride	0·125
i-Inositol	0·0125
p-Aminobenzoic acid	0·0125
Vitamin A (crystalline alcohol)	0·025
Vitamin D (calciferol)	0·025
Vitamin K (Menadione)	0·0025
Vitamin E (disodium α-tocopherol phosphate)	0·0025
Vitamin B_{12}	0·01 mg/ml

Inorganic salts	
Sodium chloride	680·0
Sodium bicarbonate	220·0
Potassium chloride	40·0
Calcium chloride	20·0
Magnesium sulphate	20·0
Sodium phosphate (monobasic)	14·0

Culture medium *NCTC*-109—*contd.*

Miscellaneous	mg/100 ml		mg/100 ml
D-Glucosamine (amino sugar)	...0·320	Tween-80	1·25
Glucose (Dextrose)	100·0	Sodium acetate	5·0
Glucuronolactone	0·18	*Antibiotics*	μg/ml
Sodium glucuronate	0·18	Oleandomycin phosphate	3·33
Phenol red	2·0	Tetracycline- HCl	6·67

Preparation of stock solution concentrates

Double distilled water is used throughout.

1 Amino acids

These are made up in Earle's saline (containing 3 times the normal concentration of salts) at 8·5 times the final concentration (omitting L-cystine and L-tyrosine).

L-cystine and L-tyrosine (52·45 mg and 82·2 mg respectively) are dissolved in 0·075 N HCl and brought to a volume of 50 ml with distilled water.

2 Vitamins

(a) Water soluble B vitamins

(i) 12·5 mg niacin and 25 mg *p*-aminobenzoic acid are dissolved in boiling distilled water and made up to 25 ml.

(ii) 12·5 mg niacinamide, 12·5 mg pyridoxine hydrochloride, 12·5 mg pyridoxal hydrochloride, 5 mg thiamine hydrochloride, 5 mg calcium pantothenate, 25 mg *i*-inositol and 250 mg choline chloride are dissolved in distilled water and made up to 25 ml.

(iii) 10 mg riboflavin are added to 10 ml 0·075 N HCl then 5 ml 0·2 N NaOH are added and heated very gently. Finally the solution is made up to 20 ml with distilled water.

(iv) 25 ml of (i) are combined with 25 ml of (ii) and 10 ml of (iii) and made up to a final volume of 100 ml with distilled water.

(b) Biotin

10 mg of D-biotin are dissolved in 50 ml distilled water acidified with 1 ml N HCl and made up to a final volume of 100 ml with distilled water.

(c) Folic acid

10 mg folic acid are dissolved in 100 ml distilled water at 80°C.

(d) *Lipid soluble vitamins, A, D and K*

An alcoholic tincture of each of these 3 vitamins is used for the first stage solution. 10 mg of calciferol(vitamin D) are dissolved in 2 ml ethanol in a 100 ml volumetric flask. 10 mg of vitamin A alcohol are dissolved in this solution. 0·1 ml of menadione (vitamin K; 10 mg/ml alcohol) is then added. 10 ml of 5% aqueous Tween 80 are also added to the pooled vitamins and the final volume made up to 100 ml with distilled water.

(e) *Vitamin E*

10 mg disodium α-tocopherol phosphate are made up to a volume of 100 ml with distilled water.

The above 5 vitamin stock solutions are combined in proportions of 2 ml (a); 1 ml each, biotin and folic acid (b & c); 10 ml (d) and 1 ml (e) and made up to 26 ml with distilled water.

Store at 4°c.

3 *Reducing agents*

Ascorbic acid, 20·8 mg; cysteine hydrochloride, 108·3 mg; Glutathione, 4·2 mg are made up to 25 ml in distilled water.

4 *Co-enzyme mixture*

Diphosphopyridine nucleotide, 2·1 mg; triphosphopyridine nucleotide, 0·3 mg (65% pure); Co-enzyme A, 0·75 mg (70–75% pure); thiamine hydrochloride, 0·3 mg; flavine adenine dinucleotide, 0·3 mg (58·2% pure); uridine triphosphate, 0·3 mg (90% pure).

Make up to 15 ml in distilled water (this mixture is made up freshly each time the defined medium is prepared).

5 *Nucleic acid derivatives*

(i) Deoxyadenosine, 3·0 mg; (ii) deoxycytidine hydrochloride, 3·0 mg; (iii) deoxyguanosine, 3·0 mg; (iv) thymidine, 3·0 mg; (v) 0·01% solution of 5-methylcytosine in distilled water.

(i)–(iv) are added to 10 ml distilled water. 0·3 ml of (v) is added and the whole is made up to 15 ml in distilled water.

6 *Glucuronic acid mixture*

Sodium acetate, 100 mg; glucuronolactone, 3·6 mg; sodium glucuronate, 3·6 mg; glutamine, 200 mg are made up to 100 ml in distilled water.

7 *Phenol red*

Five hundred milligrammes phenol red are dissolved in 15 ml of 0·1 N NaOH and the solution is made up to 100 ml in distilled water. This is dispensed in 1·0 ml aliquots, autoclaved and freeze dried for storage. Reconstitute before use at 2·0 mg/20 ml in Earle's saline.

Volumes of stock solutions to make up final medium

	ml
Amino acids	12·0
Tyrosine and cystine	1·0
Vitamin mixture	0·65
Reducing mixture	6·0
Co-enzyme mixture	5·0
Nucleic acid derivatives	5·0
Glucuronic acids	5·0
Double distilled water	1·05
Phenol red	20·0
Earle's saline (single concentration)	44·3
Total	100·0 (per cent by volume)

Unused aliquots of medium may be stored for up to 1 month at 5°C and warmed to 37°C just before using.

Eagle's basal media for the cultivation of HeLa cells and, in brackets where different, mouse fibroblasts (Eagle, 1955).

L-Amino acids   mM

Arginine	0·1	
Cystine	0·05	(0·02)
Glutamine	2·0	(1·0)
Histidine	0·05	(0·02)
Isoleucine	0·2	
Leucine	0·2	(0·1)
Lysine	0·2	(0·1)
Methionine	0·05	
Phenylalanine	0·1	(0·05)
Threonine	0·2	(0·1)
Tryptophan	0·02	(0·01)
Tyrosine	0·1	
Valine	0·2	(0·1)

Vitamins

Biotin	10^{-3}
Choline	10^{-3}
Folic acid	10^{-3}
Nicotinamide	10^{-3}

    mM

Pantothenic acid	10^{-3}
Pyridoxal	10^{-3}
Thiamine	10^{-3}
Riboflavin	10^{-4}

Salts

NaCl	100
KCl	5
$NaH_2PO_4.H_2O$	1
$NaHCO_3$	20
$CaCl_2$	1
$MgCl_2$	0·5

Miscellaneous

Glucose	5
Penicillin	0·005%
Streptomycin	0·005%
Phenol red	0·0005%

Serum	5–10%

A further modification of this medium appears on p. 239, for the cultivation of *Taenia crassiceps*.

Eagle's minimum essential culture medium (Eagle, 1959).

L-amino acids	mM	mg/l.
Arginine	0·6	105
Cystine	0·1	24
Glutamine	2·0	292
Histidine	0·2	31
Isoleucine	0·4	52
Leucine	0·4	52
Lysine	0·4	58
Methionine	0·1	15
Phenylalanine	0·2	32
Threonine	0·4	48
Tryptophan	0·05	10
Tyrosine	0·2	36
Valine	0·4	46

Carbohydrate		
Glucose	5·5	1,000

Serum	5–10%	

Salts	mM	mg/l.
NaCl	116	6,800
KCl	5·4	400
CaCl₂	1·8	200
MgCl₂.6H₂O	1·0	200
NaH₂PO₄.2H₂O	1·1	150
NaHCO₃	23·8	2,000

Vitamins	
Choline	1
Folic acid	1
Inositol	2
Nicotinamide	1
Pantothenate	1
Pyridoxal	1
Riboflavin	0·1
Thiamine	1

Medium 199 (Morgan et al., 1950).

Amino acids	mg/l.
DL-Alanine	50·0
L-Arginine	70·0
DL-Aspartic acid	60·0
Cysteine	0·1
L-Cystine	20·0
DL-Glutamic acid	150·0
L-Glutamine	100·0
Glycine	50·0
L-Histidine	20·0
L-Hydroxyproline	10·0
DL-Isoleucine	40·0
DL-Leucine	120·0
L-Lysine	70·0
DL-Methionine	30·0
DL-Phenylalanine	50·0
L-Proline	40·0
DL-Serine	50·0
DL-Threonine	60·0
DL-Tryptophan	20·0
L-Tyrosine	40·0
DL-Valine	50·0

Vitamins	
Thiamin	0·010
Riboflavin	0·010
Pyridoxine	0·025

	mg/l.
Pyridoxal	0·025
Niacin	0·025
Niacinamide	0·025
Pantothenate	0·010
Biotin	0·010
Folic acid	0·010
Choline	0·500
Inositol	0·050
p-Aminobenzoic acid	0·050
Vitamin A	0·100
Calciferol (Vitamin D)	0·100
Menadione (Vitamin K)	0·010
α-Tocopherol phosphate (Vitamin E)	0·010
Ascorbic acid	0·050
Glutathione	0·050

Inorganic salts	
NaCl	6800·0
KCl	400·0
CaCl₂	200·0
MgSO₄.7H₂O	200·0
NaH₂PO₄.H₂O	140·0
NaHCO₃	2200·0
Fe₂(NO₃)₃.9H₂O	0·1

24

Medium 199—*contd.*

Miscellaneous	mg/l.		mg/l.
Adenine	10·00	Tween 80 (oleic acid)	20·00
Guanine	0·30	Cholesterol	0·20
Xanthine	0·30	Sodium acetate	50·00
Hypoxanthine	0·30	Adenosine triphosphate	10·00
Thymine	0·30	Adenylic acid	0·20
Uracil	0·30	Ribose	0·50
		Desoxyribose	0·50

Medium 150 (Morgan *et al.*, 1955).

Medium 199 with the substitution of Hanks's balanced salt solution (p. 350) for Earle's balanced salt solution as shown above.

CMRL-1066 (Parker, *et al.*, 1957; see Parker 1961, p. 74)

Amino acids	mg/l.		mg/l.
L-Alanine	25·0	Pyridoxine-HCl	0·025
L-Arginine-HCl	70·0	Riboflavin	0·01
L-Aspartic acid	30·0	Thiamine-HCl	0·01
L-Cysteine-HCl.H_2O	260·0	Ascorbic acid (Vitamin C)	50·0
L-Cystine	20·0	*Inorganic salts*	
L-Glutamic acid	75·0	NaCl	6800·0
L-Glutamine	100·0	KCl	400·0
Glycine	50·0	$CaCl_2$	200·0
L-Histidine-HCl.H_2O	20·0	$MgSO_4.7H_2O$	200·0
Hydroxy-L-Proline	10·0	$NaH_2PO_4.H_2O$	140·0
L-Isoleucine	20·0	$NaHCO_3$	2200·0
L-Leucine	60·0	*Miscellaneous*	
L-Lysine-HCl	70·0	Deoxyadenosine	10·0
L-Methionine	15·0	Deoxycytidine	10·0
L-Phenylalanine	25·0	Deoxyguanosine	10·0
L-Proline	40·0	5-Methyldeoxycytidine	0·1
L-Serine	25·0	Thymidine	10·0
L-Threonine	30·0	Cocarboxylase	1·0
L-Tryptophan	10·0	Co-enzyme A	2·5
L-Tyrosine	40·0	Diphosphopyridine nucleotide	7·0
L-Valine	25·0	Flavin adenine dinucleotide	1·0
		Triphosphopyridine nucleotide	1·0
Vitamins		Uridine triphosphate	1·0
p-Aminobenzoic acid	0·05	Tween 80 (oleic acid)	5·0
Biotin	0·01	Cholesterol	0·2
Calcium pantothenate	0·01	Glucose	1000·0
Choline chloride	0·50	Glutathione	10·0
Folic acid	0·01	Sodium acetate.$3H_2O$	83·0
Inositol	0·05	Sodium glucuronate.H_2O	4·2
Niacin	0·025	Ethanol (as diluent for fat	
Niacinamide	0·025	soluble constituents)	16·0
Pyridoxal-HCl	0·025		

Grace's (1966) insect tissue culture medium

Used for the cultivation of *Macacanema formosana* (see p. 312).

Media for plant tissues

(i) *White's medium* (1934, 1939; see Paul, 1965 p. 107)

	mg/l.
$Ca(NO_3)_2$	200·0
$MgSO_4$	360·0
Na_2SO_4	200·0
KNO_3	80·0
KCl	65·0
NaH_2PO_4	16·5
KI	0·75
$Fe_2(SO_4)_3$	2·5
$MnSO_4$	4·5
$ZnSO_4$	1·5
H_3BO_3	1·5
Glycine	3·0
Thiamine	0·1
Niacin	0·5
Pyridoxine	0·1
Sucrose	20,000

(ii) *Gautheret's medium* (1942; see Paul, 1965 p. 107)

	mg/l.		mg/l.
$Ca(NO_3)_2$	100·0	Glucose	30,000·0
KNO_3	25·0	Agar	6,000·0
$MgSO_4$	25·0	Cysteine-HCl	10·0
KH_2PO_4	25·0	Thiamine	1·0
$Fe_2(SO_4)_3$	50·0	Calcium pantothenate	0·1
$MnSO_4$	2·0	Biotin	0·1
KI	0·5	Inositol	100·0
$ZnSO_4$	0·1	Naphthalene acetic acid	0·3
H_3BO_3	0·15		
$Ti_2(SO_4)_3$	0·2		
$NiSO_4$	0·05		
$CoCl_2$	0·05		
$CuSO_4$	0·05		

IV. TISSUE CULTURE

Several parasitologists have endeavoured to cultivate parasites in the presence of the tissues of their hosts. For this reason, the basic methods of tissue culture will be outlined here.

1. PREPARATION OF TISSUES

1   *Vertebrate tissues*

Tissues may be obtained from two fundamentally different sources, either embryos or adults. Embryonic tissues are initially sterile and grow more readily *in vitro* than adult tissues. Thus embryonic, or immediately post-natal chick, mouse or rat tissues are probably the most useful for the cultivation of the vertebrate phase of the parasite's life-cycle. Great care must be taken to ensure that the desired tissue remains sterile during and after removal from the donor animal. Before use the tissue must be cut into small fragments suitable for the desired culture method.

Generally it is best to set up cultures as soon as possible after the tissue has been obtained (within 2–4 hr) but it is possible to store tissues for 2 days before use in a nutrient solution in the refrigerator.

2   *Invertebrate tissues*

The tissues used by parasitologists have been mainly insect tissues. The greatest difficulty encountered here is that of maintaining sterility. The insect donor should be washed well in iodine, merthiolate or other sterilizing solutions before the required tissue is aseptically removed. Where the tissue itself is likely to be contaminated, washing several times in solutions of antibiotics in a balanced saline solution reduces such contamination to a minimum. Specialized culture media have been devised for insect tissues and have been referred to earlier (p. 312 and Grace, 1966; Jones, 1962; Trager, 1959).

3   *Plant tissues*

The same principles apply here as for animal tissues, namely aseptic removal of tissue and or disinfection, the main difference being the composition of the culture medium. Plants can be prepared aseptically with comparative ease. For example it is only necessary to break open a disinfected carrot and remove a small piece with a sterile cork borer, to obtain very good material for culture purposes. Similarly potato, beetroot and other root tissues can be obtained and these are frequently used for the cultivation of plant parasites, particularly nematodes.

Culture of carrot callus (see Paul, 1965)

The tissue is grown on a solid substrate. Several test tubes (15 × 2·5 cm) are prepared by inoculating each with 10 ml of White's medium and adding a pad of 4 thicknesses of filter paper. A healthy carrot is cleaned thoroughly, broken to expose a sterile surface and a core of about 5 mm diameter removed with a sterile cork borer. This is transferred to a Petri dish and sliced into discs. One or two of these are placed on the filter pad in each tube, which is then capped with aluminium foil and placed at an angle in a rack so that the paper is kept moist but the explants are not immersed. A modification of this technique involves replacing the filter pad with agar in the medium to form a semi-solid substrate and the explants are then grown on the surface (see Gautheret's medium, p. 357).

2. CULTIVATION OF ANIMAL TISSUES

Most of the methods are similar in principle, the main difference being the types of vessels used for growing the tissues. The most common ones used by parasitologists are slide cultures, Carrel flasks and test-tube cultures. In addition to these some workers have used specially designed apparatus for continuous flow cultures and these are described under the relevant sections.

1   Slide cultures

These are more suitable for protozoan cultures than for helminths; they may be prepared, with the usual sterility precautions, as follows.

The prepared tissue explants should be placed in culture medium in a watch glass. Coverslips are laid out on a sterile surface, the small pieces of tissue drawn up into a Pasteur pipette and one piece deposited in the centre of each coverslip. Any fluid can be drawn off and one measured drop replaced on the tissue. The fluid is then spread out in a thin circular film with the tissue protruding from the centre of it. *Immediately*, a depression slide, ringed with petroleum jelly, must be applied to the coverslip and the whole turned over quickly to prevent any fluid running between slide and coverslip. The coverslip should then be sealed to the slide with paraffin and the slide incubated in the upright or inverted position; the cells of the explant should grow directly on the glass coverslip.

Slide cultures are most suitable for short-term experiments since transferring them to fresh media is both difficult and tedious. They are however useful for microscopical studies on parasitic protozoa *in vitro*. Various perfusion chambers have been devised for long-term cultures (Pitts & Ball, 1958, see p. 267; Paul, 1965, pp. 309–312) which enable the culture medium to be constantly changed without disturbing the coverslip. In addition the effect of different media on the activity and/or morphology of the organisms can be followed easily with the phase-contrast microscope.

2 Carrel flask and test-tube cultures

The wide necks of the vessels facilitate manipulation of the tissues and changing of the media; larger volumes of media can be used which make it possible for chemical assays to be carried out. In addition to this the gas-phase can be readily controlled; such cultures can be maintained for as long as the tissue or parasite will survive *in vitro*. Good Carrel flasks have an advantage over test tubes in that they have excellent optical properties and thus the cultures can be examined microscopically during the experiment; this is more difficult with test tubes but can be achieved with special techniques (Leland, 1961; Trevan, 1961). However, in in both cases large numbers of cultures can be set up at one time which is an advantage over slide cultures.

(a) Technique of preparation

A plasma clot is used both as a fixative to maintain the explants in position and as a substrate on which the tissues can commence growth.

(i) A drop of plasma is placed in position (on the floor of the Carrel flask or on the wall of the test tube) and spread out into a thin area with a spatula.

(ii) The desired number of explants is then transferred to this and clotting allowed to take place.

(iii) After the plasma has clotted, thus firmly fixing the explants in position, the culture medium can be added.

(iv) The vessels can be gassed when desired, and then quickly stoppered.

(v) Carrel flasks should then be stood in an incubator. Test tubes may either be incubated in racks (standing position) or in a roller culture apparatus (supplied by Matburn Ltd).

(b) Renewal of medium

(i) The old fluid is drawn off by means of a pipette and put aside for chemical assay if required.

(ii) This is then replaced with an appropriate volume of fresh medium.

(iii) The vessel is again gassed before stoppering if required.

V. BAERMANN APPARATUS
for the collection of nematode larvae

This consists of a funnel leading into a rubber tube closed with a clip. In the funnel rests a metal sieve with a 1 mm mesh and of a size which permits fluid in the funnel (usually 0·85% NaCl) to rise about 2·5 cm above the bottom of the sieve. This is lined with cotton fabric to prevent particles such as soil from falling through the sieve. The larval culture is allowed to stand in this apparatus for some time during which the larvae tumble through the interstices of the soil and collect in the rubber tube. As soon as the clip is opened they are washed out into a vessel set to catch the first drops which escape.

VI. HANDLING OF PROTOZOAN CULTURES

Almost all cultures of parasitic Protozoa (except those of the Sporozoa) are grown in simple containers such as test-tubes, screw-capped bottles, or flasks. Removal of small volumes of medium for examination or subinoculation can be done with either a bacteriological wire loop, sterilized by heating to redness in a Bunsen burner flame, or a sterile Pasteur pipette.

NOTE: Cultures containing organisms pathogenic to man (e.g. *Entamoeba histolytica*, *Balantidium coli*, *Trypanosoma cruzi*, *T.rangeli*, *T.rhodesiense*, *Plasmodium* spp. and tissue cultures of *Toxoplasma*), must be autoclaved or otherwise sterilized before disposal. Apparatus used for sampling and examining such cultures must also be sterilized immediately after use.

REFERENCES

CHEN T., KILPATRICK R.A. & RICH A.E. (1961). Sterile culture techniques as tools in plant nematology research. *Phytopathology* **51**: 799–800.

DIAMOND L.S. & DOUVRES F.W. (1962). Bacteria-free cultivation of some parasitic stages of the swine nematodes *Hyostrongylus rubidus* and *Oesophagostomum quadrispinulatum* (*O.longicaudum*). *J. Parasit.* **48**: 39–42.

DROPKIN V.H. (1966). Physiology of nematodes of the soil. *Ann. N.Y. Acad. Sci.* **139**: 39–52.

EAGLE H. (1955). Nutrition needs of mammalian cells in tissue culture. *Science, N.Y.* **122**: 501–504.

EAGLE H. (1959). Amino acid metabolism in mammalian cell cultures. *Science, N.Y.* **130**: 432–437.

EARLE W.R. (1943). Propagation of malignancy *in vitro*. IV. The mouse fibroblast cultures and changes seen in living cells. *J. Nat. Cancer Inst.* **4:** 165–212.

EVANS V.J., BRYANT J.C., FIORAMONTI M.C., McQUILKIN W.T., SANFORD K.K. & EARLE W.R. (1956a). Studies of nutrient media for tissue cells *in vitro*. I. A protein-free chemically defined medium for cultivation of strain *L* cells. *Cancer Res.* **16:** 77–86.

EVANS V.J., BRYANT J.C., McQUILKIN W.T., FIORAMONTI M.C., SANFORD K.K., WESTFALL B.B. & EARLE W.R. (1956b). Studies of nutrient media for tissue cells *in vitro*. II. An improved chemically defined medium for long-term cultivation of strain L-929 cells. *Cancer Res.* **16:** 87–94.

GAUTHERET R.J. (1942). *Manuel technique de culture des tissus végétaux:* 172. Paris: Masson.

GRACE T.D.C. (1966). Establishment of a line of mosquito (*Aedes aegypti*) cells grown *in vitro*. *Nature, Lond.* **211:** 366–367.

HANKS J.H. & Staff of the Cooperstown Course (1955). *An introduction to cell and tissue culture*. Minneapolis: Burgess Publishing Co.

HANKS J.H. & WALLACE R.E. (1949). Relation of oxygen and temperature in the preservation of tissues by refrigeration. *Proc. Soc. exp. Biol. Wash.* **71:** 196.

HOUSE W. (1964). Toxicity of cell culture medium due to filtration through asbestos filter pads. *Nature, Lond.* **201:** 1242.

JONES B.M. (1962). The cultivation of insect cells and tissues. *Biol. Rev.* **37:** 512–536.

KHERA S. & ZUCKERMAN B.M. (1963). *In vitro* studies of host-parasite relationships of some plant parasitic nematodes. *Nematologica* **9:** 1–6.

KRUSBERG L.R. (1961). Studies on the culturing and parasitism of plant parasitic nematodes, in particular *Ditylenchus dipsaci* and *Aphelenchoides ritzemabosi* on alfalfa tissues. *Nematologica* **6:** 181.

LELAND S.E. JR. (1961). A simple prismatic device for viewing nematode parasites *in vitro* cultures. *J. Parasit.* **47:** 623–624.

LOCKE F.S. (1901). Die Wirkung der Metalle des Blutplasmas und verschiedener Zucker auf das isolierte Säugerthierhertz. *Zentbl. Physiol.* **14:** 670.

McQUILKIN W.T., EVANS J.V. & EARLE W.R. (1957). The adaptation of additional lines of NCTC clone 929 (Strain L) cells to chemically defined protein-free medium NCTC 109. *J. Nat. Cancer Inst.* **19:** 885–907.

MORGAN J.F., CAMPBELL M.E. & MORTON H.J. (1955). The nutrition of animal tissues cultivated *in vitro*. I. A survey of natural materials as supplements to synthetic medium 199. *J. Nat. Cancer Inst.* **16:** 557.

MORGAN J.F., MORTON H.J. & PARKER R.C. (1950). Nutrition of animal cells in tissue culture. I. Initial studies on a synthetic medium. *Proc. Soc. exp. Biol. Med.* **73:** 1–8.

NYDEGGER L. & MANWELL R.D. (1962). Cultivation requirements of the avian malaria parasite *Plasmodium hexamerium*. *J. Parasit.* **48:** 142–147.

PARKER R.C. (1961). *Methods of tissue culture*. 3rd ed. London: Pitman Medical Publishing Co.

PARKER R.C., CASTOR L.N. & McCULLOCK E.A. (1957). Altered cell strains in continuous culture: a general survey. *Spec. Publ. N.Y. Acad. Sci.* **5:** 303.

PAUL J. (1965). *Cell and tissue culture*. 3rd ed. Edinburgh and London: E. and S. Livingstone Ltd.

PITTS T.D. & BALL G.H. (1958). A chamber for helminth culture. *Trans. Am. microsc. Soc.* **77:** 280–283.

RINGER S. (1895). Further observations regarding the antagonism between calcium salts and sodium, potassium and ammonium salts. *J. Physiol.* **18:** 425.

SANWAL K.C. (1959). A simple method for rearing pure populations of the foliar nematode *Aphelenchoides ritzemabosi* in the laboratory. *Can. J. Zool.* **37:** 707–711.

SILVERMAN P.H. (1963). *In vitro* culture of parasites. In *Techniques in parasitology:* 45–68. Taylor A.E.R. (ed.) Oxford: Blackwells.

SLEIGH J.D. (1965). Sterilisation. In *Medical microbiology:* 679–721. Cruickshank R. (ed.) Edinburgh & London: E. & S. Livingstone.

STRUMIA M.M. (1954). The preservation of blood plasma and blood products by freezing and drying. In *Biological applications of freezing and drying:* 129–149. Harris R.J.C. (ed.) New York: Academic Press.

TINER J.D. (1966). Collection and storage of axenic inoculum of plant parasitic nematodes in the laboratory. *Ann. N.Y. Acad. Sci.* **139:** 111–123.

TRAGER W. (1959). Tsetse fly tissue culture and the development of trypanosomes to the infective stage. *Ann. trop. Med. Parasit.* **53:** 473–491.

TREVAN D.J. (1961). Examination of roller-tube cultures. *Jl R. microsc. Soc.* **80:** 97.

TYRODE M.V. (1910). The mode of action of some purgative salts. *Arch. internat. pharmacodyn.* **20:** 205.

WALLACE H. (1963). *The biology of plant parasitic nematodes.* London: E. Arnold.

WEBSTER J.M. & LOWE D. (1966). The effect of the synthetic plant growth substance, 2,4-dichlorophenoxyacetic acid, on the host-parasite relationships of some plant-parasitic nematodes in monoxenic callus culture. *Parasitology* **56:** 313–322.

WEINSTEIN P.P. (1953). The cultivation of free-living stages of hookworms in the absence of living bacteria. *Am. J. Hyg.* **58:** 352–376.

WEINSTEIN P.P. & JONES M.F. (1956). The *in vitro* cultivation of *Nippostrongylus muris* to the adult stage. *J. Parasit.* **42:** 215–236.

WENYON C.M. (1926). *Protozoology* **2:** 1302. London: Baillière, Tindall & Cox. (Reprinted 1966 by Baillière, Tindall & Cassell).

WHITE P.R. (1934). Potentially unlimited growth of excised tomato root tips in a liquid medium. *Pl. Physiol.* **8:** 489.

WHITE P.R. (1939). Potentially unlimited growth of excised plant callus in an artificial nutrient. *Am. J. Bot.* **26:** 59.

WHITE P.R. (1954). *The cultivation of animal and plant cells.* London: Thames and Hudson. New York: Ronald Press.

NAMES AND ADDRESSES OF
SUPPLIERS MENTIONED IN THE TEXT

ABBOTT LABORATORIES, Queensborough, Kent, England.

ALBRIGHT & WILSON, Knightsbridge Green, London S.W.1, England.

ALCONOX Inc., New York 3, N.Y., U.S.A.

ARMOUR PHARMACEUTICAL Co. Ltd, Hampden Park, Eastbourne, Sussex, England (or Kankakee, Illinois, U.S.A.)

ASHE LABORATORIES Ltd, Kingston Road, Leatherhead, Surrey, England.

BALTIMORE BIOLOGICAL LABORATORY Inc., 1640 Gorsuch Avenue, Baltimore 18, Maryland, 21204, U.S.A.

BRITISH DRUG HOUSES Ltd., Poole, Dorset, England.

BURROUGHS, WELLCOME & Co., Euston Road, London N.W.1, England.

CALBIOCHEM (California Corporation for Biochemical Research), P.O. Box 54282, Los Angeles 54, California, 90054, U.S.A. (or 13 Barlows Road, Tadley, Basingstoke, Hampshire, England).

CLOROX CHEMICAL Co., Oakland, California, U.S.A.

DIFCO LABORATORIES, Detroit 1, Michigan, U.S.A. (or Baird & Tatlock Ltd, Freshwater Road, Chadwell Heath, Essex, England).

EASTMAN Organic Chemicals Department, Distillation Products Industries, Rochester, New York, 14603, U.S.A. (or Kodak Ltd, Kirkby, Liverpool, England).

ESCO (RUBBER) Ltd, 35 Seething Lane, London E.C.3, England.

EVANS MEDICAL SUPPLIES, Speke, Liverpool 19, England.

GLAXO Ltd, Greenford, Middlesex, England.

HARVARD APPARATUS Co., Dover, Massachusetts, U.S.A.

HOPKIN & WILLIAMS Ltd, Chadwell Heath, Essex, England.

HYLAND LABORATORIES, Los Angeles, California, U.S.A. (or Caxton Way, Thetford, Norfolk, England).

LEDERLE LABORATORIES DIVISION, American Cyanamid Co., Pearl River, New York, U.S.A. (or Bush House, Aldwych, London W.C.2, England).

LILLY & Co., Indianapolis, Indiana, U.S.A. (or Basingstoke, Hampshire, England).

LIMBRO CHEMICALS, New Haven, Connecticut, U.S.A.

LINDSAY & WILLIAMS Ltd. Suppliers: GALLENKAMP, Christopher Street, London, E.C.2, England.

MARMITE Ltd, 35 Seething Lane, London E.C.3, England.

MATBURN Ltd, 20 Emerald Street, London W.C.1, England.

MAY & BAKER Ltd, Dagenham, Essex, England.

MEINECKE & Co., Inc., New York 14, N.Y., U.S.A.

MERCK & Co., Inc., Rahway, New Jersey, U.S.A. (or Merck, Sharp & Dohme Ltd, Hoddesdon, Hertfordshire, England).

MICROBIOLOGICAL ASSOCIATES Inc., Bethesda, Maryland, U.S.A.

MILLIPORE Corp., Bedford, Massachusetts, 01730, U.S.A. (or 109 Wembley Hill Road, Wembley, Middlesex, England).

MILTON PHARMACEUTICALS Ltd, 10 New Burlington Street, London W.1, England.

MINNESOTA MINING & MANUFACTURING Co. Ltd, St. Paul 6, Minnesota, U.S.A. (or Wigmore Street, London W.1, England).

NUTRITIONAL BIOCHEMICALS Corp., 21010 Miles Avenue, Cleveland 28, Ohio, U.S.A.

OXO Ltd, Southwark Bridge Road, London S.E.1, England.

PAINES & BYRNE Ltd, Pabyrn Laboratories, Greenford, Middlesex, England.

PFIZER Corp., Sandwich, Kent, England.

PORTLAND PLASTICS Ltd, Bassett House, Hythe, Kent, England.

ROCHE PRODUCTS Ltd, 15 Manchester Square, London W.1, England.

SIGMA CHEMICAL Co., St. Louis, Missouri, U.S.A.

SQUIBB & Sons, Ltd, Moreton, Wirral, Cheshire, England.

THOMPSON, Marvin R., Inc., Stamford, Connecticut, U.S.A.

VISKING Corp., 6733 W. 65th Street, Chicago, U.S.A.

WEST CHEMICAL PRODUCTS Ltd, Montreal, Quebec, Canada.

WINTHROP LABORATORIES, 1450 Broadway, New York 18, N.Y., U.S.A.

INDEX OF AUTHORS
WHOSE CULTIVATION TECHNIQUES
HAVE BEEN DESCRIBED IN DETAIL

INDEX

Page numbers in bold type refer to detailed descriptions of cultivation techniques.